D1546673

Coriell

To Dr. Helen Gites-Gee
May Dr. Coriell's commitment
to Camden thrive in your work.

CORIELL

The Coriell Institute for Medical Research
and a Half Century of Science

JOHN O'DONNELL

Science History Publications/USA
2002

First published in the USA
by
Science History Publications/USA
a division of
Watson Publishing International

This project was assisted by a grant from the New Jersey Historical Commission,
a division of Cultural Affairs in the Department of State.

Library of Congress Cataloging-in-Publication Data
O'Donnell, John M., 1945–
Coriell : the Coriell Institute for Medical Research and a half century of science / John O'Donnell.
p. cm.
Includes bibliographical references and index.
ISBN 0-88135-268-3 (alk. paper)
1. Coriell, Lewis L., 1911– 2. Coriell Institute for Medical Research (U.S.)—History. 3. Research Institutes—New Jersey—Camden—History. 4. Medicine—Research—New Jersey—Camden—History. 5. Research—New Jersey—Camden—History. 6. Physicians—New Jersey—Biography.
I. Coriell Institute for Medical Research (U.S.) II. Title.
RA982.C22 C676 2002
610'.7'2074987—dc21

2002026669

Designed and typeset by Publishers' Design and Production Services, Inc.
Manufactured in the USA.

CONTENTS

FOREWORD

IT IS A DISTINCT HONOR to prepare a foreword for this volume describing the first fifty years of what has become the Coriell Institute for Medical Research. My first knowledge of Lewis Coriell concerned the program that he conducted at the Camden Municipal Hospital for polio victims. I was much impressed that the professor of pediatrics of the University of Pennsylvania School of Medicine, Dr. Joseph Stokes, Jr., considered it the best program for paralytic polio in the Delaware Valley. At that time, I had no presentiment of the measure of Dr. Coriell's scientific acuity or of his organizational ability and continuing drive.

The circumstances were the following: a young cousin in Wilmington had developed an illness with beginning paralysis and I appealed to Dr. Stokes for help. He said the best place to take paralytic polio was the Camden Municipal Hospital to which he had appointed a recent resident at Children's Hospital of Philadelphia, Lewis Coriell, to become director. Dr. Stokes arranged for the transfer of the patient across state lines, and my cousin arrived in Camden in time to be put in an iron lung. His paralysis became almost total so that he was able only to move his eyelid. With Dr. Coriell's care, he survived in the iron lung and as luck would have it, the paralysis reversed and turned out to be due to Guillain Barré syndrome and not polio. The boy survived through manhood and has had a good life and children of his own.

With this unusual introduction, I became increasingly aware of Lewis Coriell and early became a member of the board of trustees of the research institute that he established on the grounds of the Municipal Hospital in Camden. Thus, I gained a closer view of his operation and his success in raising the resources to create his research institute. Poliomyelitis, one of the great threats to young people in those years, was a problem which was largely resolved by culturing the polio virus and producing a vaccine. Later, this vaccine was given not by injection but by mouth due to the work of Albert Sabin. However, the original work of growing the virus, done by John Enders and his associates in Boston, depended on the culture methods which Lewis Coriell had developed in his early days in which viruses were grown on egg embryos. Thus, while Lewis Coriell did not share the Nobel Prize, his method was essential to that development.

With the triumph of modern medicine over most of the childhood diseases, such as scarlet fever, diphtheria, whooping cough, measles, mumps, and polio, the need for municipal hospitals or contagious disease hospitals diminished and the hospital was closed. However, Dr. Coriell's institute continued its research in a number of different directions and resources were gathered and the staff grew. An important development was the preservation of cells at very low temperatures. As the institute grew and finally moved to its present location, next to the Robert Wood Johnson Medical School in Camden, this aspect of its operations became more and more important and it now houses and preserves many thousands of cell lines. A more recent development has been the preservation of stem cells and the exploration of their potential when brought to life by re-warming and their introduction into biological systems.

From 1964 to 1976 it was my privilege to serve as vice president for scientific affairs at the Institute. While I was not really qualified to do so, my activities with the National Institutes of Health in Washington led to this appointment, initiated by Dr. Coriell. In recent decades I have not been close to the scientific work, although I often hear impressive reports of it at board meetings. In the following ten chapters you will find details of the work of the Institute culled from observers who were close to it or have been key participants in it.

Fortunately, Lewis Coriell had other abilities besides his remarkable scientific acumen. He was a remarkable fundraiser, and he interested prominent businessmen in Camden and in Philadelphia in the work of the Institute. He derived support from the local United Fund and additional support from the state government of New Jersey. Important affiliations were established not only at Jefferson but also at the University of Pennsylvania and with some of the corporate enterprises such as the Merck Laboratories at West Point, Pennsylvania.

The present institute, under the able leadership of David Beck, is carrying on the traditions established by Lewis Coriell with ever expanding activities and budgets. The new building has recently been enlarged and the facilities for cell storage have been augmented and now supply cells for research workers all over the world in addition to the studies going forward at the Institute. It has close ties to the Camden campus of the Robert Wood Johnson School of Medicine of UMDNJ. It is, in a remarkable sense, the lengthening shadow of a genius who fortunately arrived at the Camden Municipal Hospital to take care of infectious disease and poliomyelitis.

December, 2001
Jonathan E. Rhoads, M.D., D.Sc.
Professor of Surgery Emeritus
University of Pennsylvania School of Medicine
Philadelphia
May 19, 1907–January 3, 2002

PREFACE

STANDARD "COMPANY" HISTORIES are often inward-looking accounts filled with collegial names, smiling images, and intramural events linked by little more than raw chronology. Ordinarily, corporate histories celebrate rather than analyze. A handy way of sizing up their narrative scope is to inspect the photographic reproductions that accompany text. Think of the usual images. Perversely sun-tanned board directors symbolically break winter ground with silvered shovels. Seated behind impressive, uncluttered desks, executives peruse important documents. Leaders "grip and grin" as they richly acknowledge one another's considerable achievements. Rarely does one photograph the sacrificial work trustees perform behind the scenes or otherwise capture the day-to-day activities that sustain and give purpose to an organization.

Eschewing historical self-congratulation, the Coriell Institute decided to search out—and portray—a more useable past. It chose to undertake a historical analysis of its origins and development in order to expand and strengthen its corporate memory. That allowed the author to endeavor to acquaint or reacquaint the reader with the larger issues that the Institute was called upon to confront and to provide a meaningful context—political, economic, cultural, and scientific—within which to view its progress. Conversely, the Institute's history constitutes an important window through which to view the development of American science in the last half of the twentieth century. This book was written in the conviction that the story of biomedical research in the United States will remain incomplete until the role of the independent research institute is more thoroughly examined.

The Institute wisely determined to locate its heritage not only by chronicling its many significant accomplishments but also by looking beyond itself. In attempting to discern and explain the interplay between the Institute and external forces and events, the author is acutely aware that many individual achievements have gone unreported or underplayed. The attempt to make the book larger in terms of theme and context has made it smaller as an embodied text honoring personal memories and contributions. Many scientists will not find herein descriptions of their discoveries or funded projects. Critical issues that occupied fine minds over long periods and whose resolutions mattered deeply to institutional progress will go unmentioned. Many individuals whose dedication and involvement made meaningful and lasting contributions to the Institute will go unheralded. It is hoped that the reader will find the book useful nevertheless.

Writing contemporary history is dangerous in at least two ways. First, one's interpretation of events is subject to the scrutiny of those who actually lived through and even shaped those events. Second, especially in situations where documentary evidence is scant, reliance on living memory poses the challenge of triangulating to truth through the subjective impressions of participants. In fact, the testimony of "oral history" is not only as reliable as any other source, but more significantly provides extraordinary insights into the very spirit of the individual or enterprise under examination.

I can think of no more apt example of this than Lewis Coriell's recollection of the ribbon-cutting ceremony on the occasion of the opening of the first laboratory building of the South Jersey Foundation for Medical Research. It was actually a ribbon-*exploding* ceremony. One celebrant exposed to sunlight a silicon disk that was transformed in a battery held by Dr. Coriell into electrical energy sufficient to trigger a small powder charge at the ribbon's center. Lew Coriell—an ardent astronomy buff and star-gazer—publicly and privately recounted that the disk was powered not by the light from our sun, but rather from the star Arcturus, which is located some unenergizing thirty-seven light years away. Regardless, it was below the eastern horizon on the afternoon the laboratory was dedicated in 1956.

Memory can play tricks even on a man wedded to hard facts. At first I considered his "false" recollection as the subconscious conceit of a scientist who realized that biological science was more difficult than physical science. I thought that this modest man was expressing in an oblique and subliminal way the conviction that—were he a physicist—he would not settle for the sun but harness the power of distant stars. Knowing Lew better than physics, I did not doubt he would have found a way to do so.

But why Arcturus and not some other star? Memories of summer hikes in Montana wilderness reminded me that Arcturus was the brightest star in the northern sky and usually overhead at summer's nightfall. Then I recalled that it was the first star of the constellation Boötis, the Herdsman, an apt stellar mascot for a rancher. But as I went beyond recollection to research, I learned that Arcturus achieved popular fame in America when its light was used to "open" the 1933 World's Fair in Chicago. Magnified rays of its light, which had left the star at about the time of the previous Chicago World's Fair in 1893, were focused on photo-electric cells at several astronomical observatories, transformed into electrical energy, and transmitted to Chicago. There the current tripped fairground floodlights on May 27. About that time Lew Coriell proposed marriage to Esther Amanda Lentz. There is no empirical evidence to support what I shall unhesitatingly accept as hard historical fact: On a summer night in 1933, beneath a celestial canopy, Lew Coriell recounted to Esther the Chicago achievement as he pointed to the bright star that would come to symbolize for him the opening of doors to nature's mysteries.

Acknowledgments

While the author alone is responsible for errors and omissions in this volume, making sense of the first fifty years of the Institute's history has been a collaborative effort. My considerable intellectual debts, I trust, are recognized in the book's "Notes on Sources." The staff at the UMDNJ and Coriell Research Library was an invaluable source of information and enthusiasm. The professionals at the Camden County Historical Society, the Paul Robeson Library at the Camden campus of Rutgers, The State University of New Jersey, and the Free Library of Philadelphia provided expert access to essential materials.

Among the many past and present participants in the Camden adventure who helped me to see the past more clearly, I must especially thank Shirley Bonnem, Earl Coriell, James Coriell, Edwin Foltz, Arthur Greene, Thomas Hedges, William Kalellis, C. Everett Koop, W. Thacher Longstreth, Robert M. McAllister, G.J. McGarrity, Warren Nichols, Jonathan E. Rhoads, Thomas F. McNair Scott, and S. Robert Wilson. Doctors Greene and Nichols gave the drafted manuscript close and critical readings, and their keen recollections and insights saved the author from many errors of fact and interpretation. Amy Leach's gentle guidance of the author and coordination of the project's myriad details brought the book to life. She deserves special thanks for authoring the captions to the images that she painstakingly selected for inclusion in this book. Jim Coriell provided enthusiastic, caring advice on many of the photographs from the Coriell family album. Had I been able to pursue the many leads that Karen Campbell produced with loving care, the narrative would be more lively and informed. Martha Allen's stewardship of the official minutes of the Institute's board eased my work considerably. She labored diligently with B.J. Swartz, another enthusiast of the project and historian in her own right, to produce a splendid aid in the form of a comprehensive bibliography of the Institute's scientific publications. The entire administrative staff facilitated my incursions into the Institute's time and space with courtesy and competence.

I cannot say enough about the gracious support of David Beck and the wondrous latitude he afforded my muse. Pressed by the future, he unfailingly provided discerning commentary, kind encouragement, and firm belief in the worth of the endeavor. Lastly, my mind and heart are filled with appreciative memories of the many fruitful interviews with Lew Coriell about his life and work. Many conversations with him predated the idea of this book, which is dedicated to his memory.

John O'Donnell, Ph.D.
The Vantage Center
January 2002

Chapter One

Introduction

The founding of the Coriell Institute for Medical Research a half century ago is still within the living memory of participants and spectators. The enterprise's longevity bespeaks a certain destiny. Yet even the drama's chief protagonist, Lewis L. Coriell, would look back on the accomplishment with wonder. Subsequent histories of the Institute may examine the organization's past from different vantages. This first full-length account, however, properly concerns itself with one big question: How did a world-renowned biomedical research institute emerge from an unendowed, independent act of will in Camden, New Jersey?

Of course, nothing occurs with complete independence or without preconditions. The career paths that Dr. Coriell and his colleagues would pursue would have been impossible before the rise of the modern American university in the last decades of the nineteenth century. And the development of higher education in the United States would depend upon the availability of huge accumulations of surplus capital, the commitment of the scholarly community to promoting specialized knowledge in graduate departments, and the maturation of a federally funded national scientific establishment. By the 1920s, Lewis Coriell's formative years, American science had come of age. Its particular genius was its institutional ability to accommodate the German ideal of advancing knowledge for its own sake and the nation's need to supply scientific and technological expertise to an expanding, modernizing society. Lewis Coriell belonged to a generation of biomedical researchers able to achieve sustainable, mobile careers that integrated the ideologies of pure science and practical service.

As the mantle of international scientific leadership passed definitively to America after the Second World War, the independent research institute came to be seen as a complementary alternative to the university-based science that facilitated it. For wealthy industrialists determined to fund investigations into specific problems and for scientists impatient with encroaching academic bureaucracy, the independent laboratory was an attractive vehicle for patronizing and pursuing knowledge. A decade after the war, the proliferation of trained investigators enhanced the viability of scientific ventures outside academe. Thus, in large terms, the stage was set for the creation of the Institute and for fifty years of substantive accomplishment.

A single yardstick measured the Institute's achievement in its founder's estimation. The purpose of the Institute was to contribute to the expansion of scientific knowledge and to discover useful biomedical information. To pursue that exclusive purpose experimentally spelled progress. To pursue it historically, however, would not only impoverish our understanding of the Institute's history but also diminish our appreciation of science itself. The following narrative is dominated by the idea that science is more than the process of cumulative empirical inquiry. Science, in the words of historian Robert Kohler, is "a complex system with many actors, in which securing resources, negotiating with patrons, creating departments and disciplines, competing for talent, designing products and services, and projecting public images [is] no less essential than bench research." Kohler continues:

> Science and scientists mean something quite different to university presidents, congressmen, businessmen, and foundation officers, and their views are no less valid and worthy of study than the view from the laboratory bench. All are essential actors. None has a privileged historical value. Science is the sum of their views and activities.

The fullest understanding of the Institute's past, in other words, meets at the intersection of a dynamic interplay of federal mandates and organizational direction; municipal power and community needs; cultural styles and scientific rubrics; professional roles and personal ambition; social, economic, and political influences and empirical findings; legislation and logic; biography and institutional development.

One biography is especially germane to the Institute's first fifty years. Ralph Waldo Emerson's hyperbolic dictum that a "great institution is the lengthened shadow of one man" seems plausible when applied to the organization that bears Dr. Coriell's name. The narrative begins with Chapter Two, a sketch of Lewis Coriell's early life. It examines forces that shaped the man and explores origins of those aspects of his intellect, character, personality, and temperament that, in turn, helped shape the Institute. This emergent portrait will serve as a touchstone through much of the subsequent narrative. Dr. Coriell's educational and military experiences during World War II prepared his arrival at the Children's Hospital of Philadelphia at an auspicious moment in virological science's ascendancy. There his precocious contributions to diagnostic research, together with his particular combination of medical and scientific training, made him the logical candidate to take charge of the municipal hospital in Camden, New Jersey.

Chapter Three looks at the three years following the new hospital director's arrival in Camden in 1949. Against the backdrop of civic efforts to rebuild a city that had fallen on hard times, this account interweaves three stories: the national fight against polio, Philadelphia medicine's administrative "takeover" of the Camden Municipal Hospital for Contagious Diseases, and Dr. Coriell's pioneering contributions on both fronts. In this brief but dramatic period of American medicine, Dr. Coriell secured his national and local reputation and also the support necessary to the establishment of a research center in Camden.

By 1953 Dr. Coriell had transformed the municipal hospital, improved the health of the region, attracted outside resources to the city, and infused the community with contagious optimism. In response, business and civic leaders conspired to charter the South Jersey Medical Research Foundation in 1953 and to raise funds to build an independent research facility in the city. The Camden researcher's growing national notoriety invigorated the campaign. Between the chartering and the groundbreaking in June 1956, Dr. Coriell and his co-workers made a signal contribution to the conquest of polio through their laboratory evaluation of the Salk vaccine trials. Chapter Four examines these events while introducing the founding trustees and the relationship of Dr. Coriell's scientific aspirations and professional ambitions to community hopes and needs.

Chapter Five is concerned with the "take-off" period of the new enterprise, the critical half-dozen years between the opening of the new laboratory facility and Dr. Coriell's announcement in December 1961 of his imminent retirement from Municipal Hospital, which would close the following year. It chronicles the growth of research staff, additions and losses of key personnel, expansion of scientific disciplines and agenda, the hospital's financial struggles, and the culture of supporting philanthropy. These developments were decisively affected by the Foundation's reorientation in the direction of cancer research, its dawning awareness of the need—and early calls—for a central tissue culture registry, and its interactions with the larger scientific community.

Growing pains, vicissitudes of financing, and competition to attract and retain scientific talent would remain endemic features of the independent research institute's landscape. But Dr. Coriell's newly won ability to concentrate on Foundation business, together with the congealing of the trustees as a working board, led to the charting in 1962 of the first pathway through that landscape to the future. In 1964, the Foundation dedicated the new Cell Bank Research Laboratory, decided to add a department of cytological biophysics, and boldly embarked on a major building expansion program. In 1966, the Foundation changed its name to the Institute for Medical Research, devised a strategy to seek annual state appropriations, committed itself to advocacy of a medical/dental school in South Jersey, and amended its charter to accentuate its dedication to the conquest of cancer. These major actions were not ad hoc opportunisms but rather strategic components of a unified vision. Chapter Six concerns itself with the organization's first strategic plan and its practical unfolding through 1968, when a series of unforeseen events and conditions would begin to jeopardize the plan itself.

Chapter Seven juxtaposes the Institute's strategy and scientific progress—including stunning epiphanies in cell biology, virology, biochemistry, and cytogenetics—against larger political troubles of the late 1960s and economic recession in the first half of the 1970s. The struggle to expand physical plant and animal quarters, build new cell banks, rebound from strained departures of key research teams, and maintain institutional viability are examined within the context of altered federal research policy and funding, civil unrest, and the political economics of the state of New Jersey.

As the Institute approached its twenty-fifth anniversary in 1978, it found itself at a crossroads, perhaps the most dramatic intersection of events, personal and professional lives, institutions, competing interests, and political and economic forces in its entire history. Its cumulative operating deficit from 1975 to 1980 approximated one million dollars just as "Reaganomic" retrenchment threatened further to diminish the flow of funds to medical research. The physical plant required renovation or relocation, but decisions were put on hold due to lack of secure funding. *And* its founding president was contemplating retirement. Respected prognosticators of IMR's capacity to sustain critical mass in an increasingly competitive environment were not sanguine about its future. Merger, affiliation, and alliance were viewed as viable options for survival, and each alternative was fraught with peril.

How the Institute coped with its greatest crisis, which altered institutional strategy and scientific foci, is the subject of Chapter Eight. Building upon relationships Dr. Coriell spent years and even decades developing, the organization launched an ambitious fund raising campaign, developed and redeveloped cooperative agreements with educational and medical institutions, and forged closer ties with the State of New Jersey. As Dr. Coriell stepped down on September 30, 1985, his Institute, thanks in part to heroic trustee involvement, had maintained its autonomy and sustained its scientific momentum in a precarious environment.

Chapter Nine recounts the period from Dr. Coriell's retirement to the resignation six years later of his successor, Dr. Gerald J. McGarrity, and the arrival of the Institute's current president, Dr. David P. Beck in October 1991. Despite its apparent transitional nature, this period witnessed significant accomplishment: successful negotiation of an affiliation agreement with the University of Medicine and Dentistry of New Jersey; construction of new headquarters and the Institute's relocation; and acquisition of a major cell repository contract with the National Institute of Mental Health. This time of unprecedented change was not without turmoil. Perhaps its most lasting accomplishment was the Institute's realization that the demands of administering an independent research institute in the last decade of the twentieth century required unique talent and exclusive dedication.

Chapter Ten essentially depicts the unfolding of Dr. Beck's plan for the Institute's future, a strategic reformation designed to catalyze an ongoing scientific renaissance. Within weeks of his arrival, the new president articulated a plan designed to build critical mass around the evolving field of human genetics and the investigation of human genetic diseases. He sought to rebuild essential intellectual connections between ongoing research and cell bank activity, and to acquire advanced research equipment and develop cutting-edge technologies. In doing so, he was strategically recapitulating the scientific vision of the Institute's founder. We now turn to the beginning of Lewis Coriell's story.

Chapter Two

Anticipations

Brought to life in western Pennsylvania by the confluence of the Allegheny and Monogahela rivers, halfway toward its thousand-mile rendezvous with the Mississippi, the Ohio River impatiently arches northward along the Kentucky-Ohio border to welcome the waters of the Scioto River. In that fertile farmland valley on June 19, 1911, Lewis L. Coriell was born not far from the site where—nearly a century earlier—his great-great-grandfather Elias had brought a raft ashore at an Indian village in order to bury his youngest child.

A native of New Jersey, Elias Coriell with his wife Lucretia and family of nine children had floated down the Allegheny and Ohio rivers when the very concept of nationhood was problematic. Their pioneering aspirations propelled them toward territories beyond statehood, but the death of their drowned daughter compelled them to stop. As a result of the family's decision never to abandon her gravesite, four generations of Coriells would prosper on the rich limestone soil of Scioto County, Ohio.

Navigating American rivers was nothing new to the formidable clan. The first Coriell[1] in the New World, Elias's great-grandfather, had settled in New Jersey in the late seventeenth century and established a barge service across the Delaware River into Pennsylvania. New Jersey already possessed more roads than any other colony, and they inevitably funneled travelers and cargoes to ferries. One such way station on the important Lower York Road connecting Pennsylvania with East Jersey and New York was a place known after 1732 as Coriell's Ferry, now Lambertville.

The progenitor of these American Coriells was aptly named Abraham. He was a French Huguenot who, along with some 400,000 followers of John Calvin, had fled his native land after Louis XIV revoked the Edict of Nantes in 1685 and ushered in a second round of persecutions of the French Protestants. Prepared to endure oppression and expatriation rather than to compromise

[1] The name was then spelled "Coryell." The present-day rendering has been maintained in the narrative for consistency.

Lew Coriell was born on June 19, 1911, in the agricultural community of Sciotoville, Ohio.

their convictions, Huguenots were independent-minded, strong-willed, hard-working individualists. As if to fortify these characteristics for future generations, Ira Coriell—Elias's son, and Lewis L. Coriell's great-grandfather—married Sirena White, a direct descendant of Peregrine White, the first child born in Plymouth Colony, the son of Pilgrims who had arrived on the Mayflower. Lewis L. Coriell would come from sturdy stock composed of generations of genuine pioneers.

The twentieth century itself failed to tranquilize the frontier spirit in the Coriell clan's imagination. The year before Lewis L. was born to Louis Alonza and Mary Effie (Lemon) Coriell, Louis and his brother Henry embarked on an extensive exploration of open land in Montana, Washington, and Canada. The historian Frederick Jackson Turner may have declared the American frontier closed in 1893, but Montana and Washington had been admitted to statehood only four years earlier. Montana was the most sparsely populated space in the Union that was humanly habitable. In 1910 the northwest landscape remained vast and vague, homesteading was being encouraged, and population mobility was as fervid as the dreams of men and women pulled westward by the prospect of improved opportunity and freedoms. The Coriell brothers chose Montana.

In 1916, when Lewis was four and a half years old, the Coriell family pulled up stakes, loaded furniture and farm machinery into a boxcar, and hopped aboard a Pullman. Through seven generations, many Coriells had earned their livelihoods transporting passengers, cargo or cattle across formidable rivers. This family—the seventh and eighth generations—was looking forward to celebrating a Mississippi River transit in rare comfort. Alas, along with two older and two younger sisters, Lewis slept as the steam engine carried him across that mighty waterway.

There were other rivers to cross before they reached their final destination not far from Montana's geographic center: a 640-acre ranch nestled next to Coyote Creek in what shortly would become Judith Basin County. Louis and Henry had chosen well. From their fields and pastures, they could see mountains in every direction: the compact Highwood Mountains some twenty miles to the northwest; farther eastward, the Judith Mountains; south of them, the Big Snowies. Twelve miles to the southwest, the Judith River—named by explorer William Clark in honor of his cousin and eventual wife[2]—rushed down the eastern slopes of the spectacular Little Belt Mountains, welcomed Wolf Creek into which the Coyote flowed, and drained the basin northeasterly into the Missouri River. The brothers had driven a good bargain for the ranch, but it was in need of repair and new construction. The work ahead would be staggering. When one had a chance to look up from it, the beauty of the panorama could be staggering too.

The Coriells began their Montana adventure as farmers on lands littered with bleached bones of the last buffalo. Still stalking the high grass, their ghostly trails would lead to unvisited wallows rounded into streambeds. On half the land, the new Montanans planted wheat and other grains; the other half was pastureland for grazing stock and growing hay. Poultry, pigs, and gardens provided eggs, meat, and vegetables; dairy cows provided milk. Water was hand-carried. Electricity and telephone were non-existent. Wood and coal stoves warmed winters that could plunge temperatures to fifty degrees below zero. Mules and horses, not tractors, helped the humans perform field work. The days were long and laborious—and rewarding.

The aspects of character, personality, temperament and intellect that marked Lewis Coriell's exceptional professional life and that have given shape to the institute he founded can easily be traced to his Montana upbringing. Forging a productive farm out of untamed northwestern terrain involved extraordinary levels of organization, discipline, physical stamina, mental toughness, patience, resilience, meticulous performance of time-sensitive tasks, mastery of many interrelated bodies of knowledge, decisiveness, acceptance of high risk, humility in the face of natural forces beyond human control, and abundant good hope. As Pascal said, a man's virtue should not be measured by his special exertions, but by his habitual acts.

Farming, it seems, is a lot like science. Of course these qualities form a handy catalogue for success at any endeavor. But just east of the continental divide at the beginning of the twentieth century a thing called danger intensified

---

[2] Louis and Effie would name their last daughter Judith in honor of the cherished place and the explorer's sentiment.

A view from the Coriell homestead to the log cabin originally built as a stage coach station between Fort Benton and Helena. Every side of the building houses a rifle port, and the young Coriell boys, Lew and Earl, delighted in extricating bullets from the exterior walls.

the need to acquire such virtues. Where failure to smell a wolf could spell the loss of a calf or inability to sense barometric change could result in hypothermic death, proper cultivation of these qualities suggested more than polite success; it meant mortal survival. Graduates of this school, if inclined toward a life in science or medicine, would have a head start in those disciplines that Louis A. Coriell might have reckoned less demanding than ranching.

Life in Montana fostered virtues beyond those of self-control. Ranches and farms were island communities, microcosms of interdependence. In a place and era where the family was the corporation, estrangement was especially dysfunctional. At the end of what we would call the workday, "employees" did not disperse to their separate cells. Tensions had to be readily resolved or—more characteristically—obviated by a gentleness of personal, familial regard that daily defused animosity. Prosperity was linked to posterity.

Associates and patients who encountered Lew Coriell in his later life in the eastern United States would be disarmed by the conjunction of his gentle demeanor and passionate intensity, of his homespun social grace and august professional stature. There are regional cultures of character building. Lew Coriell assimilated his and never discarded its lessons.

Beyond the interdependence of family and ranch was the larger dependency upon the local community that encouraged the cultivation of kindness, cooperation and teamwork. The myth of the self-reliant frontiersman is balderdash. To be sure, the Coriell farm aimed at the highest standard of self-sufficiency. Yet, in an age when the equivalent of a "911" phone call might be saddling a horse for a midnight ride, survival depended on mutual aid. Even in commerce, there were no Yellow Pages where a dissatisfied customer could find an alternate source of shotgun shells. Time and place demanded a social compact forged in reliable, stable relationships. Such an environment helped fashion Lew Coriell's principles and style of leadership. He would select his colleagues carefully, make clear his organization's dependency on their performance, and give them room to work. Paradoxically, such dependence fostered dependability.

As Lew Coriell began to learn these lessons, the schoolbell summoned him for more formal studies. From the ranch house it was a five-mile trek to the town of Stanford, the geographic center of the county. Thanks to its situation midway along a new automobile road between Great Falls and Lewiston and alongside the branch line of the Great Northern Rail Road, built in 1908, Stanford was a thriving metropolis of some five hundred inhabitants. It was destined to become the county seat. Cousin John, Henry's son, ran the horse-drawn covered school wagon from the ranch to the livery stable close by the schoolhouse. Along the way six Coriells would collect another half dozen scholars. In wintertime, sled runners would replace wheels and a portable coal stove would do its best to keep the pupils from freezing.

By the mid-Thirties, tractors replaced horsepower. Louis Coriell, the father of Lew and Earl, stands (right) atop the combine.

A successful rancher had to be a good veterinarian, and Lew Coriell learned about doctoring from an early age.

At first, Lew preferred the education he received on the ranch to that of the schoolroom. His marks during the first four years of schooling reflected his lack of enthusiasm. In the fifth grade, however, he fell under the spell of a beautiful teacher named Margaret Asman. He began to enjoy learning and became a straight-A student thereafter. To his last days, his placemark in whatever book he was reading was a small lower-case "m" pencilled in the margin in her honor. His mother, who had been a teacher in Ohio, reinforced his academic awakening and provided constant encouragement. In the statewide examinations at the end of his eighth grade in 1925, he received a combination of high and perfect scores.

That was an especially exciting year for Lew Coriell. He was looking forward to attending high school in the fall, and that spring the family purchased and moved to Phillips Ranch on Wolf Creek. They had prospered as farmers and now were becoming ranchers too. Phillips Ranch was a 1,600-acre spread with a sizeable herd of cattle, a band of six hundred sheep, thirty-five dairy cows, and ten horses. Lew's father had become a county commissioner, member of the school board, and ardent conservationist. From his father's example, Lew began to understand the importance of community pride, service, and leadership. By the year's end he had started displaying these traits on the athletic fields of Stanford High School.

The young man's enthusiasm for sports was unbounded. Wiry, quick, and confident, Lew Coriell was an excellent athlete. By high school football standards, however, he was diminutive, and for this reason his father discouraged his playing games in which the ball was not round. Undeterred, Lewis made the team as halfback his freshman year. He returned from the season opener against Geraldine with a black eye seemingly acquired to distract attention from his broken ribs and collarbone. The next year at quarterback he played against a much bigger high school in Great Falls and lost 108–0. Half his team had to be carried to the train for the long ride back home. As testimony to his resilience, he stuck with the sport, captained the team, and in his senior year earned honorable mention on the All-State squad.

The best pitcher on the baseball roster and one of the best in the league, he threw two no-hitters, but was deprived of perfect games by his team's defensive errors. His frustration over that failure would convince him of something that he would later command but that high school sports could not supply—the ability to surround one's self with excellence and be in the position to pick one's teammates. Almost reflexively, he gravitated to the key "skill" positions where an athlete has the best chance of influencing a contest's outcome. Athletics enhanced Lew's self-confidence, showed him that he possessed natural qualities of leadership, and reinforced his belief that hard work was rewarded. It was worth the occasional cracked rib.

In high school, Lew Coriell excelled in sports.

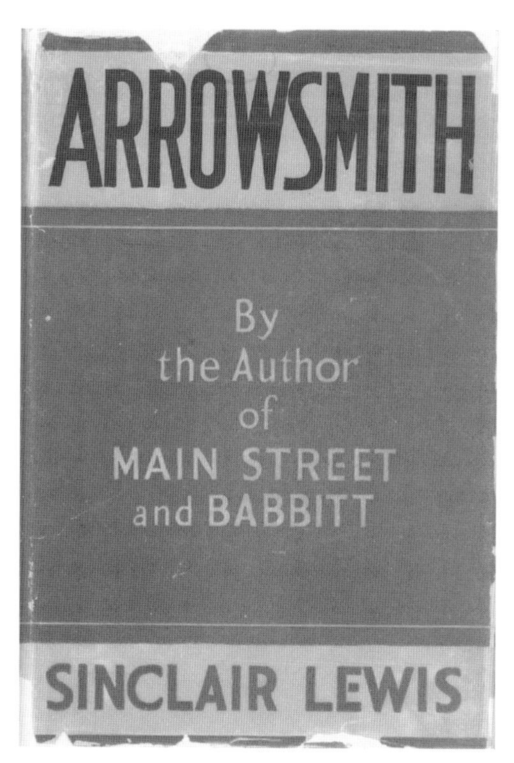

Published in 1925, Sinclair Lewis's Arrowsmith *profoundly influenced Lew Coriell.* Courtesy of Roger Lathbury

Off the playing fields, the young Coriell was likewise excelling. He received mostly "A" grades in his courses, but—more importantly—was becoming aware of his intellectual powers and preferences. Concentrating on one's strengths is a natural inclination for someone highly motivated to achieve. Lew Coriell came easily to mathematics and the sciences. It was more difficult for him to appreciate poetry or understand Shakespeare. But there was something more to his choices. To this son of a rancher, geometry and biology were highly practical subjects that possessed immediate utility. Reinforced by generations of forebears, the practicalist frame of mind clearly dominated Lew Coriell's maturing intellectual temper.

Given Lew Coriell's preference of the slide rule to the sonnet, it is ironic that his vocational awakening was initially stimulated by a novel. Sinclair Lewis's 1925 publication of *Arrowsmith* introduced the American public to a new kind of modern hero, the medical researcher. Martin Arrowsmith was a bacteriologist whose scientific endeavor required the highest standards of personal and intellectual integrity in the pursuit of an altruistic cause threatened by an enveloping materialistic culture. As if to grab the young Montanan's attention, the novel begins with a vignette set in the western frontier: Arrowsmith's great-grandmother, then aged fourteen, is holding the reins of a wagon while her father lies in its bed racked with fever and begging for relief that never comes.

To Lew Coriell such scenes were vividly realistic. As an impressionable seven-year-old, he and every member of the family saw his mother come down with influenza as the great pandemic spread terror and death across the west. A few years later he watched his bedridden father suffer painfully from rheumatic fever, the closest hospital fifty miles away. His cousin Roy collapsed in a race at a local track meet and died a few weeks later of rheumatic endocarditis. Martin Arrowsmith had dedicated his life to finding answers to such sad mysteries.

Sinclair Lewis had patterned his fictional hero after Paul de Kruif, the brilliant young bacteriologist from the Rockefeller Institute for Medical Research. The scientist actually helped the novelist structure the work. The very next year de Kruif published *The Microbe Hunters*, a benchmark in the history of the popularization of science. De Kruif's romantic promises of ultimate conquest of disease fascinated Lew Coriell, who would voraciously read the prolific author. Both books were powerful persuaders as Lew Coriell contemplated a vocation.

Reflecting de Kruif's personal opinions, the character Arrowsmith exhibits a noticeable hostility toward the clinician. No such prejudice infected

Lew Coriell with rifle and his father with shotgun bracket their prey. Gun ports in the building in the central background signify the precariousness of their historical environment.

Lew Coriell's ideology. His father was constantly demonstrating to Lew and his younger brother Earl the practical aspects of care and cure of farm animals. He had in fact aspired to the medical profession and would fondly recall to his sons his youthful days riding with Dr. Thomas McCann[3] on the general practitioner's horse-and-buggy house calls in Ohio. His apprenticeship, however, was abbreviated. The eldest male offspring in his family, he was needed on the farm and thus deprived of the opportunity to go to college. But every night at dinner he gently planted the seeds of desire for a medical education in the minds of Lew and Earl, both of whom became physicians. Lew would follow the examples of both his fictional hero and his real-life one.

Louis planted other seeds to insure that his son would attend college. When Lew was a high-school senior, his father sowed a 29-acre crop of wheat with the intention of reaping sufficient profit therefrom to defray college expenses. Lew graduated from high school in 1929 with a tuition scholarship to the University of Montana, but in August just prior to his de-

[3] Dr. McCann married Louis's eldest sister, Hattie May, in 1895. She died the following year, and in 1901 he married Louis's elder sister Lida.

High school yearbook portrait.

parture a severe hailstorm destroyed the fine crop and delayed his matriculation.

His arrival in Missoula some three hundred miles to the west of Stanford for the fall semester in 1930 opened up a world for which he was unprepared. Out of the habit of studying, exhilarated by the freedoms of campus, and unfettered by the discipline of the farm, Lew competed in intercollegiate athletics, rushed a fraternity, and never missed a dance. As a result, he lost his scholarship at the end of the first semester because of poor grades. The experience is what theologians call the *felix culpa*, or fortunate fall—an alarm sounded prior to perdition. Hearing the call, he limited his extracurricular activities, studied hard, and earned back his scholarship for his sophomore year.

The hailstorm that had impeded his academic progress was followed two months later by a catastrophe of larger proportions. The stock market crash that ushered in the Great Depression had not severely affected his ranch due to its agricultural self-sufficiency. But the economic malaise left the collegian cash-strapped, and he resorted to a host of time-consuming menial jobs in order to make ends meet. In his junior year, he became the medical proctor in South Hall, the men's dormitory. The experience solidified his interest in medicine.

From his first day on campus the man from Stanford was preoccupied with another interest that did not require reinforcement. Standing in one of two registration lines, he was captivated by a beautiful young woman in the other. Her name was Esther Lentz, a Missoulan and daughter of a prominent district court judge. Lew watched her graciously orient fellow freshmen to her hometown. It took over three years for him to convince her to date him. Most things in Lew Coriell's life had come easier. With characteristic calm persistence, however, he succeeded in the fall of their senior year. They were going steady by Christmas and engaged by graduation day.

By graduation Lew Coriell had set his academic as well as his romantic course. At Montana, he had majored in biology and minored in bacteriology, which became his favorite academic pursuit. His professor was Alvin Wells, a recent recipient of a Ph.D. from the University of Kansas. Impressed with Coriell's intelligence and promise, Wells arranged through his Kansas mentor, Noble Sherwood, to have his student appointed assistant instructor with a salary of $50 per month. In 1935 Lew was admitted to both the graduate and medical schools with advanced standing while Esther would begin her teaching career at Thompson Falls across the Rockies in a beautiful river valley in the Bitterroot Range. After centuries of westward migration, the Coriell family—in the person of Lew Coriell traveling to Kansas in a cattle train—would begin its journey eastward toward its American roots.

In the spring of 1936, Coriell received his Master's degree in bacteriology and immunology with the completion of a thesis on antibody formation.

He returned briefly to Missoula for the wedding, and Mr. and Mrs. Coriell set out to Kansas in the fall to begin their life together. Majoring in immunology and minoring in physiology and anatomy as a prelude to medical schooling, Lew completed his doctoral dissertation entitled "Studies of Natural Immunity in Cats" and received his Ph.D. in immunology in 1940. The year before, he published his first article. It dealt with a subject that he would ultimately revolutionize: the storage of cells by freezing. Some two hundred publications would ensue during his prolific career.

Moving at a relentless pace, Lewis Coriell began his medical schooling at Kansas before his doctoral work was completed. Despite working an array of odd jobs including dispensing first aid at an aircraft factory, he achieved honors in his last three years and was inducted into Alpha Omega Alpha, the prestigious honorary medical society. In 1941, in his third year of medical school he got his first taste of pediatric medicine. Uncle Sam had drafted into the army the residents at Children's Mercy Hospital in Kansas City. He was one of four students judged capable of replacing them. For sixteen months before and after classes, he staffed the hospital, while managing in 1942 to graduate first in the medical school class of which he was president. What destiny his

Wedding Day, June 19, 1936, Lew Coriell's twenty-fifth birthday.

At the University of Kansas.

voracious curiosity and prodigious accomplishment had prepared him for was yet unclear. But he was convinced that the intersection of immunology, applied research, and preventive medicine was his proper destination. He was confident that he had arrived.

It was eastward again in the summer of '42. Lewis Coriell had applied for and was awarded an internship at the Henry Ford Hospital in Detroit, Michigan. He was accepted strictly on the basis of his academic record. No collegial network existed between his Kansas professoriate and the hospital's medical staff. The new M.D. picked Henry Ford primarily because it was one of the few hospitals that offered interns remuneration along with the usual room and board. Driving to the Motor City to a hospital named after the world's most famous automobile manufacturer seemed like the economic equivalent of transporting coals to Newcastle. So the Coriells sold their first car and boarded a bus for a hot, dusty journey to Detroit. Arriving in Detroit, they made their way straight to the hospital, suitcases in hand, and—estimating that they had traveled far enough—found accommodations on an alley adjacent to the hospital.

As Dr. Coriell began his residency in cardiology, Esther supplemented his meager wages by substitute teaching in the city's school system. Cardiology was not the young doctor's intended specialty, but it was a paying job. The young doctor already knew that he would devote his professional life to the conquest of infectious disease. It made sense for the newly minted M.D. to specialize in pediatrics, since so many bacterial infections were diseases of childhood. With characteristic alacrity, he won certification from the American Board of Pediatrics in the spring of 1943. His residency at Henry Ford, however, was interrupted by the arrival of a second anticipated certificate: a notice of military conscription.

A decade earlier, Lewis Coriell had done his share of summertime soldiering as a young instructor in the Civilian Military Training Corp at Fort Missoula. In 1933, during one of the most pacifist, isolationist eras in American history, close order drills were voluntary exercises of sunshine patriotism. But Hitler's depredations catalyzed the nation's first peacetime draft registration in the fall of 1940, and the Japanese raid on Pearl Harbor on December 7, 1941, triggered a massive call to arms. Typically, new medical school graduates, including most of his Kansas colleagues, were getting their residency training in civilian hospitals before being drafted. In the summer of 1943 he received orders to report to the Medical Officer Training School at Carlisle Barracks, Pennsylvania, for six weeks of instruction.

In 1942 the young Dr. Coriell chose the Department of Medicine at the Henry Ford Hospital for his internship.

As the world conflict escalated across expanding theaters of war, Dr. Coriell could not have foreseen that he would remain on the East Coast for the "duration," much less for the rest of his professional life. In fact, towards the end of his indoctrination at Carlisle Barracks, he received orders to Santa Anna, California, the "jump-off" for the South Pacific scene of a furious American counteroffensive against the Japanese forces. Shortly before he shipped, however, the Army changed his orders. Someone had somehow matched his biomedical expertise with a military mission. He would report for duty at the U.S. Army Medical Command's Biological Research Division at Fort Detrick. The newly commissioned second lieutenant understood military euphemisms; biological research meant bacteriological warfare.

Commissioned a second lieutenant in June 1937, Dr. Coriell was later stationed at Fort Detrick, Maryland, where he acquired a top-secret security clearance for his work in the Chemical Warfare Service.

Nestled in the eastern foothills of the Appalachian Mountains some forty miles northwest of the District of Columbia is the rural town of Frederick, Maryland. Proximate to the nation's capitol yet sufficiently secluded, it was a perfect spot for a top-secret military installation. What happened behind Fort Detrick's secured gates through which Dr. Coriell daily rode his bicycle was shrouded in mystery; a topic of townsfolk gossip, the stuff of imaginative children's nightmares. Cases of "occupational illness"—the official terminology for laboratory infections—were commonplace; deaths therefrom, not undocumented. Far from the front, Fort Detrick was nevertheless a battleground where scientists raced to mobilize potential microscopic invaders and prepare them for combat.

The United States inaugurated its biowarfare program in 1941 and headquartered it at Fort Detrick the following year. Under the auspices of the War Research Service, the Biological Research Division was organized into two departments: offensive and defensive. The former endeavored to develop biological weapons; the latter, to develop antidotes for or prophylaxis against such weapons. In 1943, the medical order of battle clearly revealed the military's strategic emphasis. Some two thousand workers were investigating offensive weaponry, while only five scientists, including Lieutenant Coriell, had been assigned to develop immunologic agents. This disproportionate personnel ratio was no measure of Allied inclination to employ weapons. Rather, this massive offensive buildup—together with the construction of a huge biowarfare munitions factory near Terre Haute, Indiana—was intended to alert the Germans through their spy channels that the Allies were prepared to retaliate against any enemy who made the bacteriological first strike.

With democracy itself at stake, the United States government had little difficulty collecting in one small central Maryland post many of the leading biological scientists of the allied countries. Fort Detrick became the Los Alamos of microbiology. Dr. Coriell acknowledged that there he had met everybody important in the field from the United States and Great Britain. At the end of the long day's work, the researchers would customarily repair to the Officers Club for postprandial songs. British Lord Trevor Charles Stamp served as the distinguished piano accompanist. In later years these scientists would celebrate the excitement of the enterprise and the camaraderie of their association. At the time, however, everyone knew that the excitement involved danger, the associations were imposed, and the enterprise was clandestine. "We lived and worked," Dr. Coriell recalled, "in a bubble."

After the war, those portions of Dr. Coriell's laboratory investigations that could be declassified began appearing in the *Journal of Bacteriology*, the *Journal of Immunology*, and the *Journal of the American Medical Association* (*JAMA*). They revealed that he and his section colleagues had been working on *tularense*, a bad-tempered bacterium that can produce the infectious, debilitating disease tularemia. In fact, in the succeeding Cold War decade (by the end of which Fort Detrick had become the world's leading consumer of

Esther and Lew at Flathead Lake on Lentz Point, 1939.

Guinea pigs), the Maryland laboratories had converted the bacteria causing tularemia into an effective weapon capable of inflicting intolerable mortality rates or prolonged convalescence for the two out of three casualties who survived death. Recently declassified documents show that the organism was being mass-produced as a probable "agent of retaliation."

In 1943, however, the defensive unit at Fort Detrick was concerned with eviscerating not exaggerating the impact of the disease. Cora Downs, a foremost expert on *tularense* and one of Dr. Coriell's former professors at the University of Kansas, was stationed at Fort Detrick when the Montanan arrived. She requested his assignment to her unit, and soon Lieutenant Coriell would become the project's leader. Following the scientific dictum that holds that in order to cook a rabbit one must first catch a rabbit, the section's early work involved attempts at cultivating *tularense* in embryonated eggs. As we shall later see, the cultivation techniques Dr. Coriell mastered at Fort Detrick would lead to his seminal contribution to a chain of discoveries that ultimately led to the conquest of polio.

Dr. Coriell's later work in Camden would draw on other scientific accomplishments in Frederick. For example, one wartime preoccupation that adumbrated his peacetime achievements involved comparing the susceptibility of various laboratory animals to tularemia. Rats, mice, and monkeys filled the ranks of a sizable non-volunteer army at Fort Detrick. As a pliant bacterium and not a stubborn virus, *tularense* was susceptible to a number of antibiotic agents, such as streptomycin. Dr. Coriell's team needed to ascertain relative bactericidal responses of various animals in order to gauge proper dosage levels of the new wonder drugs. Throughout his twelve-year tenure at Camden's Municipal Hospital for Contagious Diseases, Dr. Coriell would dramatically improve infant health through his establishment of safe pediatric dosage levels of antibiotic drugs. His earlier experiments on conscripted mice would eventually help him save the lives of Camden County children.

During his tour of duty at Fort Detrick and ever after, Dr. Coriell doubted the strategic efficacy of biological agents. He and his colleagues would not know until after the conflict that Adolf Hitler had reached the same conclusion and had originally proscribed biowarfare research. Ironically, it was the Third Reich's awareness of the vigorous Allied effort—created to counter the non-existent German program—that prompted the Wehrmacht High Command to authorize its own endeavor in July 1943, the month of Dr. Coriell's conscription.

By the time of Germany's defeat, the lieutenant had been promoted to captain and was chief of the division of research and development of defensive measures against biological warfare. Following Japan's surrender on September 2, 1945, President Harry S. Truman, capitulating to immense popular and political pressure, ordered rapid military demobilization. Dr. Coriell's last official responsibility at Fort Detrick involved organizing and overseeing a sudden, massive effort to convert thousands of military billets to civil service positions. When asked to consider occupying one of those top new civilian posts, he politely but unequivocally declined. Biological warfare, aptly labeled "public health in reverse," would remain the principle focus of research activity at Fort Detrick for the next quarter century.[4] For Coriell, now a captain, however, the war was over. It was time, in his words, "to get on with the business of curing disease, not causing it."

For three principal reasons, the war itself would make the business of curing disease a bigger business than it had been prior to the hostilities. First, the mobilization of an entire nation on behalf of the overriding goal of military victory in a worldwide conflict demanded higher levels of centralization, bureaucratization, and mission-oriented federal funding of the private sector. Such patterns tended to persist in the post-war environment, particularly for the winners. Science had contributed decisively to the Allied victory. Government sponsorship of scientific research exponentially increased as a result of wartime experiences. Biomedical research in particular had proved its worth. The U. S. Army emerged comparatively unscathed from infectious disease, the grimmest reaper of the battlefield.[5] World War II has often been called the physicist's war, but in statistical terms American's fighting men owed more to biomedical scientists.

A second reason for expanded postwar investment in research was simply the availability of more dollars. The war itself, not the New Deal, ended the Great Depression. Economic dislocation would persist for several years, but prosperity was just around the corner. Postwar America saw an especial commitment to biomedical research due to the escalating propagandistic competition of the Cold War. Quite simply, the health of a population came to be seen as one of the most sensitive indicators of the moral worth of vying political and economic systems.

To be sure, the government's support of biomedical research had been gradually improving before the war. The creation of the National Cancer Institute in 1937, for example, testified to a growing awareness that the challenges of medical research were beginning to exceed the capacities of the traditional sources of support: private philanthropies and university budgets. Nevertheless, between 1938 and 1940, the Institute dispensed only $220,000 in grants. Right up to the beginning of World War II, in the words of one prominent historian, "financial malnutrition remained a serious malady throughout the American scientific community."

The war itself was the watershed. In 1951, for example, of the $24 million available for sponsored research in basic biological research in the U.S.,

[4] President Nixon's announcement on November 25, 1969, that the United States "shall renounce the use of lethal biological agents and weapons" caused a short-lived economic recession in the city of Frederick, Maryland.

[5] Malaria, however, continued to be a major problem.

approximately $20.7 million came from five federal agencies. About two-thirds of that federal total came from the National Institutes of Health (NIH). Its sweeping reorganization in 1944 insured its stability and growth within the federal government and gave a number of its cherished goals the force of law. Forging proverbial swords into plowshares, decommissioned medical officers such as Captain Coriell would find their research fields fundamentally altered by the rich fertilization of federal dollars.

The sea change was not only financial but psychological as well. Medical research hardly lacked transcendent values or an ideology of service to humanity. The war, however, superimposed upon that ideology a reinforcing sense of patriotic purpose. Coriell and his compatriots participated in an urgent crusade that could be exciting without being traumatic. They had gone to war, but not quite. They made genuine contributions without suffering grisly casualties, and emerged from their wartime experiences in a mood of ebullient optimism. Their postwar evocation of military symbolism, captured in such phrases as the "fight against polio" or the "war on cancer," was more than opportunistic rhetoric designed to catalyze support for medical research. It had become a deeply implanted motivational dynamic, an essential element of their worldview. For Dr. Coriell there were also some practical consequences of his military experience. Never lacking in confidence or disinclined to lead, he had gained valuable experience organizing and administering a huge high-stakes operation at Fort Detrick. There he also met the man who would be his next civilian boss.

Thomas F. McNair Scott, M.D., had been the director of research at Children's Hospital of Philadelphia for less than a year when the war intervened. Dr. Coriell had taken an immediate liking to the cherubic pediatrician with his animated British accent when they first met in the summer of 1945. Scott had fallen under the spell of American medicine as one of seventy members of Cambridge University's Medical Students Association that toured the elite medical schools of North America's eastern seaboard in 1926. He began his cisatlantic career in Boston in 1930, spent three years in residency at Harriet Lane Home, the Johns Hopkins University's pediatric center, devoted two more years to virological research at the Rockefeller Institute, married, and returned to England to practice medicine. But the favorable impressions of his post-graduate sojourn irresistibly drew him back to the United States in 1938; this time—finally—to Philadelphia. He accepted the call to become head of pediatrics at the Temple University School of Medicine and, two years later, found himself at the Children's Hospital of Philadelphia.

As a volunteer member of the Harvard–Red Cross Unit, Scott had been assigned to the laboratories of an infectious disease hospital in Salisbury, England. He joined the U.S. Army in June 1942 when the hospital became its responsibility. In March 1945, he was assigned to Fort Detrick. Dr. Coriell assumed Scott had arrived there to muster out. In fact, he was on a classified assignment to document the Surgeon General's Office's historical involvement with biological warfare. Scott would return each weekend to his civilian job at the Children's Hospital of Philadelphia (CHOP). When he learned of

Dr. Coriell's career plans, he asked him to consider choosing a pediatric residency at CHOP in hopes of attracting him to his own research laboratories. Coriell readily accepted. Scott's weekly commute to Philadelphia gave him ample opportunity to negotiate the necessary institutional commitments to bring the young doctor to CHOP. Later, Scott would recall that his recruitment of Coriell was "one of the best things I ever did for Philadelphia."

Likewise, it was not a bad stroke of luck for young Coriell. In 1946 Children's Hospital was arguably the institution best able to take advantage of his training and talents while providing the optimal environment in which he could flourish. Founded in 1855 in the birthplace of American medicine, CHOP was the first children's hospital on the North American continent, a principal incubator[6] of the modern science of pediatrics. From its earliest days, the hospital had achieved renown for its excellence in patient care and teaching. In the 1940s, however, it greatly enhanced its research capacity in the area of neonatal and childhood diseases. Joseph Stokes, Jr., physician-in-chief and head of pediatrics at CHOP and the man who had recruited Dr. Scott, is widely credited with transforming the hospital into a world-class pediatric center in the 1930s and '40s. The hospital's virus diagnostic laboratory—the first in any clinical department in the nation—was established in 1940. Throughout that decade, CHOP vigorously forged the sciences of bacteriology, virology, immunology, biochemistry, and epidemiology into a dynamic program of research, education, and clinical care that earned it international acclaim.

Dr. Coriell's arrival coincided with several other encouraging developments. First, unprecedented amounts of money were being dedicated to medical research by the federal government, new national foundations, and corporate and industrial interests. Stokes, a powerful member of the Armed Forces Epidemiological Board, exerted a considerable influence on the distribution of certain federal funds. Second, a seismic demographic shift helped direct a large share of those funds to pediatrics and to childhood infectious diseases. The post-war "baby boomers," who currently help dictate funding policies for the elderly, then more innocently accounted for a funding boom for pediatric medicine and research. Third, a 1946 agreement between CHOP and the University of Pennsylvania solidified a relationship inaugurated in 1919 and considerably magnified the hospital's stature, resources, and capability. Dr. Scott was able to procure for Dr. Coriell through the University's School of Medicine a National Research Council fellowship under the auspices of famed gastroenterologist T. Grier Miller, the co-developer of the Miller-Abbott tube. Coriell became an NRC Senior Fellow in Virus Research. He was also provided a research residency, courtesy of Dr. Stokes, and a modest salary as a member of the research staff.

A kindly yet commanding administrator and a distinguished scientist who found time to make daily rounds and to lunch with residents, Joseph

[6] The epithet "incubator" is apt. Dr. Charles C. Chapple developed the first incubator for newborns at CHOP in 1938.

Children's Hospital of Philadelphia, 18th and Bainbridge Streets (1916–1974). Lew arrived for his pediatric residency in 1946. Courtesy of The Children's Hospital of Philadelphia

Stokes had assembled a brilliant staff. Its collective acumen was enlarged by the disciplinary and institutional cross-fertilization he encouraged. Dr. Coriell worked next door to the laboratory of Werner and Gertrude Henle, where in 1943 this internationally famous pair of scientists had demonstrated the first effective vaccination against influenza. In an adjoining laboratory another nationally renowned couple, T. N. and Susanna Harris, made seminal contributions to the study of rheumatic fever and its relationship to streptococcus. Klaus Hummeler, together with Mary Crawford, were developing diagnostic methods that utilized electron microscopy to differentiate a score of viral diseases. The brilliant Milton Rapaport engaged Dr. Coriell's interest in biochemistry. Biological bull sessions, the sociological substance of scientific progress, stimulated research and researchers at CHOP. Microbiology, virology, and biochemistry were next-door neighbors on a friendly block. It was an environment tailor-made for Dr. Coriell. He would recreate it in Camden.

Another aspect of CHOP's success that appealed to the young Montanan's pragmatic instincts was the intense interactivity between the laboratory and clinical research. C. Everett Koop, M.D., had also arrived at Children's at the end of the war and had begun to transform pediatric surgery by creating instruments, techniques and support systems appropriate to fragile baby bodies. Margery Van Norden Deming's anesthesiological innovations contributed greatly to surgery's triumphs. Benefiting obstetricians throughout the region, Neva Abelson's research in the hospital's Rh laboratory and its inter-hospital service known as the Serum Exchange improved transfusion techniques and dramatically lowered infant mortality. Aims McGuinness and his colleagues produced sera against whooping cough and other childhood diseases, and CHOP shipped their vaccines around the world. Irving Wolman contributed to public acceptance of homogenized milk for infants by proving it readily digestible. Charles Chapple, who grew up not far from Lew Coriell in Billings, Montana, developed the first incubator for premature infants.

Coriell's associations and experiences at CHOP reinforced his conviction that pure science and medical progress could thrive most heartily in an environment that placed them in close proximity. A man of equipoise, Lewis Coriell balanced his M.D. and Ph.D. like wings of a plane designed to fly smoothly between bench and bedside. His ultimate destination, however, was always the improvement of the human condition. When he decided he could best fulfill that goal by dedicating his life to research, he never forgot the purpose of his undertaking. The research institute that bears his name would embody his scientific ideology and be sustained by the example Joseph Stokes set at CHOP.

C. Everett Koop in 1952. Dr. Coriell's long-time colleague at the Children's Hospital of Philadelphia, he would receive the Coriell Medal in 1993 after an illustrious career as U.S. Surgeon General.

If the constellation of scientific stars Stokes had assembled impressed the young resident, it soon became clear to them that Dr. Coriell belonged in that firmament. "He was very brilliant," said McNair Scott of his chief laboratory assistant, "I learned an awful lot from him." Scientifically, Scott was interested in herpes simplex virus. He had clinical responsibilities too. As the director of research, however, his preoccupations were chiefly administrative. Most often recognized by his flying coattails en route to some organizational séance, he was affectionately known to his colleagues as "McMeeting" Scott. In short order, as he did at Fort Detrick, Dr. Coriell became the laboratory's scientific leader as evinced from the primacy of his name in citations of articles that issued from the little research group.

Herpes simplex virus is commonly associated with fever blisters. In children, however, it can be responsible for many devastating diseases, including encephalitis. Dr. Coriell and his colleagues documented ways of identifying the virus. They became the leaders in the field of herpes simplex. They made similar contributions to the solution of the problem of acute herpetic gingivostomatitis, a troublesome virus that infected almost all infants in the United States at the time.

The key to the laboratory's breakthroughs was CHOP's remarkable progress in applying advanced techniques of culturing viruses in order to make vaccines. Remarkably, prior to the 1930s there existed only two serendipitously-discovered virus vaccines: Jenner's against smallpox and Pasteur's against rabies. In an era when wonder drugs were helping populations combat hordes of bacterial diseases, virus-disease prevention was in a relatively backward state. One reason for the disparity was the virus's size. Unlike the comparatively portly bacterium, most viruses are too small to be seen by optical microscopes. The electron microscope had only begun commercial production in the United States in 1941. By 1946 only some five dozen or so viruses had been identified by all methods, including charting symptoms and tracking the antibodies they produced.

The biggest problem, however, was the virus's recalcitrance. Whereas bacteria can happily multiply in the sterile, lifeless medium on a glass plate, the virus insists on inhabiting a living cell, and is often quite particular about the location and type of the cell and the species of its host. Many viruses that infect humans also infect certain animals, but growing a virus in a live laboratory animal is messy, expensive, and often confusing. The animal can have other diseases that distort results or can have undecipherable, dismaying immunological responses.

Tissue culture, a robust research area since the 1920s, provided one method of cultivating viruses outside of living organisms. At the Rockefeller Institute, Alexis Carrel deposited living tissue under cultivation along with plasma and other nutrients in sealed test tubes set horizontally on a rotating machine that exposed the tissue alternately to fluid and air. Properly incubated, the tissue could be kept alive for years. In 1928, Hugh and Mary Maitland demonstrated that incubated cowpox virus could be grown in a broth of minced chicken kidney, serum, and salt solution sealed within glass flasks. These unperfected *in vitro*, or under glass, methods failed to overcome the problem of bacterial contamination. The only way to keep the bacteria from overwhelming the researchers' cultures was to move them to fresh flasks every few days. Most viruses, however, rebelled against such frequent changes of venue and stubbornly refused to grow.

A more promising avenue involved growing viruses in the embryonic tissues of chicks inside fertile eggs, bacteriologically sterile media. Just inside the shell, the second sphere called the chorioallantois is a blood-thickened membrane through which unborn chicks breathe. Ernest Goodpasture and Alice Miles Woodruff succeeded in growing fowlpox virus on this membrane. The announcement of this trailblazing achievement in their 1931 *American*

Journal of Pathology article opened the possibility of preparing large quantities of non-contaminated virus on a cheaply obtained and readily available host. Chroniclers would argue about which development in the 1930s was most important to virology's rapid advance in the 1940s: was it the electron microscope for detecting viruses, the ultracentrifuge for purifying them, or the chick embryo technique for growing them in sufficient quantities to produce cost-effective vaccines? It is no chicken-and-egg question. Without Goodpasture's breakthrough, the other developments would have had little practical effect. Actually, it was a chicken-and-egg *answer.*

Had it not been for Stokes's commitment to research as an essential function of a pediatric hospital, such abstruse answers, tucked away in esoteric journals, would provide little sustenance to clinicians. CHOP's medical staff was witnessing the devastating effects of measles, mumps, chicken pox, and poliomyelitis. Those who recovered from these diseases enjoyed permanent immunity. Why then, wondered Dr. Coriell and the doctors who dealt daily with the complications of these diseases, were there no preventive vaccines? The answer became apparent to Dr. Coriell and other virologists on staff. These viruses were usually human; ordinarily, they did not infect other species; therefore, vaccines could not be produced from experimental animals. In studies conducted through the early '40s, Goodpasture and his British colleagues succeeded in grafting human skin onto the chorioallantoic membrane of embryonated eggs. Then they showed that such viruses as the herpes simplex could be grown on the grafted skin as well.

Using the previous system where viruses were grown directly in the tissue of the chicken, Dr. Coriell and his colleagues laid human skin directly on the outer membrane of the egg. Courtesy of the National Library of Medicine.

The ramifications of these studies were not lost on researchers at CHOP. The ability to grow human skin in a sterile host that does not produce its own antibodies held the key to the cultivation of strictly human viruses. Drs. Coriell and Scott, together with Harvey Blank, a NRC Fellow in the Department of Dermatology at Penn's School of Medicine, successfully replicated and thus confirmed Goodpasture's experiments. Koop had donated the human skin used in the study: discarded foreskin from neonatal circumcisions. Young, vascularized, and morphologically distinct, it was a perfect choice of tissue. With it, the research team developed a comparatively simple procedure for keeping bacteria-free human skin growing by serial transfer from egg to egg. Their sterilization techniques resulted in markedly reduced rates of bacterial contamination. In short order, they became the first researchers to inoculate the human skin with chicken pox virus, thus opening up the possibility of culturing chicken pox in order to develop effective vaccines. In the tangled scientific web of slow cumulative progress, somersaulting inspiration, and serendipity, Dr. Coriell's pioneering techniques would ultimately contribute to the successful cultivation of poliovirus, as we shall see in the next chapter.

Dr. Coriell's passion and talent for research would not dissuade him from writing his own next chapter as a clinician. Determined to pursue a full pediatric residency, he spent a good many waking hours in his second and third years at CHOP on call and on rounds. With 140 beds and over 300 admissions per month, Children's Hospital was an intensely busy institution with a challenging clinical panorama. Dr. Coriell was acutely aware of the initial skepticism of his medical staff that a physician who had spent his first year of residency in a basement laboratory could know much about patients. Indeed, the mental discipline of the scientist is like the endurance of a long-distance runner. Hospital medicine requires a sprinter's agility. It's a rare feat of intellectual and emotional athleticism that allows excellence in both arenas. Perhaps it was Lewis Coriell's supreme confidence in his scientific abilities that accounted for the fact that his greatest satisfactions at CHOP came from his accurate, decisive diagnoses of medical cases. Time after time he "nailed" diagnoses and cured the patients in his charge.

As his residency was concluding, Dr. Coriell secured his reputation as a brilliant scientist, seasoned administrator, and superb diagnostician, who knew most of what was known about infectious diseases. It was not surprising, therefore, that Stokes approached him in the fall of 1948 with an extraordinary proposition. He asked Dr. Coriell if he might be interested in becoming the medical director and chief of staff of the Camden Municipal Hospital for Contagious Diseases across the Delaware River from Philadelphia in Camden, New Jersey. It was not an opportunity to be dismissed, and after analysis and negotiation, Dr. Coriell decided to accept the offer.

The 90-bed Camden Municipal Hospital (CMH) was one of the few remaining contagious disease hospitals in the United States. Since 1920, Dr. Joseph C. Lovett, a 1911 graduate of Jefferson Medical College and one-time resident of the Philadelphia Municipal Hospital, had run it as a virtual one-man institution. When an illness that would shortly take Lovett's life forced

William Thackara ("Thack") Read, M.D.

his retirement in 1948, Dr. David Kayser, Camden City's health officer, assumed provisional leadership of the facility. The city commission tasked city director of public welfare, E. George Aaron, with initiating a search for a permanent successor. A commissioner himself, Aaron sought the advice of the Camden County Medical Society.

Ruben Sharp, M.D., president of the medical society, and William Thackara ("Thack") Read, M.D., the society's secretary, asked Dr. Stokes for help in identifying and recruiting viable candidates. Stokes saw the transition as an opportunity to forge a mutually beneficial alliance between CHOP and CMH. For years he had declined to send his residents to the Philadelphia Municipal Hospital for Contagious Diseases because he did not feel it was an adequate teaching facility. With the help of Sharp and Ruben, Stokes initiated discussions with Aaron that resulted in a novel arrangement, which the city commission approved at its final meeting in 1948.

Not until February 1949 was the agreement announced. Under its terms, CHOP and Penn's School of Medicine assumed control of CMH, which would become a clinical center for contagious diseases for the staffs and students of both Philadelphia institutions. Coriell would spend the first half of the year at Johns Hopkins University's Sydenham Hospital in Baltimore, Maryland, as assistant chief resident with a specific assignment to learn the ropes of hospital administration. Dr. Charles O. Tyson, an assistant visiting physician at CHOP, would assume day-to-day management of the Camden hospital until the new director returned from Baltimore.

There would be few surprises for the new director. Because he had signified his willingness to accept the assignment early on, Dr. Coriell was given a major role in planning the transition and charting a strategy for productive interaction. The city of Camden would pay the $10,000 salary of the new director and the salary of a chief resident. Grants would support laboratory and research technicians. Dr. Coriell would retain appointments as assistant professor of pediatrics at Penn and assistant physician at CHOP. Both Philadelphia institutions would support a teaching service and provide clinical and research laboratories. It was a classic win-win situation. Philadelphia would gain an invaluable source of clinical information and experience, and Camden would garner, as George Aaron exclaimed, "a million dollars worth of services" and a hospital director with a formidable reputation.

On June 1, 1949, just weeks before his 38th birthday, Dr. Coriell would once again set down roots in New Jersey. From Camden he would begin a series of crossings of the Delaware River that would transport people, ideas, and dreams no less precious or significant than those that traversed it centuries earlier at Coriell's Ferry.

CHAPTER THREE

CAPTURING CAMDEN, CONQUERING POLIO (1949–1952)

HAD THE NEW HOSPITAL director possessed a quantity of what was beginning to be called "leisure time," he might have taken a ferry between the two Delaware River cities. The water route, after all, had been around since 1688, about the time his ancestor Abraham established his own service upriver.[1] But, in the age of the automobile, the Camden Bridge (renamed the Benjamin Franklin Bridge in 1956), then the world's largest single-span suspension bridge, had become the preferred if problematic alternative to the boat ride.

Nearly two million vehicles per month crossed the span at the time of Dr. Coriell's arrival. At its eastern terminus it spewed congested traffic onto unfinished highways and potholed roads that had fallen into disrepair during the Great Depression and World War II. Opened in 1926, the bridge had promised to link a prosperous Camden to a more solid metropolitan future. Instead, it created snarled traffic, air pollution, and suburban sprawl. Conceived as the centerpiece of the Greater Camden Movement of the 1920s, the bridge came to symbolize the post-war plight of the New Jersey city. To appreciate Camden's history is to understand better the origins and growth of the Institute.

CAMDEN

Even as late as 1949 it still would have been possible to recognize Camden as a once-resourceful city that had fallen upon hard times. In the 1920s, when

[1] Ferry service between Camden and Philadelphia ceased on March 31, 1952.

Camden's teeming waterfront abounded with tanneries that imported hides from around the world. When diseases such as anthrax rode these skins into town, the Municipal Hospital would confront the consequences of this dangerous commerce. John Terrell Collection, Courtesy of Haddonfield Public Library

the business of the country—in the words of President Calvin Coolidge—was business, the city was thriving. The Victor Talking Machine Company had merged with the Radio Corporation of America, and RCA Victor made Camden "the radio capital of the world." The Campbell Soup Company was marketing local agriculture produce nationwide. A resurgent shipbuilding industry rivaled electronics as the dominant employer throughout the decade. Under the banner of the Greater Camden Movement, business and political leaders were realizing their ambition to mirror Philadelphia—albeit on a smaller scale—as a civic and industrial anchor within a larger regional economy.

Camden County's diversified industrial base, busy port, booming real estate, and modern roadways encouraged madcap construction of public buildings, medical and educational centers, banks, hotels, industrial complexes, business offices, theaters, and restaurants. For a time Camden's Central Airport was the major hub for Philadelphia's airborne passengers, mail, and freight. Camden became a place where national celebrities were happy to be seen. "It looks almost like Philadelphia," observed one visitor, "only it's cleaner." Even after the October 1929 stock market crash, the area's boosters dauntlessly foresaw progress without end and prosperity without peril.

Two decades later, however, the Greater Camden Movement had succumbed to the worst economic depression in the country's history and the wartime conscription of industry to military purposes. From 1945 to 1949, after sixteen years of crisis, Camden confronted the aftershocks of postwar inflation, housing shortages, industrial pollution, violent labor unrest, civil strife, and rising crime. Some of these conditions were structural deficiencies that pre-Depression prosperity had masked. Such problems were not unique to Camden, but they seemed to hit the city with unusual intensity. In September 1949, for example, an emotionally disturbed veteran from East Camden used a souvenir war weapon to massacre twelve people on River Avenue. The bloodiest murder by one person in national history captured front-page headlines across America, a far cry from the time when U.S. presidents hailed the city as a model of urban development.

This was the situation that Dr. Coriell confronted as he crossed the Camden Bridge in 1949. Fortuitously, his arrival coincided with the first evidences of Camden's postwar recovery. While the urban infrastructure had suffered years of neglect, Camden had preserved the key to its revival in a tradition of business, civic, and political involvement and interaction that had infused the Greater Camden Movement with pride, purpose, and power. If anything, this culture of leadership had been mobilized and strengthened by wartime patriotism. Dr. Coriell would draw sustenance from this culture even as he nourished it. With optimism tempered by experience, the proponents of Camden's postwar restoration understood that Camden's realistic renaissance could be

Camden: "Radio Capital of the World." Photo Credit. Thomson Multimedia (RCA)

The Campbell Soup Company's enterprise in Camden was so pervasive that it became an international icon. © 2002 Andy Warhol Foundation/ARS, NY/TM Licensed by Campbell's Soup Co. All rights reserved.

best secured by relying on rather than rivaling Philadelphia. The City Commission's approval of the agreement whereby Children's Hospital of Philadelphia took control of the Camden Municipal Hospital for Contagious Diseases (CMH) was an early experiment in partnership. Its success exceeded the expectations of those who staked not only hopes but also political careers on the outcome.

THE MUNICIPAL HOSPITAL

Providentially, construction of Camden's hospital for contagious and infectious diseases had begun in 1911, the year of Lewis Coriell's birth. It was completed the following year on an isolated tract of land adjacent to the tracks of the Atlantic and Camden Railroad in order "to afford a site for the isolation of patients afflicted with the communicable diseases that they may not endanger the health of others." Sheridan and Copewood Streets eventually demarcated the hospital's corner; by mid-century the location was still relatively open and isolated.

The hospital's establishment as a place for treating contagion reflected the turn-of-the-century awareness that infectious diseases needed to be confined in institutions distinct from the general, "voluntary" hospitals that increasingly treated chronic diseases (and paying patients). The hospital's "municipal" aspect drew upon a longer tradition, going back to the colonial almshouse. Infectious diseases tended disproportionately to affect social classes least able to pay for medical care and therefore dependent on public support. "Municipal," as locals called it, played important roles in the epidemics of smallpox in 1925 and of scarlet fever in 1932.

In the United States by the 1940s, sulfa drugs were successfully controlling infectious diseases. Mortality from childhood infectious diseases was declining to the vanishing point, and infectious disease hospitals were rapidly becoming anachronisms. Generalized epidemiological statistics, however, can disguise egregious "micro-ecological" realities. Camden, in fact, was experiencing deadly outbreaks of contagious diseases throughout the decade. Polio, diphtheria, typhoid fever, whooping cough, scarlet fever, measles, mumps, anthrax, chicken pox, and their sequellae were commonplace and often virulent. As late as 1947 a patient died of smallpox at CMH. It was as though the community was caught in a medical time warp.

Several reasons explain why the Municipal Hospital was several years behind the curve of medical progress. CMH was a pre-modern facility that resembled an Edwardian hotel. It was a far cry from the hi-tech, bureaucratically complex superstructure the contemporary imagination conjures up as a "hospital." While medical science is cosmopolitan, medical practice can be remarkably parochial. Lovett, who had single-handedly and devotedly presided over the hospital's wards, was an old-school physician deprived of the institutional and intellectual connections—as well as the financial resources— to take full advantage of modern medical advances.

Second, the clinical panorama was bafflingly complex due largely to a diverse and diffuse patient population. CMH was the only contagious disease hospital south of Trenton, and it accepted patients from all of South Jersey. Migrant farm laborers constituted the largest patient population. Caribbean workers, especially, arrived seasonally without inoculation against endemic and epidemic contagious diseases. The hospital's admissions also reflected the maritime complexion of the waterfront city with a diverse industrial economy. For example, there were several leather factories in the city. As Dr. Coriell observed, "if they had an epidemic of anthrax in China or someplace where the hides came from, we saw the results in Camden." Finally, the southern portion of the state was predominately hinterland, rural areas where immunization seldom reached. In habitats such as the Pine Barrens, wells for drinking water existed in typhoidal proximity to outhouses. Residents of the poverty-ridden Barrens, the "Pineys" were fiercely independent people. Considered backward and uncivilized by suburban society, they could be persuaded to bring their children to the municipal hospital only in the direst of circumstances. Thus, CMH typically saw children with measles after they had contracted pneumonia or encephalitis, or when they were comatose.

A third reason for the hospital's parochialism was economic. In the mid-1940s local tax-supported hospitals such as CMH still held on to the almshouse tradition of free provision of services for those unable to pay for care. Residents of Camden City were routinely treated for free, and non-residents were assessed an eight-dollar daily fee, *if* the patient could afford to pay. The per diem cost, however, of treating a patient was about $12. No one was denied treatment. In other words, the more patients the hospital treated, the greater was its financial loss. And the number of admissions was annually increasing. In 1948, the year before Dr. Coriell's arrival, the hospital's operating budget was nearly $104,000. It received approximately $46,000 from paying patients. This growing fiscal burden helps to explain why the hospital was understaffed and why patients were not always afforded the highest possible levels of care.

Another economic factor complicating the situation was the impact on private general hospitals of new medical insurance plans, particularly the Hospital Service Corporation of New Jersey (or "Blue Cross"). By the end of the 1940s, at neighboring Cooper Hospital, the new economics of healthcare delivery began to erode the age-old doctrine of medical altruism, thus increasing the patient load at CMH. In 1948, faced with inner-city blight, union strikes, and the possible loss of wealthy private patients, Cooper's medical staff ignited a long and bitter internal controversy by challenging its board of managers to build a new facility outside the city limits. To make matters worse, the prospective opening of Our Lady of Lourdes Hospital in 1950 confronted Cooper with the potential challenge of increased competition. It was a volatile time to come to Camden to run a hospital.

The Camden Municipal Hospital that Dr. Coriell inherited was clinically challenged, economically imperiled, and confronted with a terrifying threat of national proportions—the mysterious, incurable, rising epidemic of poliomyelitis. In the long run, Dr. Coriell would modernize CMH out of existence, successfully champion the augmentation and rationalization of medical resources in South Jersey, and make path-breaking contributions to the conquest of polio. But it was his capture of the respect, admiration, and involvement of the Camden community in the *short* run that paved the way for a research institution of international stature.

SNAPSHOT

Within weeks of Dr. Coriell's arrival, a front-page article in Camden's newspaper of record, the *Courier-Post*, heralded a new era of medical care. "Municipal Hospital Gets U.S. Grant, New Director and Equipment Gift," the headline announced. The essay made clear the sequence of causality. An unprecedented $10,000 grant—the first such award ever given to a New Jersey hospital by the United States Public Health Service—was Camden's reward for its fortitude in acquiring "one of the country's leading figures in the field of virus diseases." The gifts of an Evelyn photoelectric colorimeter and a suctioning device for aspirating patients whose throat muscles had been paralyzed by polio were local donations from the Camden County Iron Lung Fund. The significant subtext of the article was clear. Here was a "vigorous 37-year-old nationally known" scientist who chose Camden as his professional residence, who was a magnet for federal funds, who requisitioned unimaginable technology on behalf of its citizenry, who understood how to use it, and who deserved the support of a local community. Here was a symbiotic blend of abstruse science and its immediate utility, the confluence of national reputation and community pride.

The photograph accompanying the article—the first glimpse most Camdenites received of their new physician—was even more revealing of the changing image of the Municipal Hospital. In the middle foreground, the youthful medical director in white frock coat sat before the newly acquired colorimeter, his hands competently fine-tuning the apparatus, his face expressing both the glee of a child with a new toy and the focused composure of a test pilot. In the left-hand background, bent over the contraption in rapt concentration was Frank H. Ryan, a respected, beloved pillar of the community and member of the Iron Lung Committee of the March of Dimes that had donated the equipment. Perhaps more to the point in terms of publicity, Ryan was the influential editor of the *Courier-Post*.

On the right side of the photograph, standing behind both men as if to insure good science and good press coverage, was the commanding figure of E. George Aaron, the city commissioner who had had brokered the deal with CHOP and the University of Pennsylvania. Aaron was a member of the "Non-Partisan" slate of New Deal Democrats who swept into power as commissioners on the coattails of George E. Brunner's mayoral victory in 1936. Camden's director of public affairs (at appropriate times he would use the title director of public welfare), Aaron had the city's health at heart. He also had a vested political interest in the success of the arrangement.

COURIER-POST
CAMDEN, NEW JERSEY

Publicist, physician, and politician: Mr. Ryan, Dr. Coriell, and Commissioner Aaron. Caption reads "Lifesaving equipment is installed at Camden's Municipal Hospital for Contagious Diseases." Courtesy of The Courier-Post

Throughout the 1940s local primary elections were hotly contested, and ambitious opposition candidates were not hesitant to remind voters of incumbents' misjudgments. Moreover, in the late 1940s, Brunner and his commissioners were desperately trying to clean up the city and make improvements in public health in order to defuse the emerging threat of a move to a city manager form of government. They preferred to stay in power, and saw the success of the CMH deal as proof of the efficacy of their public policies. Like so many civic and political leaders in South Jersey, Aaron became an enamored supporter of the new doctor in town, whom he would introduce to civic and philanthropic groups as a man "who looks like he's too young to shave." To insure the flow of non-tax funds to the hospital, the city commissioner arranged to become the chair of the Camden County chapter of the National Foundation for Infantile Paralysis.

Deliberately framed and choreographed, the photojournalistic image not only records events but also orders perception.[2] The first and subsequent *Courier-Post* photos of Dr. Coriell differed sharply from the emerging, stylized image of the lone medical researcher silently and in ways undecipherable to mere mortals communicating with the contents of a test tube held upward at arm's length toward the light. The *Courier-Post* was implying that medical progress and community involvement went hand in hand. Deeply interested

[2] It is tempting to view the photograph as a religious icon and to picture the colorimeter as a tabernacle on the altar of the laboratory table. Garbed in white vestments, the medical scientist is clearly the high priest surrounded by two attentive acolytes. And the liturgy is obviously ecumenical; the celebrants are Protestant, Catholic, and Jew. Science, in this metaphor, becomes—as it certainly was for many modern men and women—an interdenominational religion offering secular salvation in the form of medical cures to deadly diseases.

His scientific reputation firmly established, the thirty-five-year-old Coriell would earn renown as a physician at Camden Municipal Hospital.

in the health of the community and fascinated by the new director's vision of progress, Ryan sent reporters to the hospital on an almost daily basis. Dr. Coriell would later recall that there was a reporter at the door "every time an ambulance came steaming up with a sick patient." Regularly, the newspaper showed the new director surrounded by community members, usually at the center of attention and always in a novel setting. If Dr. Coriell were examining a filtration system in the hospital's water supply, he would invite the device's inventor and the city health director to participate. If he were inoculating a baby, mother and nurse would be pictured at the bedside. Before long there would be plenty of "grip-and-grin" shots of the seemingly omnipresent medical chief accepting checks from gratefully supportive community leaders on behalf of the hospital.

By juxtaposing charismatic images of Lewis Coriell as lofty experimentalist and caring doctor, the *Courier-Post* helped Camden County resolve the ambiguities characteristic of mid-twentieth-century America. People were hesitant to embrace the promised benefits of a seemingly detached, emotionless scientific future if it meant discarding nostalgic reliance on the cherished values of a familiar, albeit imperfect, past. As the community came to know the character, temperament, personality, and intellect of the young physician-scientist, they became convinced that they did not have to trade. Dr. Lewis Coriell was an apparent amalgam of Sinclair Lewis's Arrowsmith and Norman Rockwell's country doctor.[3] He embodied and reconciled the best of both worlds.

The Doctor Is In

However consciously posed, the journalistic images captured the reality of Dr. Lewis Coriell. Support for the hospital increased, not because of good public relations, but because the new hospital director was delivering the goods. Patients were suffering and dying at CMH, and Dr. Coriell moved swiftly and decisively to implement his plan for ameliorating the hazards of an unusually unhealthy community.

[3] Interestingly, the popular vehicle of Dr. Coriell's national notoriety was a famous 1952 article in *The Saturday Evening Post*, the magazine that featured Norman Rockwell's art on its covers from 1916 to 1963. The article featured two lead-page photographs containing Dr. Coriell's image—one at the laboratory bench and one at the clinical bedside.

Almost overnight, Camden witnessed an exponential expansion of care. After nearly twenty years of Lovett's solo clinical coverage, CMH acquired the medical manpower that the enormity of the challenge required. The first noticeable improvement was actually "woman power." As a *sine qua non* of his accepting the assignment in Camden, Dr. Coriell had insisted on the provision of an assistant director for the hospital. The city agreed to fund that post, and Dr. Coriell chose a young M.D. named Lois Murphy. Petite but formidable, Murphy had just completed her residency at CHOP and possessed the kind of stamina that would be called upon repeatedly during her three-year "tour of duty" at CMH.

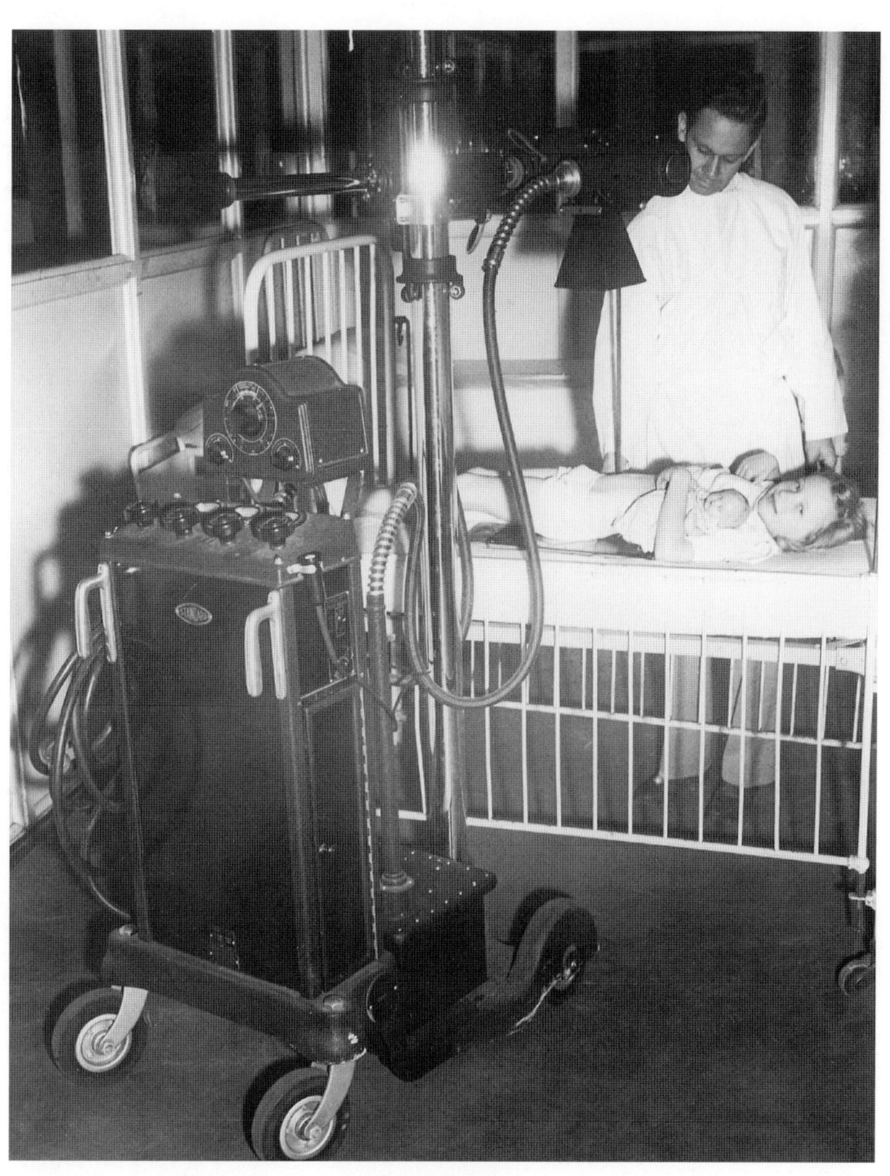

A child and her doll receive an x-ray at Municipal.

In addition to Murphy, who resided on the grounds of the hospital, CMH now had a house staff composed of two or three second-year residents, one from CHOP, one from Penn's medical school, and—less regularly—one from the Naval Hospital. Dr. Coriell had also secured agreements whereby the University of Pennsylvania and the Camden County Medical Society each would assign to the hospital a consultant in every germane medical specialty. So, in addition to four or five in-house physicians, there were always two more on call. In addition, Drs. Roy Peck and Britton Chance would take time out from their busy professional lives at Penn's School of Medicine for weekly visits to CMH, where they would supervise the rehabilitative care of polio patients. The hospital's capacity gradually expanded from ninety to nearly 120 beds. Patient care noticeably improved.

Patient, family, and community morale improved as well. CMH exuded a new spirit of vitality and bustle. There is a phenomenon known as the Hawthorne effect, which refers to a 1927–1932 experiment with lighting levels at Western Electric's Hawthorne plant in Chicago. Researchers found that worker performance increased with every change in lighting level, whether illumination was increased or reduced. The unexpected result has been attributed to an improvement in employees' attitudes simply because they were receiving unaccustomed human attention. The expansion of medical and nursing staffs undoubtedly had such an effect on CMH's patients, as did Dr. Coriell's immediate implementation of grand rounds.

For a full half-day each week, Penn medical students rotating through CHOP for training in pediatrics visited the Municipal Hospital. The institution was "blessed" with an abundance and variety of what medical people so poetically call clinical material. For the residents, who rotated through the hospital for a month or so at a time, and for the students, the training and exposure they received at CMH was a highlight of their medical apprenticeships. Dr. Coriell was a superb clinical diagnostician, outstanding virologist, and charismatic teacher. In addition to the typical clinical picture gleaned from ward visits, histories, and differential diagnoses, residents and students would complete their rounds with a visit to the hospital's new laboratory where diagnoses would be confirmed or contradicted by the evidences of cell and bacterial cultures.

It could be a chastening moment for a hotshot resident to be informed by a mere laboratory technician, "Oh, no, your diagnosis is incorrect. Your patient has meningitis. I saw diplococcus on the blood smear. Here, take a look." Such recurrent experiences, however, were salutary. Residents and students left the Municipal Hospital with a newfound respect for the laboratory. And Dr. Coriell never missed an opportunity to show Camden's leaders that clinical research related directly to the community's health.

The campaign to enhance local awareness of the value of laboratory research was an important component of Dr. Coriell's institutional strategy. The creation of the laboratory had been a sticking point in the original negotiations between Camden and the two Philadelphia healthcare institutions. Why, Camden officials had asked, should a tax-supported hospital in New Jersey fund scientific research when its incoming director retained his position on CHOP's research staff and had access to world-class laboratory facilities?[4] Stokes and Coriell had patiently explained that, without a clinical research laboratory, medical staff would be hampered in their efforts to apply the latest advances in the diagnosis and treatment of contagious disease with life-saving immediacy. Deferring to medical judgment, the city commissioners authorized Dr. Coriell to establish a modest diagnostic laboratory at CMH. They drew the line, however, between application of recent scientific knowledge and creation of new knowledge. The latter research function, they reasoned, was beyond the limited resources and statutory mission of the Camden Municipal Hospital.

Dr. Coriell appreciated the fiscal, legal, and political reasoning behind this conclusion. He could not, however, intellectually accept the distinction between applying knowledge and inventing it. He knew that both processes fed off each other in the endless interplay of focused imagination. All his training and ambition had been to unite medical science and scientific medicine, to paraphrase Robert Frost, as "two eyes make one in sight." Despite the immense gratification of curing disease, Dr. Coriell always felt that preventing disease was intrinsically more valuable to mankind. Besides, there was no known cure for the devastation he encountered every day in the hospital's polio ward. No, he would set up his laboratory per the agreement and with quiet persistence make the case for changing it.

It did not take long to make the case. As a virtual outpost of Philadelphia medicine, CMH proved to be a valuable enhancement to the teaching programs of Children's Hospital and Penn's School of Medicine. Both institutions wanted to insure the continuity of the relationship with CMH and made certain that the hospital's pharmacy was well stocked with penicillin, streptomycin, and sulfa drugs. Armed with the "magic bullets" of antibiotic medicine and superb diagnostic acumen, Dr. Coriell and his staff began to cure patients who otherwise would have suffered longer or not recovered at all.

The medical staff's achievement was not a simple matter of inducing patients to pop pills. Magic bullets had to be precisely calibrated. With the aid of the new colorimeter to measure differences in blood chemistry, Dr. Coriell began a painstaking series of successful experiments to fashion safe and effective pediatric dosages of the new, powerful drugs. His research also proved that some of these drugs could effectively combat diseases—such as whooping cough—for which they had not been designed. Properly used, such technology could even be used to monitor nursing practices. For example, when

---

[4] Ironically, CHOP had world-class science but third-rate facilities, a fact that diplomatic negotiators from Philadelphia kept to themselves. In fact, the research facilities were cramped and inefficient, and the laboratories did not rank high on administrators' lists of budgetary priorities. Dr. McNair Scott, for example, recalled running several times daily between his fifth floor office and the basement laboratory that contained the hospital's only centrifuge. Apparently, the staircase route was speedier than the antediluvian elevator. Not until 1954, with the dedication of a new research building, did CHOP's medical scientists get the quarters they merited.

patients unexpectedly failed to respond to a regimen of antibiotics, Dr. Murphy monitored trace levels in blood samples and discovered that drugs were not being administered at prescribed times. Upon interrogation, nurses confessed their reluctance to wake otherwise screaming children every six hours to swallow their medicine. This science and sociology showed the difficulty of abstractly separating application of the known from discovery of the new. Municipal witnessed stunning drops in morbidity and mortality rates among infants and children and drastic reduction in the duration of hospital stays.

Such dramatic, palpable progress persuaded community leaders that the new doctor knew best. Within months of his arrival Dr. Coriell procured an informal agreement with George Aaron. He could build a laboratory to continue his research on tissue and cell culture techniques provided he could underwrite the endeavor with external support. It is tempting to date the beginnings of an independent research institute in Camden from that handshake in late 1949. Such retrospection, however, was not available to the protagonists at the time.

The diagnostic laboratory that Dr. Coriell originally set up was located in a converted linen closet under a set of basement stairs. Soon afterward, the medical chief appropriated a small storage room for a second austere laboratory. Neither was elaborately equipped. Linen closets, historians of science suspect, are the building blocks of apocrypha. So much biological science is

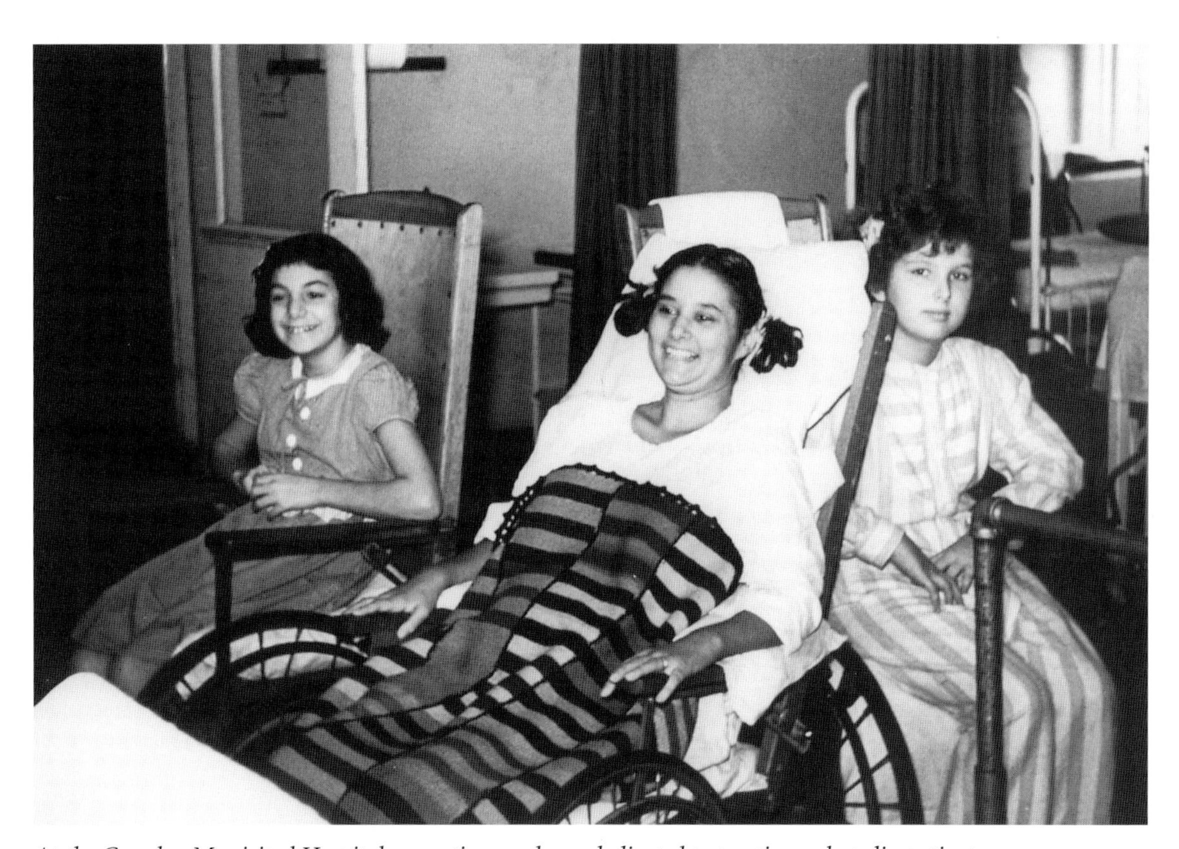

At the Camden Municipal Hospital, an entire ward was dedicated to treating only polio patients.

said to have begun under staircases that it seems that either architects were overbuilding closets or hospital employees were absconding with bed sheets. Institutional chronicles, equating growth with success, tend to concentrate on physical rather than intellectual conditions and to accentuate such humble beginnings as a way of dramatizing subsequent progress. In fact, Dr. Coriell had at his disposal well-equipped laboratories at CHOP, where he continued to work when time allowed. Collocating research and diagnostic laboratories under one roof at CMH simply cut down on commuting. It was more of a time management tactic than an institutional development strategy. In 1949 Dr. Coriell had no vision of an independent research institute in Camden. The Municipal Hospital kept him busy enough.

CMH's improved medical care altered the social and economic logic of the hospital for the community and rendered problematic the very word "municipal." Dr. Coriell's arrival completed the transformation of the facility from a public health establishment for isolating patients with communicable diseases to something resembling an acute-care institution for curing them. The social function of the earlier version of the hospital was to provide a way of segregating afflicted individuals from their families so that whole households would not have to be quarantined. Quarantine created an economic problem for the family that might require other costly state interventions.

Recognizing the deleterious economic impact of disease, in times of epidemics, neighboring municipalities and political districts would occasionally help pay the hospital bills of their economically marginal citizens. These communities, however, could not be persuaded to make *regular* appropriations in their annual budgets for what were, after all, emergencies. As a result, the old city-funded CMH resembled a one-man firehouse, which functioned quite effectively—until there was a fire.

The new Philadelphia-supported institution commanded resources and demonstrated cure rates that justified the public's reconsideration of the reasons to visit it. For example, with cardiologists to check for heart murmurs following cases of rheumatic fever and with ophthalmologists to examine measles patients for eye damage, the hospital began to be seen as the responsible alternative to home quarantine. As a result, indigent South Jerseyans began using CMH with increasing frequency, straining the hospital's limited budget. By the end of 1949, over half the admissions came from outside the city, up approximately one-third from the year before.

City, County, State

George Aaron saw the hospital's transformation as an argument for expanding its financial base by making the Municipal Hospital, in effect, a county hospital. The traditionally Republican-dominated Camden County Board of Freeholders would have summarily dismissed such a proposal. But the Republicans lost their majority in the November 1949 elections. In December Aaron persuaded the five Democrats on the incoming seven-person board to consider taking over the operation of the hospital. On Tuesday, December 20, incumbent freeholder Leslie Ewing publicly announced that the next day's meeting of the board would take up an opportunity "to provide the best facilities and medical knowledge available in combating infectious diseases, not only for children of the city but for our county boys and girls as well." One of the pioneers of the Greater Camden Movement, Ewing declared that the hospital, once a city liability, was now a county asset. He hailed the "nationally-known" medical director for his compassionate care, scientific research, and administrative talent.

At the next day's hearing, George Aaron made clear that his own administrative acumen mattered. "I have been operating this hospital for 11 years," the city commissioner testified, "and if we have done nothing else, we have brought the standards of the hospital to a point where it is on a par with any hospital of its kind in the nation." The Camden County Medical Society gave the proposal its full support, suggesting that the county's assumption of responsibility for the operation of the hospital would contribute to the fight against socialized medicine. When the meeting adjourned, the five Democratic members of the seven-person board promised to give the proposal serious consideration. On Christmas Eve, the *Courier-Post* endorsed the proposal in its main editorial, calling it an opportunity the county "should be quick to grasp."

Unfortunately, the city's reach exceeded the county's grasp. Despite its majority, the Democratic caucus of the county board could not muster the political will to increase the county tax rate by five cents in order to put the hospital on a more solid and equitable fiscal base. The reasons for this reluctance are important contextual factors for understanding the continuing challenges that state and local politics would pose for the independent research institute that would evolve from its municipal hospital origins.

At mid-century, statistically speaking, the Garden State's demographic complexion was overwhelmingly urban. But its population was densely concentrated in the Democratic-controlled northern cities of Hudson, Union, and Essex counties. The remainder of the state—especially its southern half—was rural, sparsely populated, and Republican. Thus, for most of the century, statewide elections would produce Democrat governors, while countywide contests would yield Republican legislatures. In 1941, Atlantic County elected Frank "Hap" Farley as its state senator, and for the next three decades he dominated New Jersey politics through control of the small southern counties and consequently of the Republican caucus in the state senate, better known as the "21 Club." Such malapportionment gave rural interests, controlled by Republican county bosses, inordinate control over state policy decision making. In 1950, for example, when there were only fourteen Republicans in the state senate, four Republican senators representing a mere three percent of the state's population could hold hostage any piece of legislation.

This unfair pattern of political representation was preserved by means of an outdated tax structure. As late as the mid-1950s, New Jersey remained one of only three states without both a state income tax and a state sales tax. Republicans saw a "broad-based" (that is, statewide) tax as adverse to their political hegemony. They resisted proposals for such taxes by invoking the Garden State's strong, almost sacrosanct tradition of home rule. This convenient gospel of local political control produced vast inequalities among counties and municipalities, because it made them almost entirely dependent on local property taxes for revenue. Although local property taxes were proportionately higher in New Jersey than in states possessing a better "mix" of broad-based and local sources of revenue, politicians were reluctant to raise them.

In densely urban counties like Hudson and Essex, the urban Democratic bosses controlled the county machinery. These politicos were content to secure local appropriations and patronage from the Republican legislative majority in exchange for allowing it to run the state as it pleased. As South Jersey's only legitimate city, however, Camden survived as a Democratic outpost in a rural Republican county surrounded by even more rural, rock-ribbed Republican counties. Democrats who swept onto the board of freeholders in 1949 may have seen their election as a mandate to salvage a city, but they did not interpret it as a county voting trend. In fact, the 1951 election results would reverse their gains.[5] Raising taxes threatened their precarious tenure by risking the ire of voters who might perceive the hike as a subsidy to neighboring counties that likewise sent patients to CMH. In January, the new board failed to muster the majority of votes needed to pass the measure.

Undaunted and with the blessing of the city commissioners, Dr. Coriell immediately launched a direct appeal not only to the freeholders of Camden, Burlington, Gloucester, Salem, Cumberland, Atlantic, and Cape May counties but also to every township and borough within those jurisdictions. Under his proposed arrangement, municipalities would annually transmit funds to an account that would guarantee treatment for every patient whose physician prescribed hospitalization. The process would be invisible and "without delay or embarrassment to the physician or family." If no other method of payment were available, the hospital would automatically draw from the account. From the standpoint of municipalities, the plan was better than an insurance policy because it provided for the annual remission to their coffers of unused funds.

Like politics, all disease is local. Thus, the appeal was strategically smart. New Jersey had (and still has) more municipalities per square mile than any other state. By paying homage to home rule, Dr. Coriell was able to circumvent county recalcitrance and appeal straight to those municipalities that had the highest rates of contagious disease. While county freeholders proved pre-

[5] In 1949, post-war demographic changes in the city of Camden combined with widespread dissatisfaction with county leadership to sweep all of the county's Democratic candidates save for their gubernatorial choice into local and state offices. Even Republican Albert E. Driscoll, comfortably re-elected as governor, was repudiated by his home county, then known as a "Gibraltar of Republicanism." Republican candidates for the three available freeholder slots barely but unanimously carried county municipalities outside the city. In Camden City, Democratic candidates coasted to victory by margins greater than two-to-one. In 1951, Republicans would gain back the two freeholder seats that were contested.

dictably unresponsive, particularly plagued municipalities—enlightened by self-interest—gladly subscribed to the plan. By the summer of 1950, Merchantville, Cinnaminson, Wrightown, Bridgeton, Pemberton, Beverly, Moorestown, Audubon Park, Gibbsboro, and Lower Township had signed on. The campaign to provide an equitable basis of support for the hospital while encouraging its widest possible use had served to advertise the hospital in South Jersey and had shown Camden's leadership that CMH's medical director was an ardent, convincing apologist for the city's needs. Astute observers, however, would understand what really motivated such municipalities to raise taxes for their medical self-defense. Dr. Coriell's arguments were indeed cogent, but the silent persuader was polio.

The Threat of Polio

Polio was unlike other diseases. Cholera, yellow fever, even pandemic influenza had left destruction in their wakes, but they tended to disappear for long periods of time. In the decade following World War II, public reaction to polio resembled the hysteric fear of AIDS in the 1980s. From 1945 to 1949, there were over twenty thousand polio cases reported each year nationwide. Then, through its peak in 1952 with nearly sixty thousand cases, it appeared to be increasing in incidence and virulence with no end in sight. Polio, however, differed from AIDS, whose victims once feared inevitable death. The greater horror of polio was the possibility that you or your child—mentally alert and imprisoned in an iron lung—might live.

Prior to the end of the nineteenth century, polio was probably endemic and, as viruses go, benign. The first great epidemic of 1916 left New York City with nine thousand people paralyzed and two thousand dead. Inhabitants fled in panic; quarantine was enforced at gunpoint. Shortly thereafter, epidemiologists discovered that the public health community's campaign for improved hygiene was responsible for what was commonly and symptomatically called infantile paralysis. They learned that the viruses that can cause paralytic poliomyelitis have always been with us. When infants acquired the virus neonatally, they were still protected by the antibodies from their mothers' blood and paralysis was rare. Paradoxically, modern sanitation, indoor plumbing, and soap—the sacraments of civilization—were responsible for civilization's latest scourge. When children were initially exposed to the virus after maternal immunity had ended, the results could be catastrophic.

Polio struck with peremptory impartiality and suddenness. It cut a swath across socioeconomic lines, even handicapping a patrician president of the United States. At the start of the decade, there was no cure for it—just vigilant, exhausting, expensive, and prolonged care. By the end of the decade some three hundred thousand crippled victims would be confined to leg braces, wheelchairs, and crutches in the United States. Still, other contagious and endemic diseases accounted for more deaths and disability than did polio. How did polio seize center stage as America's healthcare nightmare? Why did

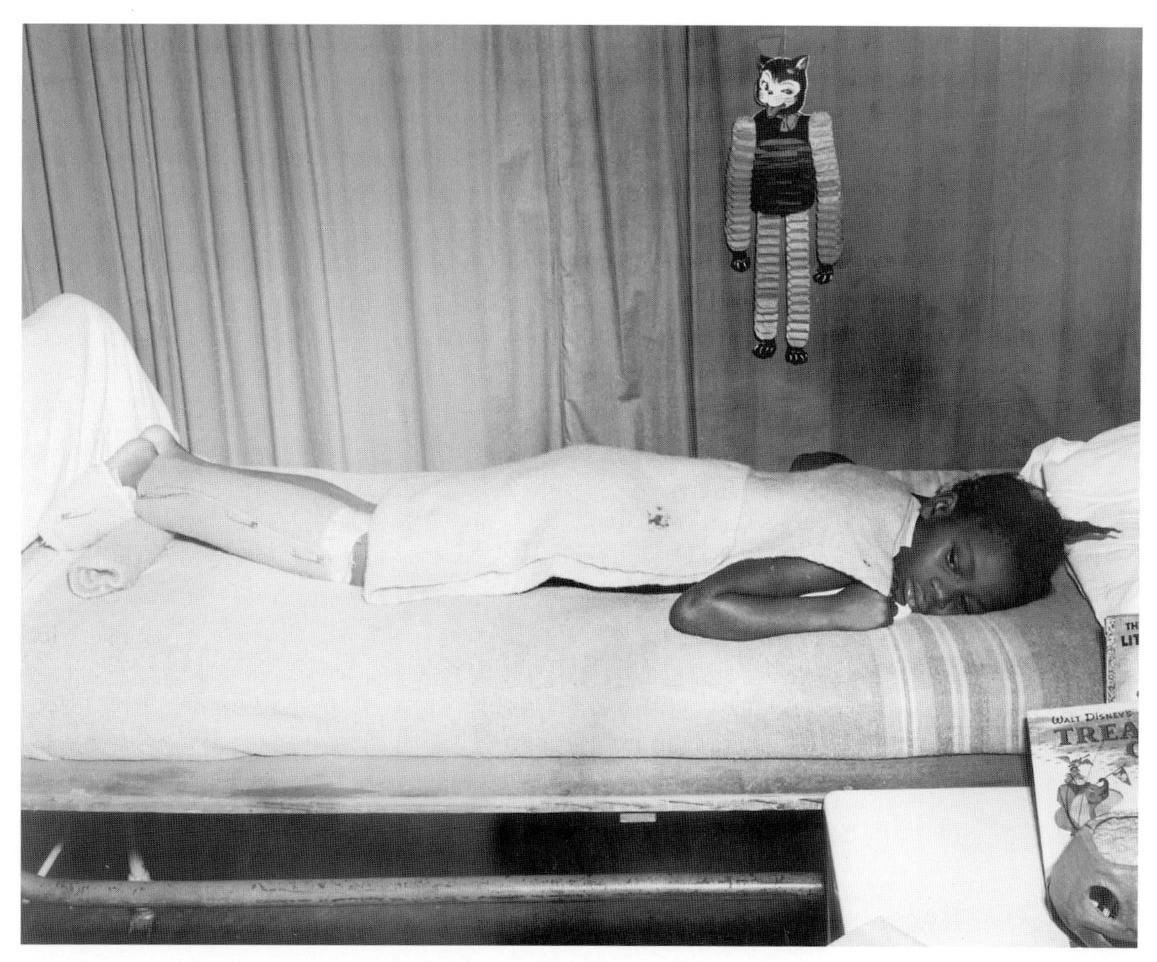

Applying hot packs to a polio patient at CMH to relieve pain.

efforts to combat its terror become an unprecedented national crusade? The answers, of course, go beyond rational explanations of epidemiological probability to the powerful arenas of cultural perception and social change.

The big social change in the United States from 1945 to 1954 was the extraordinary production of babies. In the five years preceding 1953, the U.S. population increased more than it had in the prior three decades. Next to procreation of children, the new national pastime was their care and protection, as the popularity of Dr. Benjamin Spock's books on childcare would confirm. The Baby Boom had arrived. Sadly, most polio victims were children, and the rise of the polio rate paralleled the rise of the birth rate. That coincidence fostered the impassioned engagement of parents in the cause of polio's eradication.

A larger national preoccupation with the possibility of thermonuclear war and the unpredictable ill effects of atomic radiation "fallout" reinforced this crusade. Baby boomers were born under a mushroom cloud. In March 1946 British Prime Minister Winston Churchill's announced in Fulton,

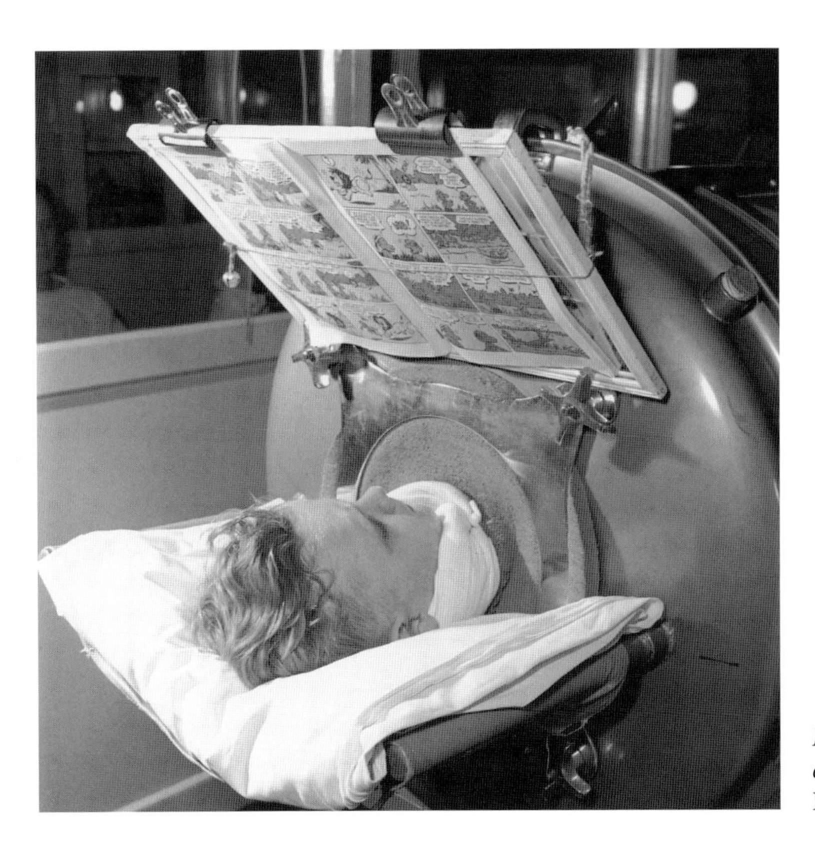

Poliomyelitis sufferer reads a comic book. Copyright Holton-Deutsch Collection/CORBIS

Missouri that an "iron curtain" of Communist domination had fallen across Europe. His speech launched the Cold War and ensuing arms race. The United States announced test detonations of atomic devices in 1948, and the Soviet Union—to the horror of Americans—exploded its first nuclear bomb in 1949. From the annihilated Japanese cities of Hiroshima and Nagasaki came reports of an extraordinary rise in the number of birth defects and of monstrous genetic abnormalities in the wake of nuclear devastation.

In Camden in January 1951, the Civil Defense Council, alarmed by the commitment of U.S. ground troops in Korea, simulated the first nuclear attack on an industrial city in the United States. Residents watched as five planes dropped paper "A-bombs" and volunteers evacuated counterfeit casualties. In the early 1950s, the children who were warned not to touch their lips to the faucets of drinking fountains for fear of contracting paralytic polio were also trained to "duck and cover" under their classroom desks from the blinding flash and fatal fallout of nuclear attack. Parents, terrified by the crippling power of polio, worried over rumors of a poisonous cloud riding global winds and raining radiation. Each threat became identified with and magnified the other. Iron curtain and iron lung: cold, hard symbols of an anxious age.

The cold war and the conquest of polio were deeply associated in America's consciousness at a psychological level as both crusades expropriated each other's basic metaphors. In the wake of world war, medical scientists commonly described viruses as "invading" the body and "attacking" cells. Conversely, anti-Communists portrayed the rival ideology as a viral disease attacking the country from within. In 1949 Congress acknowledged that the country had been infiltrated by Communists bent on the "overthrow of the U.S. government by force." The next year, a senator from Wisconsin announced that the State Department harbored Communists and their sympathizers. In 1953 the United States executed suspected "atomic" spies. Espionage, the public was told, was a cancer eating away at the body politic.

In such a paranoid period of American history, the distinction between public health and civil defense was often blurred.[6] For example, many sensible people saw fluoridation of water supplies as a Communist plot. They believed that fluoride affected a specific part of the brain, gradually rendering its victims docile and less resistant to authoritarian forms of government. (Polio, it should be noted, likewise affected the brain, immobilizing—not minds—but limbs and lungs.) Dr. Coriell advocated fluoridation, and his opinion probably carried extra weight. However, despite the fact that he chaired the New Jersey Civil Defense subcommittee on biological warfare, Dr. Coriell was unable to convince local communities to add flouride to their drinking water.

Remarkably, on Election Day 1951, the *Courier-Post*'s lead editorial was not about voting or the platforms of political candidates, but rather about the threat of germ warfare. The commentary warned of "exploding aerosol bombs, capable of spraying smog-like clouds of infectious disease bacteria over our large cities," of atomizers in the suitcases of saboteurs, and of "fifth columnists" poisoning food in canneries. It hailed the scientists at the National Institutes of Health and at Fort Detrick for their heroic work in devising countermeasures against such invasions, especially the scores of them that had suffered illness and death in the laboratories. The words "antibiotics" and "anti-Communism" were not far apart in the dictionary of Cold War politics.

The intensity of the "fight" against polio and the eventual glorification of the scientists who won the "battle" can only be understood within the context of these deep-seated public attitudes and intensely compelling events. Likewise, it is impossible to explain the overwhelming support of the Camden community for Dr. Coriell's independent research institute without appreciating the critical role he played in the conquest of the dreaded disease. Before the Second World War, the public viewed laboratory research as useful but dull business. As a result of the war, the image of science had been fundamentally altered, and the scientist was elevated to a pedestal formerly reserved for financiers or statesmen. Aided by the savvy publicity machinery of the National Foundation for Infantile Paralysis, the biomedical scientist entered the popular iconography of American heroism. In 1949, when Camden's press would refer to Dr. Coriell as a "nationally renowned" scientist, the expression conveyed local pride in the city's ability to attract a doctor whose exceptional talent was recognized by an esoteric subspecialty of microbiologists. After 1952, that label testified to broad public awareness of his vital contributions

[6] The anthrax scare following the events of September 11, 2001, provides a recent example of this blurring.

to science and society. For many individuals those three years would be worth a lifetime.

THE CONQUEST OF POLIO

Etymologically and pathologically, *poliomyelitis* means inflammation of the gray matter of the spinal cord. When polio (as newspaper editors began abbreviating the word in headlines) damages the motor cells of the spinal cord, the muscles they control are immobilized and atrophy. When polio infects the medulla oblongata, which is the spinal bulb at the top of the cord, breathing is impaired, chest muscles become paralyzed, and death can result.

Since 1908 biologists knew that polio was a virus, but finding a vaccine was proving problematic. Post-mortem examinations of polio victims showed evidence of damage to nerve cells, but the virus could not be found in the blood or other tissues. Furthermore, scientists who succeeded in growing poliovirus in tissue culture from brain cells could not duplicate the feat in other human tissues. Virologists incorrectly inferred from these studies that polio, like rabies, attacked nerve cells directly and exclusively.

In fact, the virus commonly enters the gastrointestinal tract. By the 1940s the fallacious conception of a neurotropic poliovirus retarded vaccine research because of the enormous difficulties in harvesting viruses from a culture medium containing nervous tissue cells. Virologists were painfully aware that, should any of the nervous tissue contaminate the vaccine, inoculation could cause an immune response that could produce fatal brain damage. An additional deterrent was the ostensible fact that polio attacked only man, monkeys, and chimpanzees. One could not effectively or consistently develop the virus in economical, controlled experimental animals such as mice. Monkeys—for a variety of reasons—were difficult experimental animals.

Prior to World War II, therefore, polio research inspired comparatively few investigators. The National Foundation for Infantile Paralysis dedicated most of its money to the care of polio victims. During the war, polio research took a back seat to investigation of diseases that seriously threatened American troops. Ironically, these troops may well have brought polio home from the battlefields. As polio epidemics intensified after the war, the National Foundation began spending boldly to find a prevention or cure of polio. It directed funds to investigators whose war work had enhanced their appreciation of the value of mission-oriented research. These scientists may not have been primarily interested in polio, but the Foundation's dollars supported their "pure" research and subtly induced them to consider the implications of their research for the conquest of polio. The mobilization of scientists interested in everything but polio during the war paved the way for the eventual conquest of polio after it.

Noted epidemiologist Thomas Francis, Jr., for example, had barely arrived at the University of Michigan in 1941 to direct its School of Public Health when the Armed Forces Epidemiological Board asked him to take charge of the Army's effort to make a killed-virus vaccine for mass use against influenza, the disease that had plagued the earth during the First World War. For this endeavor, he hired Jonas Salk, who had no interest in polio at the time. Francis's wartime experience made him the National Foundation's logical choice as director of the 1954 field trials of the Salk vaccine against polio.

Similarly, John Enders was not experimenting with poliovirus. At Harvard—having fallen under the spell of Hans Zinsser, one of Lew Coriell's boyhood heroes—Enders was working in Cambridge with William McDowell Hammon on cat distemper when the Epidemiological Board recruited him and CHOP's Joe Stokes to work on mumps. The affliction could produce meningitis, which was a major problem at World War I training camps. The Stokes-Enders team produced a killed-virus vaccine against the disease. Had that collaboration not occurred it is unlikely that Enders would have met Dr. Coriell and learned from him the tissue-culture techniques that resulted in the key breakthrough in polio research.

As the 1950s dawned, Dr. Coriell likewise had not focused his attention on the cure of polio. He was preoccupied with the care of polio patients. As hospital director, he had to confront an array of medical challenges; consequently, his research agenda was diversified. CMH was one of about three thousand hospitals nationwide that accepted polio patients. It was recognized as one of the best. Retrospectively overlooked in the panoply of its director's accomplishments was his mastery of techniques for rapid diagnosis of polio; of the technology of iron lungs, respirators, and rocking beds; and of rehabilitation regimens of polio victims. There were plenty of diseases to contend with at CMH, but increasingly the public's attention—and support—focused on the affliction called the Crippler.

As a prelude to his campaign to garner tax support of South Jersey counties and municipalities, Dr. Coriell had captured the commitment of the leaders of the local county chapters of the National Foundation, who dedicated the proceeds of their "March of Dimes" fundraising drives to CMH. The county chapters of Camden, Burlington, Cumberland, Cape May, and Salem donated $3,200 to equip a new hospital receiving ward which the city commission had underwritten with an emergency appropriation of $6,000. Officials dedicated the space on Monday, January 16, 1950. January was a good month to renovate and re-equip the hospital. The winter frost had put an end to the polio season and the first infectious wave of winter ills had not yet hit. The medical director's design of the renovated space coupled his insistence on providing the best medical care with his passion for efficiency. The previous layout was an ergonomic disaster. Patients were carried up a flight of stairs to a receiving room where the hospitalized could not be segregated. The new plan combined a first-floor receiving ward with three modern examining rooms, a covered ambulance entrance, and two adjacent laboratories. Essentially, Dr. Coriell had created an emergency wing in which diagnosis and treatment could commence the moment the ambulance door opened. The renovation was the first in a series of facilities developments that would bear the stamp of Dr. Coriell's determination and vision in the second half of the twentieth century.

While Dr. Coriell was establishing a reputation as one of the country's foremost authorities on the care and treatment of polio patients, the race for a cure for polio was intensifying. Serendipitously, almost inadvertently, Dr. Coriell had supplied a key to a lock that had to be opened before a polio vaccine could be developed. It was perhaps his most significant but least known contribution to the conquest of the disease. John Enders had moved from Harvard to Boston Children's Hospital after the war. With support from the National Foundation, he had hired two bacteriologists, Thomas Weller and Frederick C. Robbins, to help him conduct experiments using tissue cultures to diagnose the various infectious diseases they were witnessing at the hospital. Weller was interested in chickenpox. Enders continued to work on mumps and kept in touch with CHOP's chief Joe Stokes, his wartime collaborator on the mumps vaccine. In early 1948, Stokes told Enders about Coriell's success in growing chickenpox on embryonated human skin. Enders came to Philadelphia to visit Coriell's laboratory and learn this technique, which Enders later imparted to Weller.

One day in March, Weller prepared a few too many culture flasks in his quest to grow the chickenpox virus using Coriell's techniques. Enders recalled that he had a tube of poliovirus in the freezer and suggested that Weller seed his flasks with some of it. After all, the National Foundation was funding their research. To everyone's amazement, the poliovirus grew, even though there were no nervous tissue cells in the mixture. The team succeeded in keeping the polio strain growing for 224 days and published their report in *Science* in January 1949. This staggering breakthrough meant that poliovirus could multiply *in vitro* in cells other than those of the nervous system and that a non-neurotropic polio vaccine could be produced. The discovery, which might not have materialized without Dr. Coriell's inspiration, earned Enders and his colleagues a Nobel Prize.

Jonas Salk was best positioned to take advantage of these findings. After developing the killed-virus vaccine against influenza, he had left "Tommy" Francis's laboratory for the University of Pittsburgh. There, on the vacated floors of that city's municipal hospital, he ran the Virus Research Laboratory, which was established by the National Foundation to type polioviruses. Researchers had identified three types of poliovirus; there may have been others. The Foundation was paying Salk to find out. By January 1950, the laboratory had begun tissue-culture production of poliovirus. In short order, Salk had developed a killed vaccine against poliomyelitis and had shown its effectiveness in preventing paralytic polio in monkeys. Foundation officials and public health authorities, however, were justifiably cautious about approving the vaccine until more tests could be conducted to demonstrate its safety and efficacy in humans. There were too many unanswered questions. In the meantime, children were succumbing to polio in increasing numbers.

One alternative to a potentially dangerous vaccine was gamma globulin injection. Gamma globulin is that fraction of the blood serum containing the antibodies that fight off reinfection of certain diseases. Virologists, epidemiologists, and clinicians suspected that most people become infected with polio and that the infection—either imperceptible or mildly symptomatic—confers subsequent immunity. Joe Stokes had pioneered the use of gamma globulin. In fact, during Philadelphia's polio epidemic of 1932, Stokes and his associates at CHOP had attempted to provide passive immunity to nearly 2,500 children by inoculating them with *whole* blood obtained from their parents. Even though antibodies could not be delivered in sufficient concentrations by means of this process, the results of the experiment were encouraging if inconclusive. After 1941, when scientists learned how to separate globulin from blood plasma, Stokes proved that globulin could temporarily immunize against epidemic hepatitis. During the war, working with Enders's former colleague William Hammon, Stokes showed that globulin injection was a safe and effective method for preventing or attenuating measles. He approached the National Foundation in 1944 with a plan to use globulin to protect chil-

The Philadelphia Inquirer

WEDNESDAY MORNING, OCTOBER 29, 1952 h★ 31

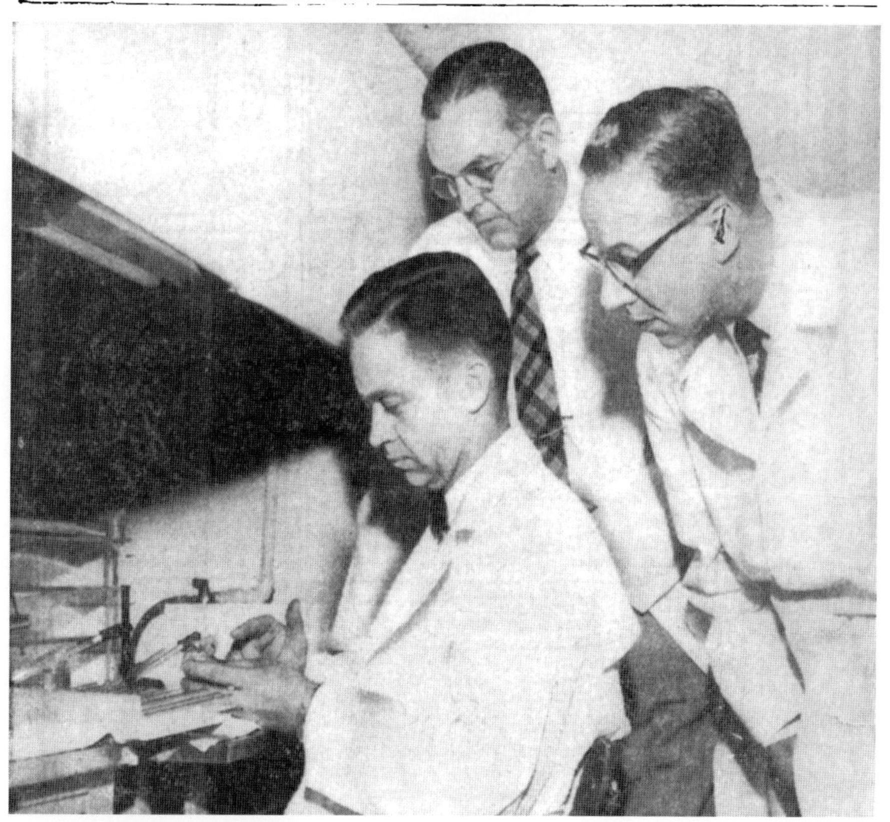

Dr. Lewis L. Coriell (seated), deputy director of the recent successful gamma globulin polio immunization studies, examines virus growing on tissue culture in laboratories at Children's Hospital of Philadelphia. Looking on are Dr. Joseph Stokes, Jr., consultant for project, and Dr. William McD. Hammon (right), project director.

Courtesy of The Philadelphia Inquirer

dren against polio. The reviewing committee axed the plan. One of its principal objections involved the fear that globulin's temporary conferral of passive immunity would compromise the processes by which children acquire natural active immunity through contact with the actual disease.

By 1948, Stokes and others had shown that artificial passive immunity did not suppress the development of natural active immunity. Stokes joined forces with Hammon to press for a hearing before the Foundation. The alliance was propitious. A fellow member of the Epidemiological Board, Hammon had recently arrived as professor of epidemiology at the University of Pittsburgh's Graduate School of Public Health, a stone's throw from Salk's Virus Research Laboratory. He had even helped the Foundation establish the protocols for Salk's virus typing project. Besides, before he had entered Harvard Medical School, he had been a missionary preacher in the Belgian Congo. He knew how to persuade. On July 6, 1951, the Foundation's special committee on immunization unanimously approved the Polio Prevention Study, a pilot project involving the gamma globulin inoculations. Hammon would be the project director; Stokes, the general consultant; and Coriell, the field director and deputy project director.

The project was huge. It was simply the biggest human field trial in medical history, the world's largest field test of a deterrent to a disease, and the most complex experiment ever conducted in the United States. It represented the first and only time a private concern directed and funded a nationwide medical experiment. At a time when the National Institutes of Health expended some seventy thousand dollars per year for polio research nationwide, the National Foundation was committing one million dollars to this endeavor alone. The Red Cross was furnishing a treasure of globulin procured from the blood of tens of thousands of Americans throughout the war years. The risks were enormous, and the level of media surveillance was unprecedented. It was not a diversion for the faint-hearted.

The selection of Dr. Coriell as second-in-command was a natural choice. In addition to sharing the burden of planning the study and selecting the most promising sites for its implementation, Dr. Coriell was the chief of operations. He had to set up the clinics, engage and train the personnel, direct public and media relations, insure the integrity of the trials, and analyze and certify the results. Probably no one else in the country possessed his combination of qualifications. The physician was an expert in the diagnosis and treatment of polio patients. The virologist was a master technician of cell culturing. The administrator had managed an empire at Fort Detrick. The man had indefatigable energy.

Dr. Coriell would spend the remainder of the summer in Pittsburgh to plan the study. Fortunately, his leave of absence did not compromise medical care at CMH. Prior to departure, he appointed Robert Milton McAllister, the hospital's chief resident. Eleven years younger than the director, McAllister was a Pennsylvanian who had graduated from Penn's School of Medicine in 1945 and spent the next two and a half years in the U.S. Army Medical Corps. He returned to Philadelphia and was pursuing a residency at CHOP in 1948 when he attended one of Dr. Coriell's lectures on virology. He was mesmerized. "Lew Coriell," McAllister recalled, "spun my head around!" Financial indebtedness incurred at medical school persuaded him to open a private practice, but Dr. Coriell's influence inspired him in a different direction. A gainful private practice in Salisbury, Maryland, proved painful. One of only two pediatricians on the entire Eastern Shore of the Delmarva Peninsula, McAllister found his work unpredictable and exhausting. His body weight dropped from 180 to 137 pounds. He wrote to his mentor an S O S.

Dr. Coriell responded by arranging for his appointment as assistant physician and member of the research department at CHOP. Armed with introductions from his new boss at CMH, McAllister traveled to the laboratories of virology's giants. He visited Yale's Joseph Melnick, who was experimenting with a live-virus polio vaccine. He worked with John Enders in Boston, then journeyed to Minnesota to learn about HELA cells from Jerome Syverton. In 1952, when Dr. Murphy left the hospital for the Sloan-Kettering Institute, "Mac" (as his colleagues would call him) assumed the assistant directorship. Forged from common challenges and bound by mutual respect and affection, the collaboration of McAllister and Coriell would span the decade and prove enormously productive. At its beginning, the partnership insured the success of the gamma globulin field trials.

Gamma globulin was certainly less dangerous than an insufficiently attenuated virus vaccine, but it did have its drawbacks. It was expensive and scarce. All the globulin in the world would not suffice to inoculate a fraction of the people at risk. And, because the antibody was a foreign protein that the body rapidly expelled, its effects were short-lived. Inoculation of gamma globulin was not the same as a vaccination that conferred permanent immunity. But if it were proved safe, if it lasted long enough, and if it could prevent paralysis in humans who had just contracted polio, then post-trial shots of the gooey substance could at least be administered to those most at risk during epidemics. Moreover, it would show scientists that it was possible to confer artificial immunity against polio. Public health spokespersons confidently informed the public that a virus vaccine was on the horizon, but—in order not to prompt panicked impatience—they took care to say that the horizon might be five or ten years away. Gamma globulin was an interim measure, but one that might bring hope to a worried country. The trial was worth the effort and expense.

There was, however, another reason for the trials that foundation officials and project officers hesitated to avow publicly. They knew that a mass vaccination against polio was inevitable. It would be useful to have had experience in mass production, purchasing, and distribution of serums. Beyond logistical considerations were larger questions. How would the public react to the unprecedented prospect of lining up their children for such tests? What would be the response of school systems, of local public health officials? This was all virgin territory. Retrospectively, the mass distribution of gamma globulin was a grand rehearsal for the main event. Prospectively, this realization only added to the tense pressure to produce a successful outcome.

Hammon was convinced that a double-blind study would be necessary in order to validate the trial results. That is, half of the children would be given in intra-muscular injection of gamma globulin and half—the control group—would receive an innocuous gelatin solution. Neither the subjects nor the administering physicians would know who got what until a secret coded record was opened at the conclusion of an outbreak. Teams were trained to rush to areas of the country that were experiencing polio epidemics. The logistics would be as complicated as the science. Nothing was left unconsidered: for every shipped dose of globulin or gelatin there would be a corresponding lollipop as a reward for bravery.

The statistical standard for an epidemic was fifty-eight victims per one hundred thousand. On August 31, 1951, when Utah County's population of 81,912 experienced its fiftieth case of polio, the Polio Prevention Study team packed up for Provo. Moving with lightening speed and accompanied by nine physicians and twenty nurses, Dr. Coriell arrived in the county on Sunday, September 1, established five inoculation centers, and began the history-making tests on Tuesday. They inoculated 5,731 youngsters. The results of that first trial would remain sealed until a larger and more statistically significant

Polio Prevention Study team prepares to board bus in Provo, Utah.

Drs. Hammon and Coriell greet polio study team member and supervising nurse Claudia Crownover on arrival from Houston, Texas.

population could be included in the final tabulations. As that year's polio season ended, the study team carefully researched some two hundred prospective cities of convenient size and support apparatus. The following spring they monitored those sites carefully for early warning signs of epidemics.

In late June 1952, Houston, Texas, became the study group's next tinderbox. An expanded team that included Bob McAllister descended on the area. Eleven exhausting days later, they had inoculated 33,074 kids. Just as they were completing their meticulous follow-up procedures in Texas, they were ordered to charter a plane for Sioux City, Iowa, which had plunged into the maelstrom of an extremely virulent outbreak. There they inoculated 15,968 children in Woodbury and Dakota counties. During the mission, McAllister succumbed to what he was pretty certain was polio. He worked nevertheless through sore bones and bouts of nausea, until he began experiencing severe chest pains. That, he recollected, "made me feel wonderful," because it suggested to the experienced diagnostician that he was suffering from a Coxsackie-virus infection.

It was time to break the double-blind code and interpret the results of the trials. On October 22, the world's attention was focused on the American Public Health Association's annual meeting in Cleveland, Ohio. Dr. Coriell had co-authored the report that Bill Hammon read to the attentive crowd. The report, which would be published later that year in the *Journal of the*

The polio study targeted children throughout the city of Houston, including the (above) Jacinto City Elementary School and the (below) Lyons Avenue Health Center.

Residents of Sioux City, Iowa, flock to participate in the Polio Prevention Study.

American Medical Association, announced that a total of 54,773 children had been inoculated. Of the 27,402 children who actually received gamma globulin, only twenty-six contracted paralytic polio. That meant that less than one person in one thousand became paralyzed, compared to 2.3 cases per thousand among the control groups. The bottom line: gamma globulin administered in the midst of an epidemic reduced one's chances of contracting paralytic polio by nearly sixty percent. After decades of depressing news about polio, the world finally saw proof of a procedure that offered hope. What's more, officials at the National Foundation and the U.S. Public Health Service recognized the public's readiness to accept national trials of a mass-produced vaccine. The announced results of the Polio Prevention Study stimulated the pace of the development of the Salk vaccine, set the stage for its national trial in 1954, and played a key role in the eventual conquest of a great epidemic scourge that afflicted children.

A Hero's Welcome

The next day banner headlines throughout the nation celebrated the success of the experiment and honored the triumvirate of Hammon, Coriell, and Stokes. Newspapers in Sioux City, Houston, and Provo praised the contributions of their cities to the progress of medical science and paid homage to Dr. Coriell and his team for their brave expeditions. The Montana papers ap-

★ AN INDEPENDENT NEWSPAPER—COVERING CENTRAL MONTANA LIKE THE STARS ★
WHEAT • STOCKRAISING
FARMING • MINING
OIL • RECREATION
Lewistown DAILY NEWS
Lewistown, Montana Sunday, November 16, 1952 63rd Year—No. 188

Former Central Montanan Gains National Recognition
For His Work In Gamma Globulin Experiments On Polio

DR. CORIELL

The local Montana press noted with pride Dr. Coriell's extraordinary success on the national scene. Courtesy of Lewistown Daily News-Argus

plauded their favorite son. The *Kansas City Times* reminded its readers where the young deputy director had received his medical training. In the Philadelphia area, of course, coverage was especially extensive and celebratory. With the substitution of a few words, the opening sentence of the *Courier-Post*'s lead story might have been written by a war correspondent. "A resounding victory," it declared, "that may well spell the end of devastating polio epidemics, has been won by American medical forces." The next week's *Saturday Evening Post*, one of the country's most popular weekly magazines, featured a major feature story, "The Best News Yet on Polio!" "Seldom," the article began, "does an army win a victory at the moment of the enemy's greatest and most damaging advance." The feature's opening page contained two photographs; one of Stokes, Hammon, and Coriell in a laboratory at CHOP and another with Hammon, Coriell, and another medical teammate inoculating a child in Sioux City.

Within a week of the Cleveland report, the National Foundation announced a $36,437 grant to Dr. Coriell to conduct continuing experiments on gamma globulin's effectiveness at CMH. The city of Camden perceived the award as an accolade. Dr. Coriell was bombarded with requests for interviews—and with lucrative offers of employment from prestigious academic medical research centers. Camden swelled with pride and competed for the doctor's attentions. In November Dr. Coriell received the County Bar Association's William T. Boyle Award as the county's outstanding citizen of 1952.

The Saturday Evening

POST

November 1, 1952 – 15¢

The Best News Yet on Polio!

By STEVEN M. SPENCER

Here are the results of the historic experiment with a new polio inoculation. They prove that, although polio isn't licked yet, we have at last come to a turning point in the long fight against it.

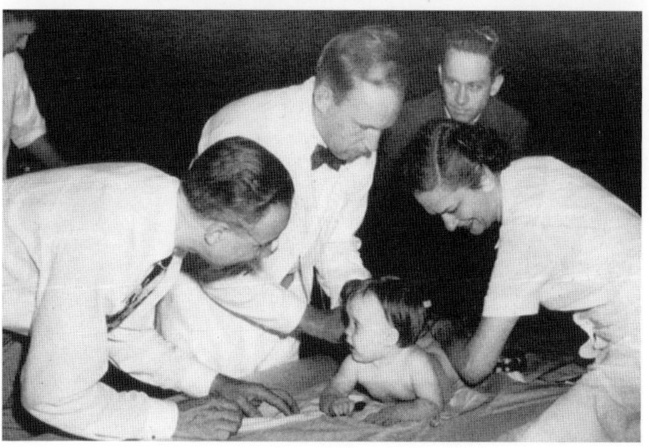

On March 11, 1953, over four hundred people filled the ballroom of the Walt Whitman Hotel to celebrate the eightieth anniversary of Camden County's Chamber of Commerce. The Chamber highlighted the gala evening by bestowing its prestigious Distinguished Service Award on Dr. Lewis L. Coriell.

Camden had good reason to salute their famous physician. Dr. Coriell had arrived at a time of urban challenge and had invigorated with his optimism, resilience, and sense of high purpose the hopes of community leaders attempting to launch a second renaissance for the city. The quick progress he had made in improving the health of the region and in attracting outside resources to the city not only mirrored the hopes and intents of civic progressives but also provided them with a model. His transformation of the institution entrusted to his care became a symbol for the kind of metamorphosis the city itself wished to make. His smooth transition from wartime to peacetime contributions inspired the city's confidence that its businesses and industries could do the same. Modestly unaffected by his growing national reputation, he embodied those virtues that Camden most valued about itself. He personified progress, inspired love and loyalty, and encouraged local pride. In honoring Lewis Coriell, Camden County's citizens were honoring themselves.

There is a difference between fame and greatness. Great people know how to manage fame to support large visions and lasting achievements. Community leaders knew that by supporting Dr. Coriell's altruistic endeavors they were enhancing their own civic fortunes. What could they do to aid his important work, they asked? Dr. Coriell did not wait for the mercurial glow of national notoriety to dim. He suggested they build him a research laboratory facility.

CHAPTER FOUR

BRICKS, MORTAR, DREAMS (1953–1956)

IN 1953 THE CITY FATHERS could take justifiable pride in—and would exact political mileage from—the unassailable fact that their troublesome pest house had been transformed into one of the country's leading hospitals for contagious disease. When they brokered their deal with Children's Hospital, however, they could not have contemplated the prospect of a hitherto-unknown cattle wrangler from Montana persuading them to surrender a city acre of tax-ratable land upon which he would build an independent research laboratory with other people's money. Yet in November 1953 the South Jersey Medical Research Foundation (SJMRF) would be formed by some of the most powerful business and civic leaders in the region. In June 1956 the organization would break ground for the construction of a research facility and institute. How did that happen?

Lewis Coriell's national celebrity may have triggered the community's energetic backing of this bold initiative, but Camden's underlying enthusiasm sprang from something else. It stemmed from its surprising and prideful discovery that a man who had devoted so much of himself to his local community had anything left to contribute to a larger crusade beyond. After all, famed scientists, Nobel laureates, in relentless pursuit of a cure for mankind's woes, hardly had time to care for a little boy or girl. They were the eponymous ones who single-mindedly withdrew from the world in order to make fabled contributions to it. Dr. Coriell, on the other hand, was the caring physician, alert to each ambulance siren, promoting patient morale and improving patient care at every turn. Surely, research must be of secondary importance to such an active physician.

Under Dr. Coriell's direction, his comrades tore down walls that separated iron-lung patients from polio victims with less severe handicaps, installed game machines and televisions in the wards, enlarged the parking lot to encourage visitation, and stood ready to implement the director's next idea. Inspired by the medical director's example, his colleagues developed volunteer

Daily care of patients fortified Dr. Coriell's and his staff's determination to find a cure for polio.

programs to augment staff and coddle patients. From procuring and mastering life-saving equipment to ushering Santa Claus on grand reindeer rounds every December, he was omnipresent and indefatigable. He devised what was perhaps the first "portable" telephone system ever seen in a hospital with a series of phone jacks connected to a dial-out-only line for patients calling home. And, investing every dime into patient care, he managed this progressive enterprise implausibly from a single small desk that he shared with the assistant director and chief resident. That this modest person so dedicated to his patients was simultaneously conducting path-breaking scientific research and directing national experiments simply amazed and humbled his neighbors.

It was difficult to say no to Dr. Coriell because he never said no to the community. He always accepted invitations—and they were legion—to address civic groups on matters of health and disease. Despite the fact that Camden County had competent public health officials, the media and community organizations would routinely seek out Dr. Coriell as medical advisor and epidemiological prognosticator. The following observations by a participant at one breakfast club's encounter with Municipal's medical director typified the effect of his charismatic personality upon Camden's citizenry:

> Dr. Coriell didn't talk like a learned physician who wanted to display what wonderful things he had helped to accomplish. He didn't try to im-

> press the men around him with his knowledge . . . He talked as a friend and as a neighbor. He spoke very simply in language we could all understand. . . . We were all very much impressed by Dr. Coriell's simplicity, his earnestness and his utter humility . . . He was exceedingly patient, and I felt as I sat listening to him that here was a truly big man who took the time to be human. Like many men in the medical field, he looked overworked but his smile was wonderful. His face was filled with that rare something one always finds in quiet men who do big things. . . . [I]t was a great privilege to have breakfast with this man who is so big but who takes the time to be a good neighbor.[1]

This newcomer's appreciation of community inter-relatedness, forging of strong personal relationships, and sacrificial commitment to Camden's well-being deeply touched his neighbors. What they saw as *exceptional* manifestations of the polite, suburban middle-class virtue of neighborliness the transported Westerner took for granted as normative conduct ordained by the social compact of mutual aid that he had assimilated in the isolated Montana community of his youth. On rugged ranchland, neighborliness meant survival. Dr. Coriell's genius was that—by quiet force of steady example—he taught his new neighbors that, in a modern city threatened by polio and other epidemic diseases, that iron law still obtained. As Camdenites practiced their philanthropy for the sake of their municipal hospital, they came to understand the indivisibility of altruism and self-interest. And that may just be the definition of a viable community. When the opportunity arose to allow Dr. Coriell to perfect his dream, Camden unhesitatingly and joyfully championed his vision.

The Beginning of an Institute

Aptly, the impetus for the development of an independent medical research institute in Camden sprang from Dr. Coriell's compassionate counsel to a deeply distressed neighbor. Kenneth N. MacDonald, a recently married, twenty-nine-year-old advertising executive, was serving as vice president of the Camden County Junior Chamber of Commerce[2] when he first met Dr. Coriell. In early 1951, MacDonald and his wife suffered the loss of their first child to leukemia. The tragedy provoked MacDonald's impassioned interest in childhood diseases and deep involvement in the progress of the Municipal Hospital. When he became president of the "Jaycees" in 1952, he threw the resources of the Junior Chamber behind a vigorous drive for hospital improve-

---

[1] The occasion was a meeting of the Men's Breakfast Club of St. Mary's Episcopal Church on December 19, 1953. The quotation is from the "This . . . and That" column in the weekly paper, *The Town Crier*, written pseudonymously by "The Oldtimer," who may have been Edith Blez.

[2] The Junior Chamber of Commerce was created in St. Louis, Missouri, in 1920. Its founder, Henry "Hy" Giessenbier, envisioned an organization in which young men could enhance their business skills while gaining leadership experience through community service. Camden County's Junior Chamber was created in 1947.

ments. Largely in recognition of these efforts, the "big" Chamber named him the county's "Young Man of the Year" in 1952.

What the community did not know was that the MacDonalds' adversity was compounded by the threat of the dissolution of their marriage. Believing leukemia a hereditary disease, Mrs. MacDonald blamed her husband for their child's death and was uncertain of her capacity to endure a marriage that implied a childless future. Dr. Coriell's sensitive guidance, backed by his medical authority, changed her mind and saved a marriage. In 1952, the MacDonalds celebrated the birth of a healthy daughter Kerry. MacDonald's tireless work on behalf of CMH was born of acknowledged sorrow and silent gratitude.

In the summer of 1951, as vice president and president elect of the Jaycees, Ken MacDonald formally introduced Dr. Coriell as guest speaker at one of the Junior Chamber's weekly luncheon meeting at Kenney's restaurant in downtown Camden. William Kallelis, who had started a securities business in Camden the same year Dr. Coriell arrived, attended the luncheon. A fairly new member of the Jaycees, he reported that Dr. Coriell "impressed us with his intensity, dedication, and sincerity." Asked what they could do to help the hospital, CHM's director suggested that they raise funds for something the budget of the January 1950 renovation had been unable to accommodate. The hospital desperately needed an elevator to transport patients in wheel chairs and iron lungs to and from the second-floor wards.

The elevator project would provide an important lift—the pun is intentional—to the prospects of an independent research institute. Significantly, it established the precedent of an innovative funding mechanism for raising capital. Because the hospital was a tax-supported entity for which the city was responsible, officials feared legal challenges to the practice of funding capital purchases with private dollars. Local "March of Dimes" drives by the county chapters of the National Foundation for Infantile Paralysis raised funds for iron lungs, portable respirators and other paraphernalia for the diagnosis and treatment of polio and the care and rehabilitation of polio patients.[3] It was okay for voluntary organizations to fund and purchase smaller items that they would then donate to the hospital because these items were seen as highly depreciable, perishable gifts. The elevator project, however, was considered a major capital addition to the physical plant of a municipal property. In order to allow privately raised money to be dedicated to this project, the Jaycees created a special trust fund. Two years later Camden's civic leadership would use this legal precedent to create the South Jersey Medical Research Foundation.

The project illustrated a feature of the greater Camden community that would be essential to the development of a research institute: its extraordinary dedication to Dr. Coriell and his mission. For eight months following that fateful luncheon, Jaycees pounded the sidewalks in pursuit of donations from local merchants, solicited coins outside department stores, and organized

[3] Technically, the national organization controlled and directed those funds and authorized what percentage of locally raised dollars could revert to the localities in which they were raised.

COURIER-POST
CAMDEN, NEW JERSEY

—Courier-Post Photo

POLIO PATIENT Shirley Dyer, of Haddonfield, snips symbolic white ribbon to put new elevator in service at Camden Municipal Hospital. The elevator was provided by the Junior Chamber of Commerce and the city. Watching Miss Dyer with interest are, left to right, Kenneth MacDonald, former Jaycees president; Richard G. Wickes, incumbent president; Dr. Lewis L. Coriell, medical director, and City Commissioner Sidney P. McCord.

Courtesy of The Courier-Post

fund raising events. When they had amassed fifteen thousand dollars for the purchase price of the elevator, an appreciative hospital chief pointed out the difficulty of utilizing an elevator prior to the installation of an elevator shaft. It was estimated that the addition would cost another six thousand dollars. Having already canvassed the business community, the Jaycees took matters literally into their own hands. "We couldn't hit the bricks again," Bill Kallelis recounted, "so we laid them instead." Working evenings and weekends, these small-business entrepreneurs and ambitious middle managers of large companies—helped by a small municipal appropriation—worked alongside skilled workers to construct the elevator's housing. Rarely do the same donors open wallets *and* blisters. In the autumn of 1952 the passenger elevator was operational. Such concrete philanthropy foreshadowed a more remarkable undertaking.

Timing may not be everything, but it counts. When the Chamber bestowed its Distinguished Service Award on Dr. Coriell in March 1953, the Jaycees announced that Ken MacDonald was Camden's "Young Man of the Year" for 1952. Following that award, the young advertising executive so immersed himself in civic and community activities that the state Chamber honored him as New Jersey's "Young Man of 1953." Both men were at the apex of local celebrity when Dr. Coriell shared with MacDonald his dream of building a research facility. MacDonald understood that such a venture would require resources beyond the capacity of the Jaycees. Fortunately, by the summer of 1953, his influence had expanded beyond the boundaries of the Junior Chamber. He promised Dr. Coriell that he would work to develop a circle of backers for the doctor's plan.

The basic strategy was to build a board of trustees with the fiduciary responsibility to oversee a trust fund and the philanthropic clout to fill it with dollars. If the venture succeeded, the board members would ultimately serve as founding directors of a not-for-profit corporation engaged in scientific research. A mid-level corporate manager, MacDonald understood that his personal reputation did not provide automatic access to the executive leadership of Camden's major corporations. He could, however, easily approach his boss's boss at Esterbrook Pen Company. Esterbrook vice president Philip E. Scott needed little persuading to head the top-level recruitment drive, an activity that almost naturally destines the doer for board presidency. He required little education into the intricacies of corporate giving and board development. Judiciously, Scott immediately approached his boss, Esterbrook president Sydney E. Longmaid, who accepted an invitation to serve as a trustee.

While it has not been recorded (or at the time appreciated) as an event of unusual historical significance, Longmaid's commitment was the key to the success of the enterprise. First, his willingness to become a trustee implicitly blessed the active involvement of Scott and MacDonald in the affairs of the new organization. Second, it guaranteed Esterbrook's forthcoming financial backing. Third, it signaled to other captains of industry and commerce that "one of their own" took seriously this new initiative in Camden. At the time, Longmaid served on the executive and finance committees of the First Camden National Bank & Trust Company, an important source of services that a fledgling corporation would require. He was a trustee of Camden's Community Chest and numerous other regional and state associations. And he knew he was about to be appointed as state director of the National Association of Manufacturers, the most influential industrial directorship in New Jersey and a position of national visibility. His involvement provided credibility to the in-

Esterbrook's commitment to Dr. Coriell's dream instilled a "buyer's confidence" in Camden's philanthropic community. Courtesy of Camden County Historical Society

cipient venture, legitimated board membership for corporate CEOs, and elevated the prestige of belonging in the eyes of other prospective trustees.

Sydney E. Longmaid's inestimable contribution, however, was not his active involvement. Indeed, from 1953 until his death in 1967 he would serve unobtrusively on the board of the South Jersey Medical Research Foundation.[4] Rather, his most precious gift was his name. His middle initial stood for "Esterbrook." His mother was the great-granddaughter of Richard Esterbrook, an enterprising Cornish Quaker who in 1860 introduced to America the steel nib fountain pen to replace the hand-cut quill. Properly churched (Episcopalian), properly educated (Yale), a member of the best clubs (Union League, Racquet Club), a commuter across two rivers from his Main Line mansion in Bryn Mawr, Pennsylvania, Longmaid was not a Jaycee. Social and economic mobility was for him a historical fact, not a personal motivation. As partial inheritor of a vast family fortune, the Esterbrook scion was pursued by many charitable organizations. He selected his charitable giving and volunteers services generously but discerningly. By backing Dr. Coriell's quest, he authenticated the Foundation for a socioeconomic elite accustomed to supporting art museums and universities. He was perhaps the only person in Camden who could have successfully approached John T. Dorrance, Jr. with the proposition of trusteeship.

Like Longmaid, Dorrance was a gifted man whose ability to run a corporate empire was acquired and whose opportunity to do so was bequeathed. At the time Dorrance served as assistant treasurer of the Campbell Soup Company, acquainting himself with the various operations of the conglomerate over which he was predestined to preside. His father, Dr. John T. Dorrance, had acquired the company in 1914 from his uncle Arthur, who in 1876 had bought out partner Joseph Campbell, who in 1869 had founded the Camden-based business. The elder Dorrance had invented condensed tomato soup in 1897 and soon thereafter transformed Campbell Soup into a national enter-

[4] In 1966, of course, the Foundation changed its name to the Institute for Medical Research. Longmaid could hardly have been expected to take an active role on a board presided over by a man who reported to him in the corporate world. (Incidentally and ironically, Longmaid's tenure on the Foundation board would bracket the twentieth-century fortunes of the Esterbrook Pen Company. In 1953, Esterbrook bought out Cushman & Denison, its chief competitor in the refillable pen business. In 1967, Venus Pencil Company took over Esterbrook.)

Sydney E. Longmaid. Courtesy of Camden County Historical Society

John T. Dorrance, Jr. Courtesy of Campbell Soup Company

prise. Receptive to Longmaid's proposal, the younger Dorrance agreed to become vice president of the board of trustees. For a third of a century afterward, he would direct needed funds to the institute from the Campbell Soup Company Foundation's coffers and give unstintingly of his personal fortune, wisdom, and advocacy. When he was in town, Dr. Coriell reminisced, "Jack Dorrance never missed a meeting."

The commitment of Dorrance and Longmaid and the active involvement of Scott and MacDonald set the stage for the board's rapid development. Bryant W. Langston, president of the Samuel M. Langston Company, became the board's treasurer. David C. Langworthy, head of Magnetic Metals of Camden, and Raymond R. Hull agreed to serve on the executive committee. Charles H. Carpenter, an executive with the Fourdrinier Kraft Board Institute; John S. Carter, senior vice president of finances at RCA, who would soon become a bank president; Wilbur H. Norton; and Thomas L. Vanderslice pledged their support. Frederick P. Greiner, co-founder of the law firm Archer, Greiner, Hunter & Read, drew up the Foundation's by-laws, mission statement, and documents of incorporation.

William A. Stretch, general manager since 1951 of the *Courier-Post*, which his family purchased from the *Philadelphia Evening Bulletin* in 1947, insured that the emergent institute would not lack free publicity. Real estate magnate Eugene Mori's membership meant that Dr. Coriell's laboratory an-

CERTIFICATE OF INCORPORATION

of

SOUTH JERSEY MEDICAL RESEARCH FOUNDATION

ARCHER, GREINER, HUNTER & READ
LAW OFFICES
CAMDEN 2, NEW JERSEY

WILSON BUILDING SUITE 1201
BROADWAY AT COOPER STREET

IN WITNESS WHEREOF, we have hereunto set our hands and seals this 10th day of November, 1953.

[illegible] (LS)
John S. Carter (LS)
Lewis L. Coriell (LS)
John T. Dorrance, Jr. (LS)
Frederick P. Greiner (LS)
Raymond R. Hull (LS)
[illegible] (LS)
David S. Langworthy (LS)
Sydney E. Longmaid (LS)
Kenneth N. MacDonald (LS)
Perry MacNeal (LS)
Eugene V. Mori (LS)
Wilbur H. Norton (LS)
Philip E. Scott (LS)
Joseph Stokes, Jr. (LS)
S. Emlen Stokes (LS)
William A. Stretch (LS)
Thomas L. VanDeralise (LS)

Signed, sealed
in the presence of

Francis James Dallett, Jr.

-3-

1953, Certificate of Incorporation.

imals would enjoy free accommodations. Mori was the president of the Garden State Race Track, where thoroughbred racehorses and experimental monkeys puzzled their proximity. The representation of medical scientists and practitioners was essential to the composition of such a board. Joseph Stokes was an obvious choice. So was his brother, S. Emlen Stokes, chief of pediatrics at neighboring Burlington County Memorial Hospital. He was not only an active member of the county medical society but also a politically active physician who had served on Burlington County's board of freeholders. Perry MacNeal, associate professor of clinical medicine at Penn, kept his illustrious institution represented in Camden. Appropriately, Dr. Coriell became secretary of the corporation and a member of the board's executive committee.

These eighteen men were the institute's *original* founders; that is, those individuals who were designated trustees in the original certificate of incorporation, executed on November 10, 1953.[5] The record of notarization makes clear that the actual execution —not unlike the signing of the Declaration of Independence—took place over a longer period of time, in this case on November 10, 12, 13, and 17. Likewise, it took months before New Jersey's Secretary of State legally certified the Foundation's corporate status. It was officially chartered in January 1954. Nevertheless, a historical fetishism understandably surrounds the establishment of any organization's date of birth. History, tradition, and common sense conspire to make November 10, 1953, the commemorative date of the institute's establishment.

The duly constituted yet unannointed board met in early January 1954 to finalize and approve the Foundation's by-laws and to consider how their new initiative would be announced. In the process, they enhanced the board's outreach and legitimacy by nominating two women as trustees. While an all-male board would hardly have been viewed as anomalous in the early 1950s, the inclusion of Mrs. Albert B. Melnick and Mrs. W.H.K. Fleck diminished the group's gender gap. A prominent social worker, Melnick had deep roots within the Jewish community in Camden County; Fleck would become the Foundation's second president in 1955. At the end of 1954, Hull and Vanderslice rotated off the board while three new trustees—Michael J. Hayes, Bill Kalellis, and Richard Wickes—joined. This twenty-one member board (the odd number conforming to the organization's by-laws) would govern the corporation through the period of fund raising and construction.

[5] Previous references to the establishment of the institute have put the number of founders at sixteen. Indeed, there were sixteen *incorporators*, trustees who put their signatures to the original certificate. That same document, however, listed eighteen trustees including two non-signatories, Carpenter and Langston. It seems probable that these two gentlemen were unavailable during the period of incorporation and that their names were deleted from the list of witnesses on the certificate.

The seemingly redundant term "original founders" is a necessary qualification. With typical inclusionary impulse, Lew Coriell considered as founding members all those who served as trustees during the critical formative period of the '50s. Appropriately, therefore, the designation "founding trustee" extends by tradition to the "recruits" of 1954 and to Dr. Reuben Sharp (1956), E. Gerald Bowman (1958), and Dr. Jonathan E. Rhoads (1958).

The certificate of incorporation captured the institution's mission concisely and perspicaciously. It read as follows:

> The purposes for which such corporation is formed is to construct, equip and support, through private and public subscription of funds or otherwise, a medical research laboratory in the City of Camden, New Jersey, which, by academic, research, diagnostic and clinical functions, independently and in association, affiliation or cooperation with other institutions, agencies and persons engaged in the field of medical science, may serve primarily the public of southern New Jersey, and, secondarily, the general public in the promotion of better public health.

The Foundation's initial publicity was more detailed and compelling. Philip Scott signed an open letter to potential supporters reminding them of the dozens of deadly diseases that had been recently conquered by medical science. Then he localized the conquest by pointing to the combined role that Children's Hospital and the Camden Municipal Hospital had played in this worldwide endeavor. Stressing that the "struggle of man against the microbe takes place in the laboratory" and that the "test tube is the birthplace of most of medicine's advances" he challenged South Jerseyans "to increase their protection against disease" by helping to make the Foundation's envisioned laboratory a reality.

Philip Scott, Dr. Coriell, and John Carter compose one of the Institute's most resonant images as they "blueprint" the new laboratory building.

Announcements and news releases emphasized the fertile collaboration between CHOP and CMH, citing particularly the development and testing of gamma globulin as a protective agent against paralytic poliomyelitis. The national prominence of CMH's medical staff did not go unreported. Spokespersons correctly stated that the flow of research grants into Camden had been retarded by the lack of space and equipment and that the necessity of conducting investigations in other institutions cost time, money, energy, and efficiency. Repeatedly, the Foundation emphasized that it did not expect tax-supported financial aid. The laboratory building would be funded by public and private subscription. Thereafter, normal operating costs would be underwritten by grants from national health organizations and the federal government.

Public exhortation stressed the practical benefits to the local community. Dr. Coriell had pioneered tissue culturing methods that could be applied to diseases that continued to plague the community. The new laboratory would provide an establishment where South Jersey physicians could diagnose those diseases that could only be determined by laboratory investigation. The laboratory could type viruses and prescribe vaccines for employees of local industries, thus promoting efficiency and reducing costs. New construction would free space in CMH that was sorely needed for the expansion of planned departments of physical and occupational therapy. A local virus diagnostic center would save lives in the event of bacteriological warfare, a plausible scenario—pundits surmised—for superpowers unwilling to risk the dangers of nuclear annihilation.

Finally, the Foundation appealed to the community's parochial pride. It reminded its neighbors that Camden's outstanding contributions to medical knowledge had been made in "borrowed facilities" with "borrowed manpower." Creating its own facility would guarantee continuity of service. It pointed not only to the possible short-lived "in-migration" of medical genius but also to the drain of local medical acumen caused by the lack of scientific research facilities in South Jersey. "Now," foundation officials urged, "is the time to give South Jersey's medical research talent its rightful and equal position with the country's best."

The price of such progress was estimated at $250,000. That figure became the goal of the campaign to build and equip the laboratory building. On March 30, 1954, the foundation commissioned Philadelphia architect Vincent Kling to design the facility to Dr. Coriell's specifications. Kling developed plans for a modern, brick-and-glass, single-story, flat-roofed rectangle, roughly fifty-nine by ninety-five feet, providing 5,600 square feet of space. Visitors would pass through a wide main entrance nearly centered on one of the building's shorter sides into a spacious lobby. A corridor ran the length of the building. Immediately on the left were offices and a conference room. Further along in sequence were men's and women's changing rooms for researchers and technicians and a series of incubation and sterile rooms. Beyond those chambers along the outer wall were five laboratories. On the right side of the corridor—again walking from the lobby to the rear entrance—were two

The March of Dimes provided critical underwriting for Dr. Coriell in his efforts to find a cure for polio. March of Dimes Birth Defects Foundation

"constant temperature" compartments, a large sterilizing room that included a kitchen, and a storage room. From back to front along that outer wall was a rear corner receiving shop, mechanical room, a chamber for sterilizing animal cages and, in the front corner, animal quarters. Between that area and the first "constant temperature" compartment was an operating room. With the exception of an internal, roofless sixteen-foot-square court on the right side of the lobby, the design was a model of functionality. Ultimately, scientific practicality and economic reality trumped architectural flourish, and the planned courtyard space yielded additional capacity for cages.

The planned laboratory facility was to be constructed on a single acre of city-owned land that was part of an approximately three-and-one-half-acre parcel behind the hospital. Rows of abandoned shrubbery recalled the parcel's former use as a horticultural nursery. The hospital itself resembled a squared-off letter "C" formed by the original elongated rectangle of a building subsequently supplemented by two eighty-foot wings extending at each end to the rear of the main structure. With its vaulted center and exaggerated appendages, it had a crab-like appearance. The laboratory building would hide behind a tree line about one hundred feet beyond and slightly to the outside of the crab's left claw. Foundation officials never failed to point out that the envisioned facility would not be far from Camden's three general hospitals. The fundraising campaign's success, however, depended on its proximity to CMH, where great progress continued to be made.

Centered in the photograph, the Camden Municipal Hospital for Contagious Diseases. The site of the new facility is inside the closest rectangle of trees in the upper right quadrant.

MEANWHILE, BACK AT BEDSIDE AND BENCH

Retrospection tends to compartmentalize history. We like to speak about the Gay Nineties, the Roaring Twenties, the Fifties and Sixties as though historical change conforms to the decimal system. Likewise, informal chronicles of the Coriell Institute for Medical Research's evolution tend to push accounts of events at CMH back into a pre-Foundation period of institutional history. There exists the tendency to view the hospital as a mere springboard for the fortunes of a research institute, as something that "went before," something from which one can turn one's attention after 1953. That was not the view of contemporaries. For them, it is important to understand, continuing improvements in health care delivery at Camden's contagious disease hospital constituted the main justification for supporting the Foundation's plan. Indeed, the building drive succeeded because its lure never distracted Dr. Coriell from the moral imperatives of delivering superb medical care, securing sound public health, and contributing to both through path-breaking diagnostic research. The years of the Foundation's incorporation, campaigning, construction, and startup constituted a time of the hospital's greatest achievement and perhaps most intensive activity. The "overlap" was not merely coincidental; it was fundamental to the institute's future.

Throughout 1953 and '54, Coriell and McAllister continued to improve the techniques they pioneered for antibiotic management and rapid viral diagnoses of infectious diseases. CMH routinely saw the worst complications of measles, mumps, meningitis, scarlet fever, and influenza. Yet in 1952, in-patient admissions accounted for 8,883 patient days but only eight deaths—three of them from among the 97 cases of paralytic poliomyelitis. That extraordinarily low mortality rate was further reduced in subsequent years. A skilled woodworker, Dr. Coriell began converting into cabinetry the hardwood from the hospital's cache of caskets.

Polio remained the greatest scourge at CMH. In 1952 there were nearly 58,000 cases of poliomyelitis diagnosed in the United States. The next year 37,000 cases were reported. The success of the national gamma globulin trials that Dr. Coriell had directed in 1951–52 not only stimulated public expectations for an ultimate vaccine but also increased demand for "GG" in 1953. Dr. Coriell was kept busy in public and medical forums across the country patiently attempting to overcome public misperceptions of the efficacy, timing, and utility of "GG" inoculations. In spring he was in Mobile, Alabama, assisting in the mass inoculation of 32,000 children in the midst of a particularly virulent outbreak. He carefully monitored other field trials in Mexico, Hawaii, and Canada. Using data from those experiments together with re-analysis of the findings from the original trials, he amassed conclusive evidence that gamma globulin was more effective than previously thought. His co-authored

The "iron lung" that provided mechanical breathing assistance to many victims of infantile paralysis meant a painful incarceration. March of Dimes Birth Defects Foundation

findings appeared in the September 1954 issue of the *Journal of the American Medical Association* and became part of a report William Hammon delivered that month to the Third Annual Poliomyelitis Congress in Rome, Italy.

Dr. Coriell's involvement with polio was not confined to medical research. In 1954 New Jersey saw over nine hundred victims, and CMH treated 150 paralytic cases without a single death. That statistic is remarkable in the year in which polio manifested its greatest symptomatic severity. Dr. Coriell's holistic treatment and team-based approach to the management of polio became a paradigm widely emulated by hospitals across the country. Committed to the "maximal recovery" of each stricken individual through continuing medical care, orthopedic treatment, physical therapy, and family counseling, the renowned scientist took time to become an expert in these related fields.

Researchers exclusively bent on discovering a cure for polio might be consoled at the prospect of preventing the next outbreak. A hospital director, however, had to look at the mounting cumulative burden of earlier annual epidemics. For every newly diagnosed case of polio, the staff at CMH treated nearly one hundred "old" cases on an inpatient and outpatient basis. The hospital's director steadfastly steered local March of Dimes proceeds toward care and rehabilitation of polio patients when he could easily have persuaded the county chapter leadership to aid the Foundation's building campaign. He unstintingly invested in the continuing education and site visitation agendas of Municipal's director of physical therapy Frances Miller and supervising nurse Elizabeth Mosely. At a time when exclusive concentration on his scientific work might have expedited the progress of the envisioned laboratory and promoted his national reputation, he was always ready to board a plane and fly to the rescue of a polio clinic that could not control the artificially aided breathing of a paralytic patient. Witnessing this balanced constancy, Camden's leaders understood that Dr. Coriell would never allow his science to baffle his humanity. Accordingly, they tried to match his endurance with their enterprise.

It was a symbiotic relationship. Dr. Coriell could trust his neighbors to build the laboratory while he labored to justify it. In fact, the very Tuesday the new trustees were signing the SJMRF's certificate of incorporation, Dr. Coriell commenced the second phase of an agreement he had entered into a month earlier with George E. Farrar, Jr, medical director of Wyeth Laboratories, the Philadelphia-based pharmaceutical company. That summer, Jonas Salk had satisfactorily tested his dead-virus polio vaccine. It was only a matter of time before companies would be asked to manufacture and test the huge quantities of vaccine that would be needed for the national trials. On October 9, Dr. Coriell agreed to train two members of Wyeth's Institute of Applied Biochemistry in general virological tissue culturing techniques. The second phase of the agreement involved propagating poliovirus in suspensions of monkey kidney cells. The trainees would become the nucleus of the Wyeth team that would prepare the polio vaccine. On November 11, 1953—the day after the SJMRF's founding—Farrar and other top pharmaceutical executives met in New York with Basil O'Connor, the National Foundation's president, to discuss their possible involvement in the polio vaccine trials.[6] On Friday, November 13, Dr. Coriell briefed scientists on "The Status of Polio Vaccine" at Wyeth's Institute.

Wyeth was slow in procuring consultation for this engagement. Most companies had retained external expertise earlier. As early as August, for example, Sharpe and Dohme had asked Jonas Salk to serve as its project consultant. All of the companies had good reason to solicit outside help. Pharmaceutical manufacturers find chemicals simple and profitable. Biologics, on the other hand, are comparatively messy and dangerous. Indeed, several firms were cut from the trials when their production methods revealed errors that resulted in paralyzed monkeys and might well have cost human life if gone undetected. Both Coriell and McAllister—especially "Mac"—spent a good deal of time at Wyeth's laboratories, and the investment paid off. Despite the company's late start and lack of prior experience with tissue culture vaccine, Wyeth was the first company to fulfill the complex criteria for production of safe and effective polio vaccine and to obtain the approval of the Public Health Service's Laboratory of Biologics Control to manufacture the Salk vaccine commercially.[7] The National Foundation fully understood that the accomplishment was largely due to the Camden researchers and quickly issued a grant of $69,930 to CMH to explore ways of producing cheaper and more reliable polio vaccine.[8]

On March 1, 1954, Dr. G. Foard McGinnes, a Red Cross public health physician in charge of the National Foundation's vaccine procurement effort, instructed Wyeth vice president John Cash to begin sending tested lots of the poliomyelitis vaccine to Thomas Francis, Jr., at the University of Michigan's School of Public Health. In January, Francis had agreed to assess the results of the imminent national field trials of the Salk vaccine after receiving the Foundation's pledge that the trials would be double-blind and that his Michigan-based Vaccine Evaluation Center would be independent of the Foundation's supervision. One of Francis's first actions was to ask Dr. Coriell if he would participate in the evaluation. It would involve setting up a laboratory to perform complex comparisons of blood samples of subjects taken at the time of vaccination and a month later in order to determine antibody formation against the three strains of poliovirus in the polio vaccine. While Francis had agonized over his own decision to take on such a grave responsibility, Coriell unhesitatingly agreed to cooperate. At the end of April, following months of

---

[6] Joining Wyeth's Farrar at the meeting were representatives of Cutter Laboratories; Eli Lilly and Company; Park, Davis; the Pitman-Moore Company; and Sharpe and Dohme.

[7] Technically, the Laboratory was under the jurisdiction of the National Institute of Microbiology, an institute of NIH, which was a part of the Public Health Service.

[8] Although it would seem logical for the National Foundation to make the grant directly to the SJMRF, it must be recalled that the chairman of the Camden County chapter of the foundation—the intermediary who publicly presented the checks to the SJMRF—was George Aaron, the elected city commissioner responsible for the progress of the municipal hospital. When Wyeth renewed its consulting arrangement in 1955, for example, it designated payment to the newly formed Foundation.

organizational pandemonium, scientific controversy and ethical trepidation, officials inaugurated the trials at 217 vaccination centers across the country. In May, the SJMRF received a $36,598 National Foundation grant to help provide laboratory evaluation of the 1954 trial.

That trial dramatically captured the nation's attention and has since been recalled as one of the most memorable events of post-war America. By Labor Day, the incidence of polio among the 440,000 children who were vaccinated in the trials appeared to be forty percent below the most recent five-year average. Authorities cautioned an expectant public against interpreting such figures as more than a hopeful indication that the vaccine may have been effective. They asked for patience pending a complete scientific evaluation. At 10:20 A.M. on Tuesday, April 12, 1955, in a University of Michigan amphitheater known as Rackham Hall, Thomas Francis began reading the results of the report Dr. Coriell had helped him write: *An Evaluation of the 1954 Poliomyelitis Vaccine Trials.* Before the world's television cameras and radio microphones Francis would talk for an hour and thirty-eight minutes. Simultaneously, a three-page summary was released to reporters. Its first line contained all the information most people needed. It read, "The vaccine works. It is safe, effective, and potent."

Rackham Auditorium on April 12, 1955. The reports that issued that day from the University of Michigan auditorium produced nationwide euphoria. Courtesy of Bentley Historical Library, University of Michigan

Dr. Thomas Francis, Jr., announces that the Salk polio vaccine is "safe, effective, and potent." Courtesy of Bentley Historical Library, University of Michigan

Dr. Coriell attended the Rackham Hall press conference and the congratulatory sessions afterward. But there was not much time for jubilant celebration. That evening drug manufacturers dispatched crates of stockpiled polio vaccine to depots around the world. Dr. Coriell rushed back to Camden to lead a drive for widespread use of the vaccine and to coordinate the 1955 immunization program throughout the eight-county Delaware Valley region. As he was doing so, the Camden community learned of the extent of his involvement in the Salk vaccine saga. Only after the Francis Report was published did the huge contribution of the SJMRF to the trial evaluation become public. Throughout the United States, twenty-two laboratories had participated in the analysis of 32,000 persons. Dr. Coriell's laboratory was so well-organized and efficient that it processed and evaluated all the samples from Maine to Virginia—in all, 8,627 persons, or over one-quarter of the entire national sample. The achievement was remarkable considering the laboratory was set up from scratch and all participating personnel were "new hires" who had to be trained by Dr. Coriell. Despite the fact that most of the equipment had to be newly purchased, the SJMRF's operation performed the tests below the average per-unit cost of the participating laboratories. Independently, because Dr. Coriell cared deeply about his region, the team also canvassed every use of the Salk vaccine in New Jersey, Pennsylvania, and Delaware.

The success of the Salk vaccine field trials did not mean that the conquest of polio was now in the dexterous hands of needle-wielding doctors. Nearly every knowledgeable researcher including Salk knew that the vaccine had to be improved. Funded by the National Foundation, Dr. Coriell and his team went to work immediately on three pressing problems. First, they improved methods of detection of Rh blood antigens in the Salk vaccine. Physicians worried that repeated injection of the vaccine prepared from virus grown in monkey kidney tissue might cause Rh sensitization of the recipients. Dr. Coriell was able to devise a very sensitive test to confirm that there were no Rh antigens in the lots of evaluated vaccine and little danger of allergic reaction. Second, the research laboratory sought a quick and cost-effective skin test for diagnosing polio. Such a method would not only assure some individuals of their natural immunity but also save valuable vaccine for non-redundant use.

Husbanding vaccine derived from monkey kidney tissue was indeed a concern for researchers and vaccine producers. The monkey population was not infinite; in fact, the search for a cure for polio had decimated it. Finding cells to replace monkey kidney cells was Dr. Coriell's third and most urgent priority. He and his colleagues were able to achieve long passages of serial cultivation of cells from human kidney and conjunctiva, the membranes of the surfaces of the eyeball and eyelid. More importantly, these cells were able to support the growth of all three polioviruses. By November 1955 poliomyelitis vaccines were being prepared from the conjunctiva cells. Over the succeeding half decade, the South Jersey Medical Research Foundation would continue to play an important role in the testing, refinement and virtual perfection of the Salk vaccine. One significant triumph went unheralded: when a near disaster threatened to derail the nationwide program of vaccination in 1955, the SJMRF helped save the day.

Within a fortnight of the Rackham Hall proclamation, the greatest nightmare of federal government and foundation officials, pharmaceutical manufacturers, and scientists became reality. The vaccine produced by Cutter Laboratories—one of the four companies that had not participated in the field trials—was causing polio. Despite all the prophylactic protocols, the company had filtered an incomplete formaldehyde activation that allowed live virus to clump in some batches of their vaccine. By April 27, the Cutter vaccine—good and bad—had been given to approximately 400,000 children. The news was terrifying and seemed to confirm gossip columnist Walter Winchell's unconscionable 1954 radio announcement that National Foundation officials were warehousing little white caskets near vaccination centers in preparation for the national field trials. Ultimately, 204 cases of poliomyelitis were traced to the Cutter blunder. Three-quarters of the victims were paralyzed; eleven died. Increased public apprehension jeopardized the entire program. Proponents were caught in a punishing crossfire of accusations. High-level federal officials were forced to resign. Meanwhile, someone had to insure that the "incident" (as it was called) did not recur.

Dr. Coriell came to the rescue. Apparent scientific setbacks can prove to be ultimate breakthroughs. In the frustrated attempt to devise a practicable skin test for rapid diagnosis of polio, Dr. Coriell and his colleagues vastly improved and simplified the method of inactivating the poliovirus. This new method provided almost complete separation of viruses from substances in which they were grown and, as such, represented the greatest purification of poliovirus yet achieved. It also provided for more sensitive, accurate testing of

A classic Berryman cartoon.

the inactivation process. Such an enhancement could insure that any given shot of vaccine would be as effective as any other in producing antibodies against poliomyelitis. It could also serve as a simple, economical safety test of the Salk vaccine. In short, it was precisely what was needed to help resolve the national crisis and restore confidence in the vaccination crusade.[9]

The information was too urgent to await release via journal publication. The American Association for the Advancement of Science hurriedly arranged a scientific meeting in New York for an "emergency report" by Dr. Coriell and his colleagues in order to get their new method into the hands of the many scientists and technicians who were producing the Salk vaccine. In June, their process of inactivating the virus became a crucial part of the revised operating procedures sanctioned by NIH's Technical Committee, a group formed in the wake of the Cutter disaster to recommend new safety measures for production of the polio vaccine.

It should come as no surprise that this critical response to a tragic emergency was never listed in the institute's inventory of scientific contributions. The unfortunate episode was a blow to science's image and scientists' self-esteem. Dr. Coriell would not advance his notoriety or his institute's fame at the expense of the reputation of science. Terrifying as it was and catastrophic as it might have been, the Cutter incident was limited and quickly contained. Fortunately, gamma globulin was available to temper the effects of polio for those who might have been exposed to live virus. Dr. Coriell's persistent efforts to analyze and improve the efficacy of gamma globulin and to insure its availability for mass inoculations likewise played an indirect but important role in the Cutter drama.

The well-chosen trustees of the South Jersey Medical Research Foundation were witnessing up close the extraordinary accomplishments of the individuals who were to be entrusted with running the research institute they were raising funds to build. Camden County was a healthier place to live. The magic potion against polio had been found. These transformations could be traced to the bench and bedside contributions of Coriell, McAllister, and their colleagues. The stewards of the foundation's fortunes could see the esteem in which the scientific and medical communities held Dr. Coriell. A palpable measure of that esteem was a strong stream of grant dollars. The physician even found that he had political "coattails." Remarkably, in the May 1955 primary elections, Mayor Brunner, Commissioner Aaron, and their Democratic associates ran on the "Planned Progress" city commission ticket that fea-

[9] In early June, a Gallup poll indicated that only thirty-six percent of the people surveyed considered vaccination.

tured—not unreasonably from their perspective—their critical contributions to the metamorphosis of the Municipal Hospital and the development of the Salk vaccine. By summer the *Courier-Post* could confidently editorialize that "Camden [Was] on Way to Fame for Medical Research." Dr. Lewis L. Coriell's dream was becoming a reality.

BUILDING THE DREAM

Chaired by Philip Scott, the fundraising campaign for the SJMRF laboratory building quietly commenced in early 1954 with the subscription of pacesetting corporate gifts. Esterbrook and Campbell Soup predictably led the way. By midyear the campaign had garnered $133,000, or over fifty percent of its announced $250,000 goal. As if to demarcate that milestone, on June 30 the National Foundation for Infantile Paralysis issued the first installment of the $69,930 grant for polio vaccine research. Coupled with the $36,598 conveyance to support the evaluation of the Salk vaccine field trials, the grant allowed Dr. Coriell to begin to build a core staff of scientists and technicians. Although nominally working under the auspices of CMH, the presence of these personnel made tangible the idea of a working research institute. Midyear publicity, however, did little to catalyze philanthropy. In October, New York Shipbuilding Corporation made a major gift. The general campaign phase of the fundraising effort, co-chaired by Michael Hayes and William Kalellis, began seeking support from individuals and from small businesses and industries.

Despite its gratifying start, the building campaign made slow progress in the fall of 1954. Competition for funds was tight. Cooper Hospital had just launched a $4.5 million "Decade of Development" drive for building construction, renovation, and equipment modernization. Children's Hospital of Philadelphia, so vitally involved in the health of Camden's youngsters, was in the middle of a major campaign in advance of its centennial anniversary celebration the following year. In this delicate ecology, the SJMRF's most likely philanthropic prospects were also Cooper's and CHOP's. Ironically, two unfortunate events helped the campaign regain its momentum.

First, the *Courier-Post*—in a momentous and widely criticized decision—moved its headquarters from Third and Market Streets in the city of Camden to its current location in Cherry Hill. As the owners and publishers of the first New Jersey newspaper to flee a center city location, the Stretch family made a special effort to strengthen the city that their exodus had weakened. They did this by charitable contribution and by extended coverage of their favorite Camden causes. Second, shortly after the controversial move, the newspaper's beloved editor suddenly died. Frank Ryan, loyal March of Dimes officer, champion of CMH and friend of Dr. Coriell, was stricken by a heart attack on November 4. Jane Stretch, the sister of foundation trustee William Stretch and author of an in-depth series of reports on CMH, replaced Ryan as editor and as treasurer of the county chapter of the National Foundation.

Courtesy of The Courier-Post

Coverage of Dr. Coriell's activities in late 1954 and 1955 increased dramatically. Quite probably this renewed attention corresponded to his unfolding role in the national drama of the polio vaccine program, but these sad contextual changes clearly helped to re-inspire the campaign by springtime.

Between July 1, 1954 and April 10, 1955, the building campaign managed to raise less than $50,000 and was thus approximately $70,000 short of its goal. One reason for the shortfall was that this period saw furious fundraising activity on behalf of the Municipal Hospital. The excitement and expectation surrounding the Salk vaccine trials provided a tremendous fillip to the March of Dimes, spurred by volunteer Lavenia S. Taylor's dedicated involvement and by memorial contributions honoring the late Frank Ryan. The county chapter of the National Foundation raised a record amount in 1955, and most of those funds were dedicated to CMH. Scores of contributions in the thousand-dollar range poured into the hospital from ladies auxiliaries and from charitable fraternal groups and sororities across the state. This dedication of funds may have hurt the laboratory building campaign in the short run, but in the long run it built bridges that would help sustain the research institute long after the hospital closed. Wisely, Dr. Coriell never sought to redirect a gift.

In April fortunes changed. The announcement of the Francis Report and the revelation that the SJMRF played a major role in the evaluation of the Salk vaccine trials swelled community pride and convincingly demonstrated the ultimate utility of research. The Greater Camden Junior Chamber of Commerce Auxiliary staged the most productive charity ball in its history, with the proceeds benefiting the foundation. Several major gifts and pledges from individuals arrived. In July RCA donated $25,000, and Foundation officials began to talk about a $300,000 goal. The new target most likely reflected increased cost of construction due both to inflation and the decision to build a full basement. But it also exhibited the foundation's confidence in the eventual success of the campaign. Records do not exist to verify the supposition that the foundation had met its original goal in July, but the gift from RCA convinced the trustees to authorize construction to begin.

Jack Dorrance gladly accepted the chairmanship of the building committee.[10] Six construction companies submitted bids. The contract was awarded to the lowest bidder, S. Levy Company, a Camden-based union

[10] The committee included Coriell, Langworthy, Fred Scholz, Frank Sleeter, and Wickes.

COURIER-POST
CAMDEN, NEW JERSEY

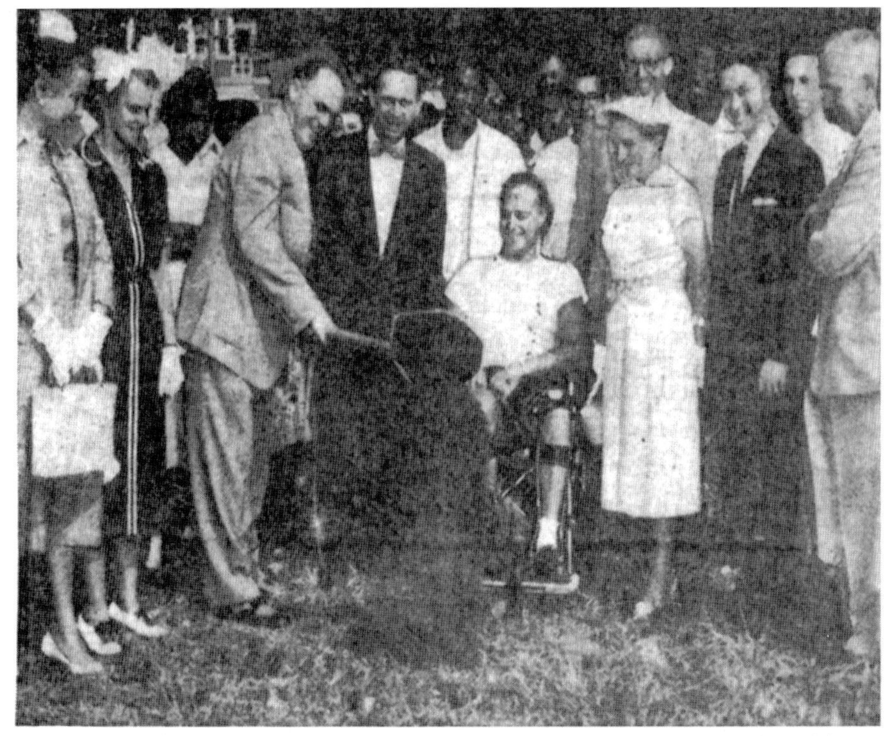

—Courier-Post Photo

MARKING THE START of construction of a new laboratory and research center adjacent to Camden Municipal Hospital, Philip E. Scott, president of the South Jersey Medical Research Foundation, is shown breaking ground today at the site. Among those looking on are (left to right) Mrs. Albert B. Melnik, Mrs. S. Emlen Stokes, Dr. Lewis L. Coriell, hospital medical director; Dr. Robert McAllister, his associate; Mrs. W. H. K. Fleck, Kenneth MacDonald and Bryant W. Langston. William Marks, of Westmont, a hospital patient, sits in the wheelchair.

Courtesy of The Courier-Post

shop,[11] with the expectation of completion before April 1, 1956. Unwilling to obligate the foundation beyond its means, the committee stipulated that certain design items would be temporarily omitted pending the arrival of additional funds. Fred Greiner arranged with the city commissioners an extension of the construction time stipulated in the original agreement of the land transfer. On Monday, July 25, in a simple groundbreaking ceremony, Foundation president Phil Scott turned over the first shovelful of earth in the presence of the hospital staff, board members, and spouses. In the center of the happy group sat William Marks, a polio patient bound to his wheelchair.

Unanticipated exigencies slowed the ambitiously charted pace of construction, but by April the research team had moved out of CHOP's laboratories in Philadelphia. Within eleven months of groundbreaking, the construction crews had practically completed the new research facility. On

[11] Dr. Coriell neglected no opportunity to improve the hospital during construction of the laboratory. In January 1955, area AFL-CIO unions pledged $7,000 to provide a free dental clinic for the handicapped at CMH.

The new South Jersey Medical Research Foundation.

Thursday, June 21, 1956, the South Jersey Medical Research Foundation Laboratory was officially dedicated. The festivities began with a noon luncheon at the Walt Whitman Hotel for board members and special guests. The dedication program began at two o'clock. For the next half-hour an impressive cast of dignitaries made remarks. After board president Scott and director Coriell came Henry W. Kumm, medical director of the National Foundation. He backed up his words of confidence in Dr. Coriell's scientific leadership with a check for $50,871 for continuing polio research. National Foundation advisor Thomas M. Rivers, CHOP's Joseph Stokes, and Penn's medical school dean John McK. Mitchell in turn addressed the gathering of over three hundred guests. Commissioner Aaron made the official dedication and was given the honor of cutting—or rather, exploding—the ribbon. The ritual symbolized the building's sophisticated scientific purpose. Aaron exposed a silicon disk to sunlight that was transformed in a battery held by Dr. Coriell into electrical energy sufficient to trigger a small powder charge at the ribbon's center. Developed by RCA scientists, the device worked like a charm. With that auspicious start, the party convened inside for an open house.

Winston Churchill remarked that we build our buildings and then our buildings build us. It is difficult to imagine that the SJMRF could have ultimately established its independent identity without a place of its own. The blurring of institutional loyalties, difficulties of recruiting scientists, and plain logistical inconveniences would have impeded if not prevented progress. For Dr. Coriell and his scientific colleagues, the opening of the new research facility marked the real beginning of the institute. In October, John Carter would arrange for RCA to provide an additional $10,000 toward the final $25,000 needed to purchase equipment for the new center. Then, as he would do for every subsequent campaign, John Dorrance completed the effort with his personal contribution. That month, Dr. Coriell could report to his board, "All research staff now work under a single roof in the South Jersey Medical Research Foundation laboratories." The dream that had come true was not the wish to have a laboratory. It was rather to build a facility capable of making many other dreams come true.

CHAPTER FIVE

HEDGEHOGS AND FOXES (1956–1961)

The half-dozen years following the opening of the research building—like the previous four years of its institutionalization—represent a brief but integral period in the Foundation's history. Sociologists of science refer to this initial, critical time of organizational growth as a "take-off" period, and the metaphor is apt. Just as a space launch must reach "escape velocity" or plummet back to earth, an institute must achieve "critical mass" in order to array scientific imaginations in dynamic and productive interrelationships, contribute to knowledge, and attract continuing support.

The SJMRF's successful take-off came in a period of significant but hazily discernible change. On the national stage, chronic maladies were beginning to supplant epidemic diseases as the public's primary medical apprehension. Patterns of research sponsorship shifted in response. At the local level, the predictable devolution of the Municipal Hospital, which closed its doors in 1962, posed opportunities and challenges for the new institute. On the one hand, its closure liberated researchers from the quotidian preoccupations of diagnostic investigation and therapeutic intervention. On the other hand, it distanced the laboratory from the more immediate purposes its local patrons had traditionally seen as justification for their support. Above all, however, locally and nationally the big change was the conquest of polio and what that meant for the philanthropists and volunteers whose energies required new outlets and for the scientists in search of new worlds to conquer.

THE ORGANIZATION OF KNOWLEDGE

The national campaign to conquer polio shaped the immediate future of the emerging institute in three critical ways. Most obviously, it catapulted virology into the forefront of popular consciousness about biomedical science. With the exponential increase in public funding for research (that is, in taxed-

The Coriell family: Tom (b. 1947), Lew, Esther, Steve (b. 1952), and Jim (b. 1945).

based dollars appropriated by elected representatives of the citizenry), such notoriety mattered. Second, the campaign provided otherwise unobtainable national funding for the technical perfection of the Foundation's tissue culturing and cell storage operations. The March of Dimes helped researchers establish stable strains of cells that were capable of reproducing themselves in test tubes without the necessity of frequent replenishment of fresh animal or human tissues. In terms of the SJMRF's institutional future, the development of these "pure lines" of cells represented a most significant and productive area of research upon which much of the institute's—and eventually, the world's—science would be based. In the beginning, one could almost view Dr. Coriell's research institute as the organizational extension of his individual scientific intelligence. Virology occupied the Foundation's intellectual epicenter, and tissue culturing comprised its methodological muscle.

The third way in which the saga of the Salk vaccine influenced the SJMRF had to do with the organization of research. The search for a preventative against polio convinced funding sources and researchers alike that a frontal assault on specific diseases could produce surefire results. Never mind that the science and technology upon which this attack was mounted took nearly a century to develop. Biomedical science, many felt, had finally developed a sufficient store of useable hard facts upon which to organize applied science. Mission-oriented research was in vogue. Independent medical research establishments such as the Sloan Kettering Institute consciously emulated Bell Telephone and similar product-oriented industrial laboratories. The SJMRF, while dedicated to fundamental research, was premised upon an ideology of imminent utility and organized itself accordingly.

The philosopher Isaiah Berlin distinguished two types of intellectuals: the hedgehog and the fox. The fox, he said, knows many, many things; the hedgehog, one big thing. A scientific institute must embody the mental dispositions of both species. Ideally those contrary imaginations are hybridized within the individual scientist, as they were within Dr. Coriell. But even so, by the middle of the twentieth century the proliferation of biomedical knowledge demanded intensive specialization, collaboration, and teamwork. Apprehension of any problem involved a wider range of proficiencies than a single individual could possess. A viable research institute would have to accommodate hedgehogs and foxes in order to maintain an unremitting focus on a big vision while displaying an agile perviousness to novel ideas, techniques, and opportunities.

Biomedical science is not only a body of knowledge, but also an organization of knowers, people who think abstractly, but—as one commentator has remarked—only for portions of each day. Like other cogitating creatures, scientists and the organizations they inhabit choose problems not only because of their intrinsic intellectual plausibility or appeal, but because their envisioned solutions appear conducive to shifting career goals, professional needs, institutional mandates, social roles, cultural values, political pressures, and funding opportunities. In the phrase "scientific community" the adjective modifies but does not exclusively govern the noun.

As the leader of a scientific organization,[1] Dr. Coriell had to attract, retain, and orchestrate a diversity of specialized talent in order to fulfill certain broad research goals or agendas. The selection of goals would depend upon an understanding of the transformations continually occurring in the structure of scientific knowledge, of the politics of funding, and of the caliber and availability of investigators. The challenge would be to create a hotbed for the growth and cross-fertilization of ideas trained on a few basic problems. Cross-fertilization of ideas in a single place inevitably involves the in- and out-migration of scientific personnel. Their selection, care, and feeding are important. The scientific director must encourage that characteristic of sci-

[1] Modern organizations have largely been comprised of those who manage what they do not understand and those who understand what they do not manage. Fortunately, one of the distinguishing characteristics of twentieth-century science in the United States is that its administrators have generally been drawn from the ranks of science. This fact not only enhances organizational strategy but also improves morale, because scientist-administrators do not impatiently demand speedy results. In his 1960 lectures on "Science and Government," C.P. Snow reminded his listeners that typical administrators are temperamentally individuals of action whose jobs make them "masters of the short-term solution." He advocated having "scientists mixed up in our affairs."

entists that has been called "mavericity" but must do so within the corral of collaborative purpose or at least cooperative intent.

In the five years following the opening of the Foundation's laboratories, Dr. Coriell would slowly but decisively incline the institute's thrust away from the conquest of childhood infectious diseases toward the study of cancer. Institutional timelines have tended to date this concentration on cancer in the period surrounding 1965 when the institute changed its charter to include cancer research in its statement of purpose. A closer examination shows that the shift was underway a decade earlier.

THE TOPIC OF CANCER

When queried about his new laboratory's scientific agenda just before breaking ground for it, Dr. Coriell clearly anticipated a future tied closely to the past. "After Polio, What?" the *Courier-Post* asked Dr. Coriell in an April 20, 1955 feature article about the Foundation's direction. The director envisioned "a campaign against other infectious diseases that menaced the young." He targeted measles, mumps, chicken pox, and the common cold using the tissue culture techniques he had perfected. Most of his early associates at the SJMRF were pediatricians. He foresaw a continuation of the close relationship with Joe Stokes and CHOP's research team.

For the next four years concerned parents would inundate Dr. Coriell with questions about proper polio inoculation protocols while his own research helped to improve his answers by making the protocols themselves more reliable and demonstrable. But it was clear to everyone that polio research had become a classic mop-up operation. The excitement was over. In 1954 Jonas Salk achieved eponymous fame; John Enders, the Nobel Prize. In 1957 Albert Sabin would produce an effective live-virus polio vaccine. That year the Camden County's March of Dimes campaign exhorted its donors with the swaggering slogan: "Let's Finish the Job." There was not much left to perfect and not much funding forthcoming. In 1958 the National Foundation itself would drop from its letterhead the phrase "for Infantile Paralysis"[2] and expand its scope beyond poliomyelitis to viral diseases, arthritis, birth defects, and central nervous system disorders.

The National Foundation would have publicly repositioned itself earlier had it not been for the immensely expensive task of funding the manufacture and delivery of the Salk vaccine. In order to compete in the outside game of fund raising, it had to maintain its celebrated identity. But already it was pursuing a different inside game. In fact, the $50,871 check that the National Foundation presented to the South Jersey Medical Research Foundation at its building dedication symbolized a subtle shift in the calculations of both organizations. Ostensibly, the gift was to continue studies of cells in which po-

[2] While it would henceforth be known as the National Foundation, its official title became the National Foundation-March of Dimes.

TIME, *November 17, 1961*. Courtesy of TimePix

liovirus grows. More interestingly, however, the National Foundation's director of research was intrigued by the fact that Dr. Coriell and his colleagues had discovered that some of those cells exhibited signs of malignancy in a way that could imply a viral etiology of cancer.

This unanticipated and baffling discovery emerged from Dr. Coriell's search for a strain of normal cells to serve as a suitable substitute for the expensive, dwindling supply of monkey kidney cells commonly used for growing polioviruses to make the Salk vaccine. He found that cells taken from human conjunctiva and kidney (both highly susceptible to poliovirus) and grown in serial passages of laboratory cultures multiplied at increasing rates and seemed to behave like cancer cells. Other scientists replicated these findings. It quickly became a very hot topic. Just weeks before the opening of the Foundation's laboratories, Tom Rivers invited Dr. Coriell to participate in a January 1957 conference at New York's Waldorf-Astoria Hotel in celebration of Basil O'Connor's sixty-fifth birthday. Dr. Coriell was asked to address the penultimate session on either the general topic of properties acquired by cells maintained in continuous culture or the specific consideration of the possibility that cells become malignant. He chose to speak about the criteria for determining malignancy in tissue culture cell lines. The chairman of the session was none other than E. W. Goodpasture.

The pendulum of research has always swung between the poles of two explanations of the causes of cancer: external or exogenous factors such as radiation, chemicals, or viruses and internal or endogenous factors such as genetic mutation.[3] In the immediate wake of the late nineteenth-century bacteriological revolution, scientists attempted to find an infectious organism and develop a vaccine against it. As early as 1907–08, researchers mounted serious arguments for a viral etiology of cancer. By the 1920s, however, scientific (and social) explanations began to favor constitutional, hereditary, and genetic factors. Not until the 1950s, with the development of tissue culture techniques for breeding viruses and of electron microscopy for examining them did viral theories of the cause of cancer reassert themselves. A basic question was whether cancer was a disease caused by infection of a tumor virus or the result of spontaneous or chemically induced factors. The resurgence of the idea of viral causation paralleled a changing social conception of the disease.

By the mid-twentieth century cancer was becoming more visible in at least two senses of the word. Mortality from cancer had been increasing since the nineteenth century. Whether this was due to a rising incidence of this group of diseases or to a decrease in mortality from infectious diseases, the perception of a growing menace deepened public anxiety. In another way, cancer was becoming more visible because there was less of a stigma attached to its victims. A glance forward and back from the mid-fifties illustrates this point. In 1987, the College of Physicians of Philadelphia was honored to have the President of the United States come to town to help celebrate the bicentennial anniversary of its founding. Auspiciously, Dr. Coriell was then serving as the College's president. He was escorting Ronald W. Reagan on a tour of the College's Mütter Museum when President Reagan's attention was drawn to one of the museum's medical curiosities: a portion of the cancerous jawbone of former U. S. President Grover Cleveland.[4] So stigmatizing was cancer in 1893 that Cleveland's offshore surgical operation was veiled in secrecy and public deception. In 1985, however, President Reagan's filmed hospitalization for treatment of colon cancer and skin cancer was a major media event. Precisely at the time Dr. Coriell began to turn his attention to cancer research, newspaper obituaries slowly began replacing the euphemism "prolonged illness" with the word "cancer."

---

[3] Correspondingly, the historiography of science is divided into, on the one hand, "internalist" explanations of scientific change that stress the cumulative acquisition of objective knowledge in an environment that is value-free, emotionally neutral, and intellectually detached and, on the other hand, "externalist" explanations that accentuate the penetration of culture into scientific thought. Alas, the intriguing speculation as to which camp could best explain the recrudescence in the 1950s of viral theories of cancer causation is beyond the scope of this work.

[4] Later in the day President Reagan remarked in a nationally televised address on healthcare that he was "the first *whole* president ever to visit the College."

Prior to the advent of genetic engineering, so long as cancer was seen as a hereditary or genetic disorder that was somehow transferred "vertically" from one generation to the next, few were sanguine about the possibility of a quick cure. But if certain forms of cancer were caused by an invading organism and could pass "horizontally" from one organism to another, there was more reason for optimism. Perhaps a cure would not be needed; perhaps a vaccine could prevent cancer's onset, as the Salk vaccine had done with polio. Dr. Coriell's preoccupation with that exciting possibility coincided with the take-off stage of institutionalization and would shape the course of the South Jersey Medical Research Foundation.

Dr. Coriell's preoccupation with cancer was in large part an aspect of his scientific humanitarianism, his desire to conquer a killer. Such a motivation, however, is not incompatible with personal ambition.[5] While his contributions to the conquest of polio were monumental, his "lack of seniority"—despite his precocious talent—had made him a lieutenant, not a general, in that victorious campaign. Some observers even contend that, in his youthful idealism, he had handed John Enders the key to the Nobel Prize. Now the head of an independent research institute, Dr. Coriell was in a position to direct a campaign against a specific disease. His opting for independence was a personal gamble for scientific seniority and perhaps even scientific fame.

The fashioning of an effective, safe polio vaccine added to the excitement of impending discovery of a viral etiology of cancer and shifted the focus of investigation in Camden from basic polio research to cancer immunity processes. After establishing exact criteria for determining malignancy in cells in 1956, researchers at the SJMRF began testing cancer cells in rats and eventually developed a serum that prevented the growth of certain malignant tumors in them. First, the investigators made the rodents highly susceptible to cancer by dosing them with x-rays and cortisone. Then they injected the rats' abdominal cavities with a strain of human cancer cells known as HeLa cells.[6] In the rats, the cells multiplied rapidly, large tumors developed, and the animals died.

In 1957, Dr. Coriell and his team found that the blood of a cow inoculated with HeLa cells developed antibodies to the cancer cells. Furthermore, they discovered that this immune cow serum could destroy HeLa cells growing in tissue culture. They procured large quantities of this serum, tested it for potency, and stored it. In the following year, they injected the cow serum into

[5] Lewis Thomas, a scientist much admired by Lewis Coriell, noted in his extraordinary book, *The Lives of a Cell: Notes of a Biology Watcher* (New York: The Viking Press, 1974), that "Scientists at work have the look of creatures following genetic instructions; they seem to be under the influence of a deeply ingrained human instinct. They are, despite their efforts at dignity, rather like young animals in savage play. When they are near to an answer their hair stands on end, they sweat, they are awash in their own adrenaline. To grab the answer, and grab it first, is for them a more powerful drive than feeding or breeding or protecting themselves against the elements" (p. 101).

[6] This widely used cell line was obtained by George Gey and his colleagues in 1951 at Johns Hopkins University from the cancerous cervix of a patient named Henrietta Lacks.

the abdomen of rats the day before inoculating them with HeLa cells and observed that tumors failed to develop and the animals lived. Dr. Coriell hypothesized that the factor that prevented tumorigenicity was an antibody against HeLa cells. Etiological hypothesizing aside, the Camden team had achieved a stunning technical feat by showing that it was possible to devise laboratory techniques to use human cancer cells to produce tumors in a different species. If Dr. Coriell's hypothesis were correct, then his experiments would seem to indicate that ordinary immunologic mechanisms operate against certain cancer cells in animals.

Throughout the five-year period under consideration here, the National Foundation provided major support for these and allied investigations. Other groups, however, were exclusively organized for cancer research and resented the National Foundation's intrusion onto their turf. Dr. Coriell recognized this political fact and, in 1957, brought onto the SJMRF's board of trustees Jonathan E. Rhoads, M.D., a prominent surgeon at the University of Pennsylvania School of Medicine and a member of the national board of directors of the American Cancer Society (ACS).[7] In 1958, the ACS began its support of the institute's cancer immunology research. By 1959, it had awarded the New Jersey organization over $100,000. By that time Dr. Coriell was being introduced as a cancer specialist as he delivered public addresses on the progress of cancer research. The Foundation was being portrayed as a center for virology and cancer study.

The gradual shift away from childhood infectious diseases to cancer research was both scientifically promising and strategically prudent. The vogue of mission-based research (catalyzed by World War II) and the optimistic implications of the theory of a viral cause of cancer (reinforced in popular imagination by the Salk vaccine) were generously nurtured within the new American ecology of unprecedented prosperity, the public's passion for guaranteed health and improved longevity, and the end of the baby boom.[8] A key figure in uniting these trends was Mary Lasker. Rich, savvy, well connected and passionate about ending the scourge of cancer, Lasker had transformed the ACS during and immediately after the war. After the death to cancer of her husband in 1952, she joined forces with James Shannon, the head of the National Institutes of Health (NIH), to lobby several influential congressmen for increased appropriations for cancer research. Largely as a result of their efforts, the budget of the National Cancer Institute (founded within NIH in 1937) increased from $1.75 million in 1946 to over $110 million in 1961.

When Shannon became NIH director in 1955, the Institutes' budget was $98 million. In 1967, the year before his departure, it was $1.4 billion. He represented a new wave of scientific leadership with which Dr. Coriell could iden-

[7] The original incarnation of the ACS was called the American Society for the Control of Cancer, founded in 1913 as an educational mission. It never gave a nickel for research until World War II.

[8] Lew and Esther Coriell's "boomers"—Jim (b. 1945), Tom (b. 1947), and Steve (b. 1952) were no longer babies.

The growth of cancer research in the U.S. owes an extraordinary debt to the perseverance and persuasiveness of Mary Lasker. Courtesy of Albert and Mary Lasker Foundation

tify. Unlike his predecessors who had risen through the ranks of the Public Health Service, Shannon was a researcher at both a university and a hospital and had served as director of the Squibb Institute for Medical Research—a subsequent supporter of the SJMRF—before coming to NIH. He understood the needs for extramural research contracts and construction grants to free-standing scientific institutes. In 1957 the NIH awarded its first grant to the South Jersey Medical Research Foundation for cancer-related research. It was the beginning of a fruitful relationship.

The Organization of Knowers

The evolution of the emergent institute can best be understood against this backdrop of opportunity and expectation involving the investigation of cancer. Its immediate organization, however, reflected its origins as a center for the study of poliomyelitis and a diagnostic laboratory peopled with pediatricians and attached to an infectious disease hospital. Historical investigative interests, funding patterns, and sources of research personnel dictated this pattern. After 1961, the research institute would successively outgrow its facilities and require an almost continual program of expansion. Before 1961, however, the challenge was to fill the five laboratories with excellent research and researchers, build a predictable funding base, and establish continuity of purpose and reputation. In the initial years, the SJMRF was a productive patchwork sewn together with funding threads of various colors and sizes by very cerebral migrant laborers.

Dr. Coriell always regarded that moment in 1956 when everyone was "under a single roof"—not the formal chartering in 1953—as the SJMRF's real beginning.[9] One should not infer institutional autonomy from that physical metaphor. Indeed, for the next few critical, transitional years the new research facility seemed to be doing everybody else's business. Drs. Coriell and McAllister remained salaried employees of CMH and continued to earn their keep. In addition to diurnal rounds of clinical teaching, they were constantly on call to handle the more severe complications of contagious disease. An epidemic of aseptic meningitis as occurred in 1958 or the unusual outbreak of eastern equine encephalitis that flared up in 1959 could wreck havoc on one's planned laboratory work. Moreover, some of the SJMRF's research assistants were hospital residents. They might become sufficiently trained to bolster their resumes by co-authoring a research article during their time at the institute, but they were quickly gone.

Like the hospital residents, doctoral candidates at the University of Pennsylvania, supported through educational fellowships and assistantships, also served as short-term research assistants. Under Penn's auspice, researchers from foreign countries would come to the institute to learn techniques for combating diseases plaguing their countries. In 1958, for example, Dr. Sombodhi Bukkavesa learned how to prepare diagnostic antigens for *endameba histolytica*, a waterborne disease causing dysentery in his native Thailand. Often, the institute would serve as a temporary oasis where medical personnel could refresh and refuel. In 1957, Helen Gaskill co-authored two studies on antibiotics before returning to her work as a medical missionary in the Belgian Congo. The useful studies transacted in the SJMRF's new laboratories were not always conducive to scientific continuity and institutional autonomy.

McAllister himself spent a large part of his time at the Wyeth Laboratories facilities in Marietta, Pennsylvania, fully ninety miles from Camden. Other SJMRF personnel likewise shuttled back and forth to the pharmaceutical company that provided nearly one-third of the early institute's operating budget in the form of grants-in-aid to perfect the Salk vaccine against polio and to test and develop other vaccines against adenoviruses and the common cold. Dr. Coriell guided an early institute research assistant, Paul Grunmeier, Jr., to his Ph.D. degree at the University of Pennsylvania in 1958, whereupon

---

[9] It is natural for a half-century-old establishment to reach back to its earliest origins in order to establish its longevity. Equally understandable is the desire of a fledgling organization to shorten the period between its founding and its present in order to show maximal progress in a minimal span of time.

Grunmeier returned to the employ of Wyeth to head up a cancer research team. The relationship with the pharmaceutical company may have been mutually beneficial at an early stage of institute funding, but Wyeth clearly controlled the agenda for the research it funded for its own commercial purposes.

While modestly underwriting the institute's operations by sponsoring tests of tetracycline, erythromycin and other antibiotics, drug companies such as Wyeth, Upjohn, and Merck Sharp & Dohme not only lowered their own overhead but also cultivated a pool of future researchers and technicians. At times, the institute resembled the training ground for future employees of pharmaceutical conglomerates, who could offer higher salaries, increased mobility, superior security, and state-of-the-art laboratories to personnel trained at SJMRF's expense. Walter Flagg, for example, served as a research assistant for two years and resigned in 1958 to work for the National Drug Company of Philadelphia. It was an oft-repeated phenomenon. The emergent institute's scientists were busy but peripatetic. Many researchers who worked together under one roof during this period entered and exited through a revolving door.

Newborn institutions may be able to accommodate the transience of its junior members so long as they can anticipate continuity among its senior principals. But even in this regard, the Foundation in its infancy figuratively crawled before it walked. In the early years, the director's[10] chief subordinates were his two *research associates*, initially Bob McAllister and Arthur E. Greene. Art Greene was a year younger than "Mac." A World War II army veteran, he was wounded in action, honorably discharged in 1946, and completed his Bachelor of Arts at the University of Pennsylvania the following year. Then in quick succession by 1952 he earned his B.S., M.S. and D.S. degrees in bacteriology at the Philadelphia College of Pharmacy and Science.

Greene immediately went to work on herpes simplex in Tom McNair Scott's laboratory at CHOP. Between 1953 and 1956, he contributed directly to Dr. Coriell's multifaceted program of polio research and mastered the complex art of establishing pure cell lines of tissue culture cells by means of serial passages of human and animal tissues. Interestingly, despite the fact that the SJMRF had been chartered in 1953, during this period Greene was on the payroll of CHOP at its research division's poliomyelitis research laboratory, which was directed by Dr. Coriell. In 1956 Greene became the SJMRF's research associate in virology and tissue culture, but even then the program was being partially underwritten by grants from the National Foundation and Wyeth to Children's Hospital. After only a year in the Foundation's employ, he resigned to take a position as research virologist at the National Drug Company. Greene's quick departure revealed the early institute's instability, not the scientist's inconstancy. Indeed, he would return in 1961 when the organization had "gained orbit" and make sizable contributions to it for the next

[10] In an organization in which the chairman of the board was titled president, Dr. Coriell appropriately chose "director of research" as his designation.

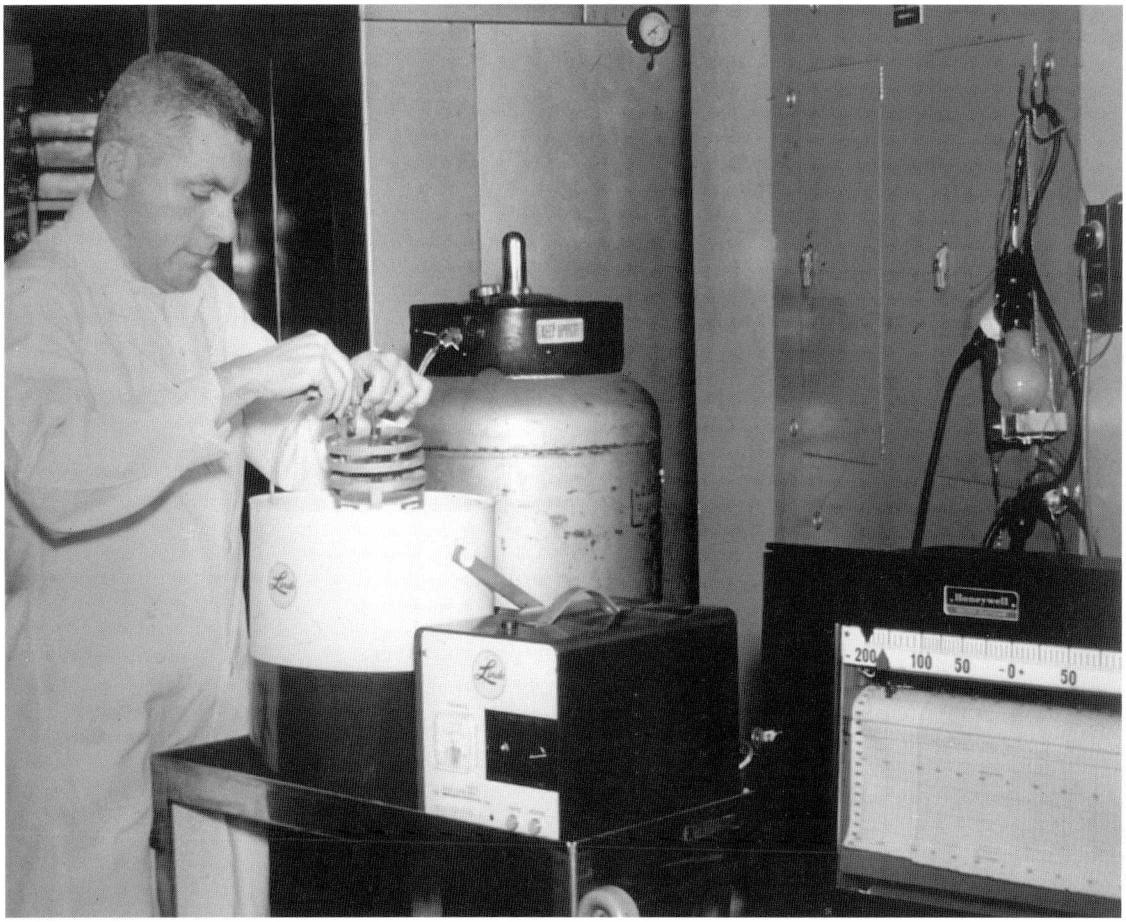

Dr. Arthur Greene assembles one of the first slow-rate cell freezing devices for preserving cells.

three decades while earning a reputation as one of the institute's most dedicated and valued members.

When he did return, he found that his former colleague and research associate had departed for California. On July 1, 1959, Bob McAllister became the director of research at Children's Hospital of Los Angeles and associate professor of pediatrics at the University of California School of Medicine. For "Mac" it was a painfully difficult but probably inevitable choice. By 1959 it was clear to him that "Camden Municipal was on its last legs." He and his wife Lois ("Dodee") had six children, and his salary as assistant medical director at CMH was $5,500. True, his supplemental income from work for Wyeth amounted to thrice that sum, but it was not *his* work and it was temporary. "We just loved Lew and Ester," McAllister recalled, "but I had family responsibilities and was getting nice offers. It was rare to find a researcher in pediatric infectious disease."

Likewise, it was rare to lose one. Dr. Coriell was not the kind of person to be devastated by any event, but the departure of his right-hand man during this critical start-up period was a personal loss as well as an institutional blow. The titles of a near score of co-authored papers, like historical signposts, signified the scientific distance they had traveled together as trailblazers. What's more, Mac's subsequent research in the viral etiology of malignancy in infants and children was precisely the course his boss would have wished him to pursue in Camden. Mac had been indispensable to the progress of scientific research and clinical medicine at CMH and hence to the birth of the institute. Its viability would depend in large measure on Dr. Coriell's ability to attract and retain a senior research associate of similar intelligence, drive, impact and collegiality.

On the positive side, Bob McAllister's move provided an opportunity to diversify research at the Foundation. Dr. Coriell did not miss that chance. His appointment in 1959 of Warren Wesley Nichols would have important consequences for the institute. The thirty-year-old Nichols was born in nearby Collingswood, New Jersey, graduated from Rutgers University, and received his M.D. from Jefferson Medical College in 1954. As a medical student intent on a clinical career, he had attended Dr. Coriell's lectures and became attracted to medical research. As a pediatric resident at CHOP in 1956–57, he rotated through Municipal and got to know his future mentor personally. Following a two-year tour of military duty as chief of pediatrics at Lake Charles Air Force Base in Louisiana, he accepted the offer of the twin posts of research associate at the SJMRF and chief of medical staff at CMH.

Mac signed his photo, given as a parting gift, "To Lew with many thanks for all the lessons in life and science."

While in residence at CHOP, Nichols had developed an interest in pediatric hematology and oncology and a belief that, by studying the mechanisms of malignancy of the blood, one could do a lot more for patients than current treatments were capable of accomplishing. Still interested in medical practice, he figured it would be easier to move from research to clinical medicine than to forsake his patients if he pursued the reverse sequence. At the time, the viral theory of cancer etiology predominated, but an alternative theory also prevalent held that chemical factors caused mutations in the genetic material of body cells. As early as 1914 it had been postulated that cancer occurred when normal separations of chromosomes in the process of cell division turned abnormal. Nichols became interested in the field of cytogenetics and the role of chromosomes in cells. Soon he had fallen under Dr. Coriell's spell and set his course upon research. Not long afterward the virologist and the cytogeneticist began to consider the possibility that the rival theories were not mutually exclusive, that viruses might have genetic effects on chromosomes. Pursuit of that possibility—as will be described in the next chapter—unlocked relatively stable sources of funding and led to some of the most exciting experimentation and collaboration in the institute's history.

Originally, Dr. Coriell's selection of Nichols as second-in-command in what was essentially a virological laboratory involved a more immediately practical consideration. One way of comparing normal cells with cancer cells

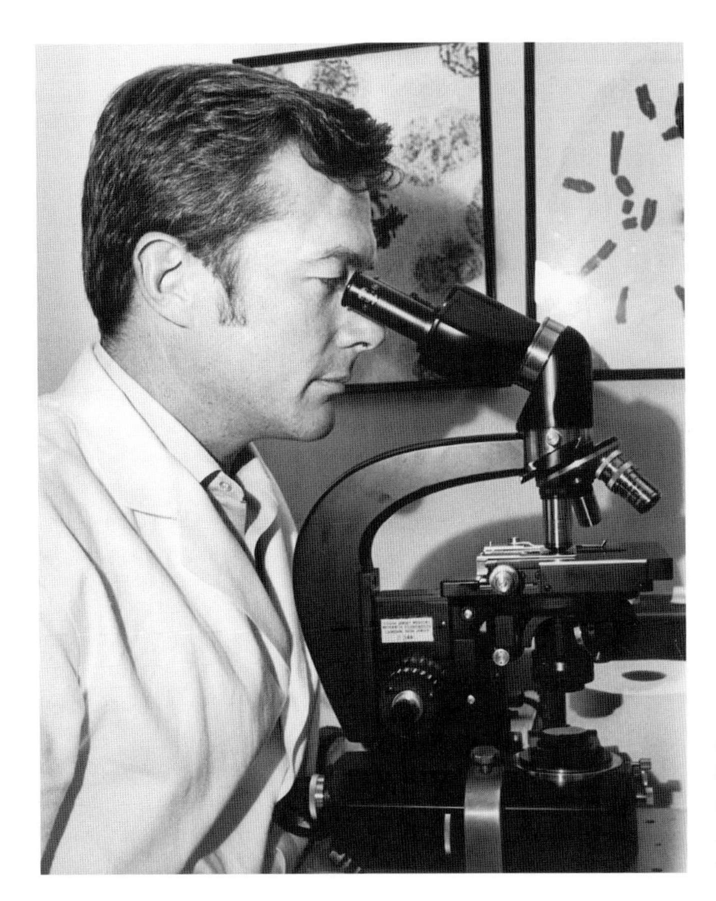

Dr. Warren Nichols established an international reputation in the field of cytogenetics. He was honored by the Institute for his accomplishments with the Coriell Medal in 2002.

in order to establish criteria for defining malignancy was to count chromosomes and inspect related details of cellular morphology. Nichols's particular expertise helped to insure experimental certainty. On an even more rudimentary level, such comparative studies meant the continual improvement of methods and media for maintaining cells in continuous culture *in vitro.* By 1957 the institute had already developed and maintained nine cancer and five normal lines. It was becoming increasingly clear, however, that cell lines procured from other laboratories were hopelessly contaminated. In 1958, for example, the SJMRF discovered that a cell line derived from normal monkey heart had been accidentally contaminated by HeLa cells in Jonas Salk's laboratory. Nichols developed a simplified method of making chromosome preparations from tissue culture cell lines. That helped institute researchers determine whether cell lines from different laboratories were infiltrated by bacteria, other cell lines, and various contaminants.

Those tests and related studies emanating from the Foundation demonstrated conclusively, in Dr. Coriell's words, "that tissue culture cell lines are unstable, prone to occult contamination, and likely to be mixed with other tissue culture cell lines." At the time there were nearly one hundred different kinds of cells under cultivation in laboratories throughout the United States. Contamination appeared ubiquitous. Since there existed no reliable method for quick identification of unlabelled tissue culture cell lines, in early 1959 Dr. Coriell called for the establishment of a central tissue culture bank and cell registry to certify and store cell cultures. His proposal gained the speedy endorsement of officials at NIH. In June the advisory panel on viruses and cancer of the National Cancer Institute established a "cell culture committee." By year's end the South Jersey Medical Research Foundation and the Child Research Center in Detroit, Michigan, were selected as the nation's two recognized cell banks.[11] According to the plan, certified samples were to be forwarded to a central repository, the American Type Culture Collection in Washington, D.C. By September 1960, the Foundation had obtained equipment, hired and trained personnel, established criteria and procedures for standardization and certification, completely processed and preserved two cell lines, and partially analyzed a dozen others. It was aided in this work by a five-year $500,000 grant awarded in June, with prospects of long-term commitment.

The cell repository at what is now the Coriell Institute for Medical Research is perhaps the most celebrated and readily recognizable aspect of the illustrious institution. While Dr. Coriell envisioned from its inception that it would become the world center for pure cell lines used in medical research, he never intended it as the organization's centerpiece. It was a store that simply had to be established somewhere in the country. And since it was his idea and he could probably do it best, there was no reason why the SJMRF should

[11] Shortly thereafter, the Naval Research Laboratory in Oakland, California, would provide a third bank.

not accommodate the enterprise. By providing the service he could strengthen the institute's emerging relationship with the NIH. The arrangement also would supply the Foundation that as yet had no endowment fund with a commodity sorely needed to achieve institutional sustainability: a reliable funding stream.

While that need seems so axiomatic as to preclude mention, it is difficult to overestimate the impact upon current and prospective researchers of those concrete things money can buy: functional space, modern equipment, plentiful supplies, technical and clerical support. Then there are the intangibles: the security of knowing one will remain employed if one's grant support is temporarily interrupted, or the ability to concentrate on one's research without the need to write several separate grants to fund a single investigation. And then there are the economies of scale: a sufficiently sized organization to facilitate intellectual stimulation among peers and to accommodate an adequate administrative infrastructure. In all these respects, during its first half-decade, the SJMRF was a work in precarious progress.

The public reception that followed the ribbon cutting in June 1956 was an "open house" in an unintended respect: the structure was under-furnished and under-equipped. When the architect finally certified the building's completion on April 18, 1957, the visitor would find the building without air-conditioning; the labs and animal rooms lacking temperature controls; the conference room deprived of ventilation and adequate lighting; and the refrigeration room and library unfinished. Seated researchers could not squeeze their legs underneath painfully low laboratory tables. The basement (which the director wisely added to the architectural plans at the eleventh hour with a view toward future expansion) was an unfinished shell. Moreover, facing that certified incompleteness, the board's executive committee had to authorize the Foundation's treasurer, Bryant Langston, to borrow money to pay the contractor's final bill. Approximately $25,000 of outstanding pledges to the building campaign explained the financial shortfall. By 1958, the fulfillment of those pledges funded the debt, but predictably unpredictable needs led to a "mini-campaign" to refurbish the building fund's exhausted coffers. New scientific ideas do not just change minds; they alter workspace. For example, publishing conclusive evidence of widespread contamination of cell lines necessitates implementing increasing cautions in one's own laboratory. In 1958, remodeling the glass-washing room and adding steam sterilizers enlarged a growing list of urgent needs.

Thus, in addition to grant writing, the small research staff perforce engaged in cultivation of essential community resources. Starting in December 1956, Dr. Coriell inaugurated a series of public programs patterned on the model he had perfected at CMH. On various evenings throughout the year, the research staff would conduct brief scientific presentations which were followed by tours of the facility that were designed both to showcase accomplishments and delineate current and future needs. By 1959, a $5,000 facilities grant from the U.S. Public Health Service—matched on a near three-to-one basis by special gifts and proceeds from the Camden County United Fund—

permitted many of the needed enhancements. On one hand, the involvement of researchers and technicians in the process of institutional development could encourage a satisfying proprietary sentiment among the staff. On the other hand, it could distract scientists from their primary focus and foster insecurity among those who recognized that the success of a local charity ball could affect the productivity of their investigative careers.

Before an organization can reach the critical mass that can enable specialization of function, hedgehogs must act like foxes. If it sometimes seemed to the scientific and technical staff that they were performing the tasks of public relations professionals, the Foundation's trustees often resembled managers. From the eleventh day of February 1955 when the first employee was placed on the payroll, Treasurer Langston became the organization's unpaid comptroller. He received and disbursed funds, handled payroll, arranged social security coverage, and stewarded grants. Fred Greiner handled the details of property, theft and fire insurance. Bill Kalellis saw to the organization's banking and investment needs. Secretarial support from the offices of various trustees reduced clerical burdens. Ken MacDonald mobilized the auxiliaries of the Jaycees to mount the charity events that helped sustain the organization. Even as philanthropists, trustees did not simply write checks. David Langworthy not only paid for but also directed the conference room's completion. President Fleck likewise personally financed and oversaw the installation of the facilities' air conditioning. The trustees and officers of the SJMRF constituted a quintessential working board. The organization and its staff learned the value of community education as an invaluable component of and complement to the research mission. The struggles of the formative years fostered an organizational style that became a corporate philosophy. *Modus operandi* became *modus vivendi.*

Four Weddings and a Funeral

From the retrospective vantage of a half-century, observers—particularly those imbued with the idea of cumulative scientific progress—might be excused for assuming that the survival and growth of the South Jersey Medical Research Foundation were inevitable. By no means was that assured, especially in the late 1950s. While there was no dearth of scientific personnel in that era, university-based science was growing and a very small percentage of the national scientific budget was dedicated to independent research institutes. The charismatic Dr. Coriell could recruit like the devil, but the institute's early structural deficiencies and growing pains made *retaining* exceptional scientists dangerously difficult. Undoubtedly, the leader's awareness of imminent access to a major funding stream for the development and maintenance of the cell bank gave him the confidence and the authority to mount an ambitious recruitment drive in the wake of McAllister's departure. Warren Nichols was the first of four key scientific personnel recruited in the months following the NIH's endorsement of the cell bank proposal who

COURIER-POST
CAMDEN, NEW JERSEY

Particles in Milk May Explain Leukemia

Research Team Reports on 'Virus-Like Discovery'

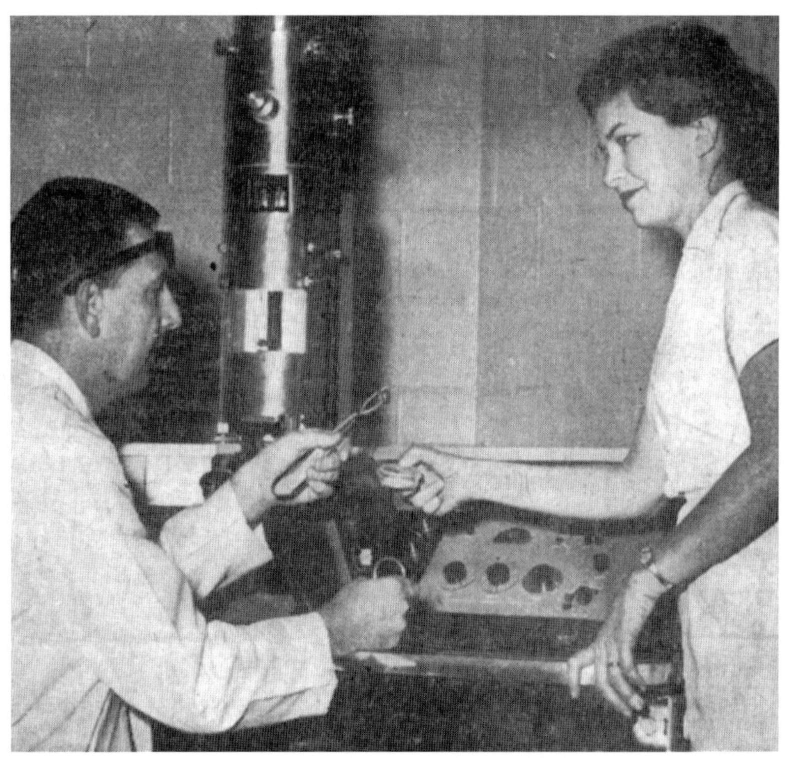

—Courier-Post Photo by Arthur C. Jarvis

LOADING MILK SPECIMEN, taken from leukemic cow and containing virus-like particles, into an electron microscope at the South Jersey Medical Research Foundation, Camden, is Dr. Ray M. Dutcher who is assisted by Mrs. Carolyn Axner of 39 Windingway, Stratford, a laboratory technician.

Courtesy of The Courier-Post

would form long-term, productive relationships with the recently stabilized Foundation.

In order to attack the problem of cancer's etiology, Dr. Coriell realized the need for disciplinary diversification within the institute. After recruiting Nichols, he found in Ray M. Dutcher a brilliant bacteriologist who possessed Mac's and his own interest in cancer research and a wide range of experience directly applicable to the Foundation's thrust. Prior to graduate schooling, he had precociously co-authored articles on tumorigenicity and on propagating poliovirus in chick embryo. A good portion of his subsequent twenty-eight months at Lederle Laboratories was spent in their neoplasm research department. While working toward his M.S. in bacteriology (University of Kentucky, 1957), he worked in veterinary research. During his doctoral studies (Ph.D. in bacteriology/virology, University of Massachusetts, 1960), he became interested in immunological processes and the relationship of viruses to tumors. In August 1960 at the age of thirty-three, he joined the Foundation staff as research associate and won an appointment as assistant research professor at Penn's School of Veterinary Medicine. He immediately took charge of a joint five-year study of bovine leukemia funded by ACS under the direction of the veterinary school's Robert Marshak, relieving Dr. Coriell of this project. To Marshak, bovine leukemia or lymphosarcoma was a common but little studied disease in cattle populations that possessed huge economic implications. To Dr. Coriell, the disease provided another avenue for exploring the possibility of a viral etiology of cancer. It closely resembled human leukemia and presented the possibility of studying large amounts of malignant tissue.

As early as 1958 Dr. Coriell realized the value of biochemical insight to understanding the differences between normal and cancer cells. In 1960 he was able to improvise a biochemical lab in the basement in order to perform comparative enzyme studies. In June 1961 he was able to retain a noted biochemist to further the study of cancer immunology. Jesse Charney was born in New York City in 1917, graduated from City College, obtained his M.S. degree from New York University in 1939, and was pursuing doctoral studies there when called to military duty. He spent a year in the Chemical Warfare Service before joining the Wyeth Institute for Applied Biochemistry in Philadelphia. From 1947 to 1952 he was involved in antibiotic research at Sharpe & Dohme and moved into the field of virological research when that pharmaceutical concern became Merck, Sharpe & Dohme in 1952. During the war he was stationed at Edgewood Arsenal, Maryland, not far from Dr. Coriell's detachment at Fort Detrick. Their scientific paths crossed in 1956 when Dr. Coriell was attempting to develop a skin test for poliomyelitis. It was Charney who had achieved the greatest purification of the poliovirus and from whom Dr. Coriell obtained his working samples. Within months of the New Yorker's arrival at the Foundation, he succeeded in isolating antigenic constituents from normal and cancer cells by means of a technique that also permitted rapid identification of the species of origin of a cell culture. This discovery was especially useful to cell line certification in the new cell bank that Arthur Greene had returned to direct in January 1961.

Under Dr. Coriell's direction, these four individuals permitted the institute to achieve critical mass. Equally valuable, they also allowed it to maintain corporate memory. Primarily interested in veterinary medicine, Ray Dutcher would move to a full-time position at Penn at the end of the term of the grant that funded the bovine leukemia study. The institute would retain the full-time services of Jesse Charney for the next fifteen years; of Warren Nichols, the next twenty-five; and of Arthur Greene, the next thirty. Such longevity is a tribute to Dr. Coriell's leadership as well as to their dedication. Observing the history of a relatively small research organization, however, allows one to realize the critical roles played by those who do not attract big grants or publish eye-opening studies. The next chapter will introduce Selena Dwight, the perfectionist whom Dr. Coriell lured from CHOP to insure preeminent quality control in tissue culturing techniques and laboratory sterilization procedures, and S. Robert Wilson, laboratory technician, supply sergeant, licensed plumber, monkey catcher, and eventual vice president of operations. Their stories and those of others are parts of the essential fabric of the institute.

By 1961, the South Jersey Medical Research Foundation had taken off. In 1956 fifteen full- and part-time staff were supported by three grants totaling $95,105. In 1961 thirteen grants amounting to $273,660 supported three dozen individuals. With the anticipation of the cell bank's expansion, the trustees were gearing up for another building campaign. For Dr. Coriell, the time had come to put his horses in one corral. On Friday, December 9, he formally announced his resignation—effective New Year's Day—as medical director of the Camden Municipal Hospital for Contagious Diseases. He also reported that Peter Vanace, M.D., had been recommended as the hospital's new director. It was a politically sensitive announcement that had to be handled with the utmost delicacy. In a letter written to the director of the county department of health, recreation and welfare, Dr. Coriell carefully and graciously thanked every organization that had associated itself with CMH during his twelve years at the helm.

Simultaneously, Mrs. Fleck, the Foundation's president, issued a statement on behalf of the trustees making clear that the board had asked Dr. Coriell to take this action "in recognition of the importance of our research commitments." The Foundation was acutely aware that many members of the community had contributed greatly to the hospital's mission and that the laboratory's future was dependent upon that community's continuing support. In order to justify the decision at the highest moral level, Mrs. Fleck accentuated the importance of the Foundation's fight against cancer and recalled Dr. Coriell's success in the battle against polio. In an interview with the media, Dr. Coriell reinforced this message. There was no mention of the fact that the hospital had outlasted its usefulness and deserved a requiem.

When Dr. Coriell had hired Nichols, he appointed him chief of staff. At the same time he appointed Vanace, another pediatrician, to serve as assistant medical director. The move was calculated to lower the medical director's high profile at the hospital. Drs. Coriell, Nichols, and Vanace rotated supervisory duties on a weekly basis in a manner that allowed them to concentrate on their research. By 1956 it was clear that the development of the Salk vaccine, antibiotics, and sulfa drugs had obviated the need for a contagious disease hospital. Indeed, during epidemics of influenza, most physicians wisely tried to keep patients on drugs and away from hospitals.

Dr. Coriell supported the reconfiguration of services that was gradually converting the facility into a modern version of the nineteenth-century dispensatory. The dental clinic had been the first move in that direction. It was followed closely by collaboration with the Easter Seal Society to use the building as a center for occupational therapy and rehabilitation. In 1958 the Muscular Dystrophy Association established a clinic there, and the Camden County Heart Association started a "heart station" for cardiac evaluation. Dr.

COURIER-POST
CAMDEN, NEW JERSEY

Last Patient Leaves Camden Municipal Hospital

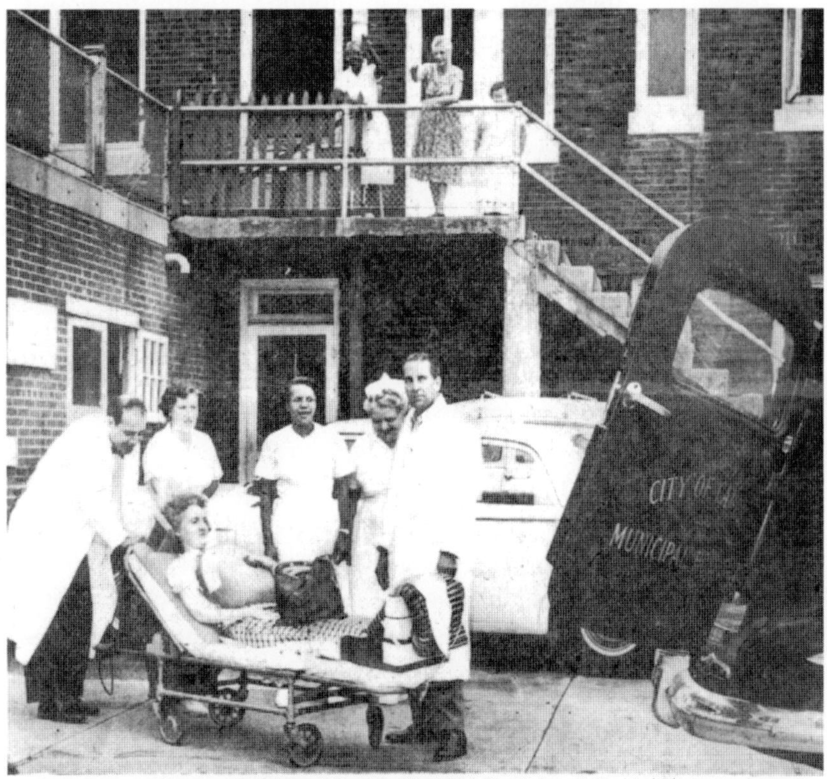

Dr. Peter Vanace (left), superintendent of Camden Municipal Hospital, and Dr. Joseph Azel, of Camden County General Hospital, at Lakeland, move Mrs. Lorean Thomson, of Haddon Heights, toward an ambulance which will take her to the Lakeland institution. Nurses and other employes say good-by to Mrs. Thomson, who was the last patient in the 50-year-old hospital, which officially closes Sept. 30

Courtesy of The Courier-Post

Coriell's acceptance of these alternatives was partially dictated by institutional self-interest. He and two senior staff members were being paid by the municipality for their services so long as the hospital remained open. Other sectors of the community—especially nearby general hospitals competing for patients—argued that, however meritorious the attempts to keep the facility viable, they came at too high a cost.

On August 10, 1962, city officials announced that the hospital would accept no patients after August 17. To justify the move it cited the findings of the Philadelphia Hospital Survey Committee's ten-week study of the institution released earlier that month. The Hospital Survey Committee (HSC) found that medical progress had made the hospital "a relic of a past era," that there were currently only eight in-patients and that the then 36-bed facility could not operate economically at twenty-five percent occupancy. The report offered assurances that these patients could be readily accommodated at other hospitals. It noted that the physical structure was unsafe and that restoration would be financially prohibitive.

The HSC was formally created in 1960–61 by a group of concerned citizens and corporations concerned with high taxes in order to analyze the need for hospital renovation, expansion, or new construction and to communicate its findings to those institutions to which the hospitals had to turn for their capital needs. It was a voluntary agency which hospitals could approach as an alternative to the Regional Comprehensive Health Planning agencies of the federal government.[12] To enable it to make its more caustic points, it utilized the services of Arthur Andersen Associates, Inc. The Andersen consultants made clear to the public in a report released along with the HSC document that Camden taxpayers were footing an annual burden of $100,000 to support a redundant hospital. Furthermore, it suggested that releasing to private development the acreage occupied by the hospital would increase the city's ratables.

Aware that the studies were being undertaken, Children's Hospital decided to offer no resistance to the findings in order to avoid antagonizing the agency. Accordingly, prior to the reports' release, it peremptorily served notice that it was withdrawing its resident physicians and retiring Dr. Vanace on September 1. That move effectively deprived the municipality of any option but closure of CMH. The *Courier-Post*'s final editorial on August 15 about the hospital it had so long championed was bluntly entitled "Municipal Hospital Closing Overdue." It seconded the conclusions of the HSC study and the Andersen report. "Recognizing these things," it said, "there is much room left for nostalgia." Thanking the "excellent and dedicated staffs," it studiously avoided mentioning Dr. Coriell by name. For his part, Dr. Coriell's workload seemed to have left him little liberty for waxing nostalgic. His scrapbook, which contained so many editorials about the hospital, did not contain this last one. The year 1962 was a year for looking ahead.

[12] In latter years, many Philadelphia-area hospital administrators suspected the HSC was an unofficial arm of Blue Cross.

Chapter Six

Of Mice and Men (1962–1968)

Dr. Coriell often said that the greatest satisfaction of his professional career was watching cured children leave Municipal. Nevertheless, his emancipation from the arduous responsibilities as head of the hospital that he had helped put out of business allowed the Foundation to concentrate on the *Foundation*'s business. In 1962 the board formulated the institute's first strategic plan. This chapter concerns itself with the plan's practical unfolding through 1968, when an unpredictable series of external events and conditions would exacerbate institutional growing pains and create a financial crisis that threatened the organization's viability.

Strategy and Stringency

The lone visionary who prefers to stay that way can strategize in secret. An organization, however, needs to articulate long-term goals and objectives if it intends to attract and retain scientific talent and secure public and private support. Internally, the planning process builds consensus and allows managers to compare design with accomplishment. Externally, a publicized plan enforces an organization's rhetorical and practical consistency and involves potential investors and employees in the institution's vision. The Foundation gave careful thought to its situation as it planned for its development. It asked itself what it would look like in a decade if it were to achieve its realistic potential and remain faithful to what it was already calling its "tradition." It honestly analyzed the strengths on which it should build, the weaknesses it would have to overcome, and the adjustments it would have to make in order to reach the brave, new world of 1972.

The nucleus of the Foundation's planning apparatus was a group of trustees called the Growth and Development Committee. The fact that the process of strategic planning was initiated in a committee of that name indicated two things. First, it signaled the board's willingness to defer to the research director in matters of scientific thrust and competency.[1] Second, it underscored the key concern for trustees who constituted the laboratories' chief financial backers and fundraisers and who were wary of unbridled expansion. Fortunately, achieving consensus on this issue did not involve much compromise. Lewis Coriell had no "edifice complex." He was an expansionist who understood the limits of growth. Development was not simply a matter of the depth of the community's pockets but of functional symmetry. Genetically engineered to scale, a one-pound *Drosophila* could not fly. Size matters.

Much has been written about the differences between "big science" and "little science." Examples of the former might include the Manhattan Project or the Genome Project. Certain kinds of investigation require bigness and massive expenditures to support it. Others do not. And in science there is no necessary relationship between the size of investment and the value of the payoff. Albert Einstein required a chalkboard, not a centrifuge. Dr. Coriell knew that the research questions the Foundation had undertaken required an interdisciplinary array of scientific talent and supporting cast large enough to cover competently the necessary intellectual, methodological, technical, and administrative bases and small enough to convince foundation and funding agency officials that its investigations were cost effective. As he often said, he did not wish to have the biggest research institute; only the best.

In 1962, with calculated imprecision, the director envisioned an institute "that is small as research foundations go, and free from the pains of uncontrolled growth, but substantially larger than the present establishment." He and the trustees set as reasonable goals for a decade of development the doubling of the number of senior investigators and the trebling both of technical assistants and of the square footage of the physical plant. The remaining goals were essentially objectives designed to achieve that single end. The plan called for the institutionalization of public relations and fund development activities. It endorsed an effort to achieve royalties by encouraging scientific staff to adopt "an aware patent outlook." It called for the "intensification" of the Foundation's educational mission to scientific professionals and the lay community. Even in this latter regard, Dr. Coriell's conviction that education was an essential intellectual obligation of a research institute never conflicted with his awareness that educational programs enhanced institutional prestige, increased public recognition of the Foundation, and helped cultivate financial support. The board's plan made this interrelationship explicit, and the institute's subsequent approach to its educational function has wisely embraced its founder's understanding. The nature of the scientific experimentation that these and other expansionist measures were intended to foster was left to the chief scientist to determine.

[1] By the mid-1960s the institute had gathered a group of respected scientists from other institutions to serve as its Research Advisory Committee. The committee would serve as a sounding board for the research director, validate his vision, and reassure the board by providing a source of disinterested strategic insight.

The planning team's assessment of the Foundation's strengths began with Dr. Coriell's past scientific achievements, robust leadership, and growing stature. As an educator he commanded a worldwide podium. In April 1957, he spent ten days in Venezuela advising its government on its plan to create an international biophysical research center and giving a series of lectures and consultations on tissue culture techniques. Three months later in Geneva, Switzerland, the Fourth International Poliomyelitis Congress bestowed upon him its Presidential Award. In 1959 he became chairman of the American Academy of Pediatrics' influential Committee on the Control of Infectious Diseases. In 1962 he joined a medical mission to Algeria to establish basic medical services in that battle-scarred country.[2] In 1963 he would receive the Delaware Valley Council's "Man of the Year" Award.[3]

The strategists likewise found encouragement in the academic credentials of the research staff, the personal and professional reputations of individual trustees, the board's collective clout, the institute's close connection to the community, its positive relationships with NIH and the ACS, and its role as a national cell repository. Since the opening of the new laboratory, its investigators had published over six dozen scientific publications. They were making important contributions to basic knowledge while sharing technical breakthroughs with the larger scientific community and producing practical discoveries that contributed to medicine and society. The conquest of cancer was becoming a national cause, and—as for the cause of cancer—viruses were becoming increasingly suspect. The board shared Dr. Coriell's optimism that the Foundation was rapidly approaching its rendezvous with scientific destiny.

The analysis concluded that there was only one bar to the Foundation's future security and growth: financial instability. "The specific major project required for further development of the institute," it concluded with simple clarity, "is therefore apparent. It is the acquisition of institutional funds." The Foundation's planners acknowledged that, not money, but the lack of it was at the root of all evils confronting the new enterprise. The institute could not afford to maintain and refurbish facilities and equipment. It had problems covering the costs of administration and depreciation. Its library was inadequate; support staff proportionately thin; pension funds, medical insurance, and other employee benefits uncompetitive; and tenure non-existent. Research grants simply failed to supply sufficient revenues to meet overhead expenses.

The principal objectives designed to remedy these weaknesses were (1) the establishment of a strong program of annual giving to support operations and (2) the creation by 1965 of a $3 million endowment "to liberate [the Foundation] from the hand-to-mouth aspects of grant-in-aid support." Annual in-

---

[2] Switzerland was surely the most relaxing tour of duty. Dr. Coriell arrived in Venezuela months before the overthrow of that country's military dictatorship. He arrived in Algeria in the year of its independence from France just as its first provisional government, following a decade of revolutionary terrorism, was anticipating the possibility of civil war.

[3] The Delaware Valley Council was a non-profit civic organization established in 1949 to plan and develop the Delaware Valley Region as an integrated economic unit.

PENNSYLVANIA MEDICAL TEAM IN ALGERIA

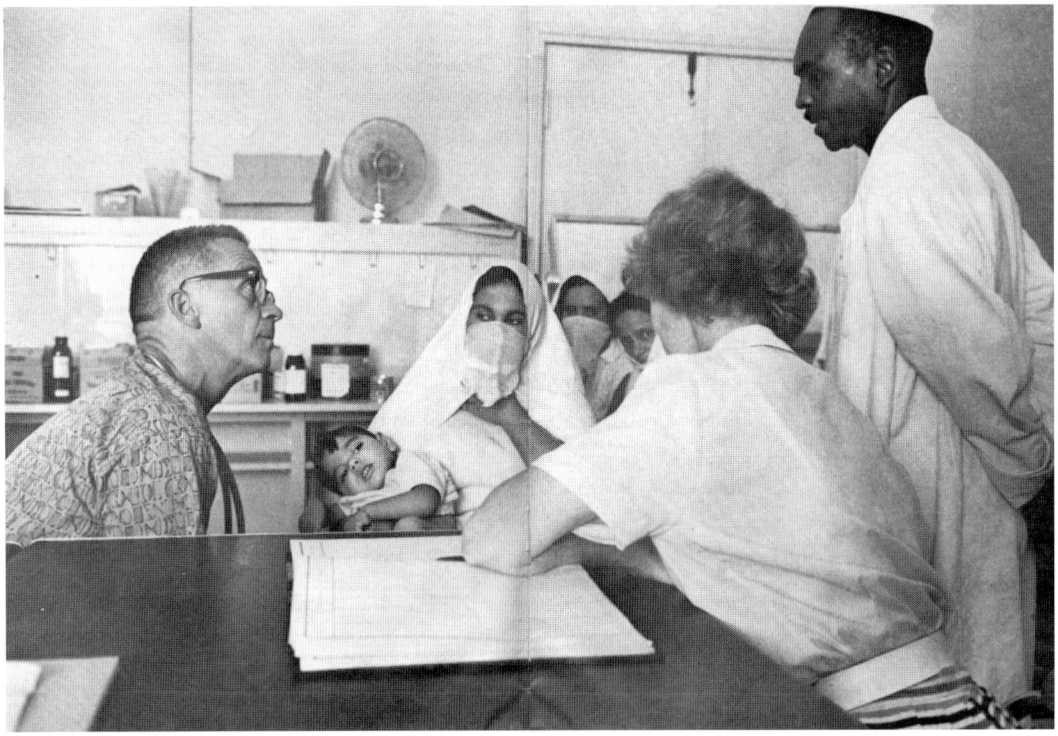

Dr. Coriell examines and prescribes for a boy with congenital syphilis during a medical mission to Algeria in 1962 (lead story of The Pennsylvania Gazette, Alumni Magazine of the University of Pennsyvania, October 1962). Courtesy of The Pennsylvania Gazette and Anders Holmquist/Blackstar

come from funds functioning as endowment would provide the administration approximately $120,000 annually for the support of new scientific investigators and supporting personnel. The single flaw in the strategic plan was its failure to incorporate into its statement of financial requirements the funds that would be required for physical expansion of its present overcrowded facility. In the United States in the third quarter of the twentieth century, for a variety of reasons involving philanthropic inclination, infrastructural need and even labor relations, it was much easier to raise funds to construct buildings than to enhance endowments. And in the highly competitive ecology of fund raising in a community with finite resources, the urgent imperative of future growth took precedence over and severely compromised the basic priority of building an endowment and an annual fund.

BRICKS AND MORTAR

Research progress spelled constant flux in the investigators' physical environment. Retrospectively regarded as the institute's second building program, the completion of the basement of the original facility in 1959—and its partial conversion into a makeshift biochemistry and cytogenetics laboratory—constituted the first expansion project. Its $18,849 price tag included the completion of and alterations to the original edifice. Proceeds from the United Fund of Camden County, special events conducted by the institute's auxiliary, and the institute's near-exhausted building fund matched the $5,000 construction grant from the U.S. Public Health Service, referred to in the previous chapter. Within months, however, the initiation of cell banking activities necessitated an immediate reconfiguration of space, the establishment of a histology laboratory, and the temporary relocation of the liquid nitrogen refrigerators to the great outdoors. In 1960 the Public Health Service, adhering to a one-to-one matching formula, pledged the institute a $92,574 research facilities grant toward the construction of a new building to house the cell bank operation. Foundation supporters braced themselves to raise an approximately identical amount.

Occupying some 7,900 square feet of space adjacent to the southwest side of the existing building, the addition would be slightly larger than the original laboratory's first floor. Officials tentatively scheduled its opening in the summer of 1962 at an estimated cost of $185,148. Both those estimates proved optimistic. When completed a year later than anticipated, the wing had become a $273,000 project, doubling the fund raising effort with essentially a *two*-to-one matching ratio. Increased costs and contingencies added only marginally to this difference. What explained the new fund raising target and the consequent construction delay was Dr. Coriell's determination to make the one-story addition a building block to future growth. Chiefly, the additional $88,000 purchased footings and bearing walls capable of supporting an eventual second floor.

The cell bank building was accepted for occupancy on August 29, 1963, and the "bankers" along with the virology section and the animal colonies moved into the new facility. Those attending the building's dedication ceremonies on January 14, 1964, witnessed the official inauguration of what would become the world's largest repository of human cells. Dr. Coriell's pioneering techniques for characterizing, freezing, and storing non-contaminated cell cultures in liquid nitrogen constitute one of the greatest contributions to modern human genetics. Indeed, attendees might have incorrectly inferred from the hoopla that the cell bank represented the new core of the Foundation's mission. To correct that misimpression they needed only to examine the roster of visiting dignitaries. NIH had sent the National Cancer Institute's associate director for grants and training. Representing the American Cancer Society was its national vice president for research. Dr. Coriell's ambition was to conquer cancer.[4]

---

[4] In January 1963, Dr. Coriell was elected to the Camden County Chapter of ACS. Over the preceding three years it had contributed $258,000 to the Foundation and was instrumental in the success of the capital campaign to build the cell bank facility.

It is tempting to imagine that, as the ritual ribbon was being scissored at the doorway of the new cell bank facility, Dr. Coriell was considering how best to retrofit the vacated laboratory spaces and animal rooms in the original facility and who best to occupy the new building's contemplated second floor. Clearly such considerations were not idle daydreams, for by summertime, with startling immediacy and seemingly inexhaustible fascination with bricks and mortar, the trustees had approved the third and boldest capital construction campaign in the institute's brief history. Once again, the Research Facilities Branch of the U. S. Public Health Service catalyzed the drive, this time with a $271,000 two-to-one matching grant. In December 1964 the Foundation announced a $540,000 appeal for a project whose construction had to begin by the end of the following year in order to qualify for the federal match.

The proposed $810,000 building program called for two major expansions. One was the addition of a second floor to the new building for a new cytological biophysics department. Biophysics would complement the institute's disciplinary cadre, particularly in the area of physical characterization of cancer cells, proteins, and viruses known or suspected to cause mutations in mammalian cells. The area would also house supporting labs and a machine shop for the fabrication and repair of instruments. The cost of this addition was initially estimated at $253,000. The other enhancement was a new administration building, an elongated structure to be built perpendicular to the original laboratory along its Sheridan Street entrance. With a basement dedicated to storage, this new facility would accommodate an auditorium, conference rooms and library, and cost approximately $356,000.

Moving administrative offices to a separate wing was designed to reduce traffic and hence microbial contamination from the laboratory facilities. Administrative space in the original facility would be converted into laboratories for studies of chromosomes, genes, and viruses related to cancer. The old library area would be converted into space for the biochemistry department to expand its studies on unusual antigens shown to be present in certain cancer cells. The compacted conference area in the new cell bank wing would be taken over by the virology department. Plans called for the construction of an $88,000 central supply building on the southern side of the original building between the cell bank wing and the administrative wing but adjoining neither. The current supply room would be converted for activities related to cell banking. Behind the cell bank building would be a detached building to house an electrical substation and emergency generators, costing $57,000. Another $57,000 would be required for research equipment. By October 1965 the need to expand sterilization and decontamination facilities brought the cost estimate to $836,000. By May 1966 the requirements of newly enlisted senior research scientists raised the goal to $978,336. When the campaign was over, the institute had successfully accomplished a million-dollar expansion effort.

The interplay of physical expansion, research activity, and scientific recruitment during this furious period of fund raising and rapid growth constituted one of the most dynamic challenges to Dr. Coriell's leadership. He had to show foundation officials and other prospective contributors that the

Gloria (Jeanne) West began her career at the Institute as a summer intern in 1960. Forty-three years later, as supervisor of the central sterilization laboratory, she is responsible for a critical element in the Institute's quality control systems.

institute's accomplishments entitled it to their support while suggesting that expansion was necessary to sustain future achievements. If supporters were satisfied with perfection, could they champion aspirations to progress? On one hand, a more modest campaign goal might insure its fulfillment and save the director some of his ample social and political capital. On the other hand, it might fail to assure the senior scientists whom he needed to recruit that the Foundation would have resources necessary to support their research programs. Dr. Coriell had to cultivate potential contributors with assurances that expansion would entice scientific talent, and he had to convince prospective scientific talent that their commitment would insure expansion. It was not a job one could accomplish serially. Faith, optimism, and persuasiveness were the keys to success. Ultimately it was Dr. Coriell's scientific reputation and the caliber of the scientists whom he had already recruited that attracted the scientists he needed to recruit. Square footage meant nothing without brainpower.

Brains and Molecules

As the Foundation plotted its institutional strategy in 1962, it was emboldened by the excitement over the scientific discoveries of Warren Nichols. His work in cytogenetics enhanced the institute's reputation for avant-garde experimentalism, bridged several disciplines within the Camden laboratory, and reinforced the educated hunch (upon which the institute's organization and activity were increasingly premised) that viruses caused cancer. The science of inheritance, modern genetics, is the biological study of the mechanisms of heredity, particularly the gene, which inhabits chromosomes, which are composed of compacted strands of DNA (deoxyribonucleic acid). *Cyto*genetics, the field of investigation concerned with chromosomes and cell division, was a newly reinvented field of exploration when Nichols made his acquaintance with it. The discovery of the structure of DNA in 1953 was followed three years later by the revelation that human somatic cells are made up of twenty-three pairs of chromosomes.

Professor J. Albert Levan and his colleague Jo Hin Tjio, a Chinese geneticist from Dutch Java, made this latter discovery in 1956 at Lund University in Levan's native Sweden. They accomplished this feat by devising a series of clever and somewhat inelegant techniques for separating chromosomes so that they could be spread out along one plane on a microscope's slide, counted, and separately examined. This new capability meant that analysis of chromosomes could now be used to characterize cell cultures, an activity at the heart of the South Jersey Medical Research Foundation's enterprise. For the work occurring in Camden, the timing of this innovation was downright providential, and Dr. Coriell rapidly added it to the repertoire of methods he and others had devised for identifying and characterizing cell lines and spotting contamination. In 1957, readers will recall, he began to use chromosome counts as one criterion for attempting to distinguish between normal and cancer cells in tissue culture. When Nichols arrived at the Foundation, the correlation of chromosomal aberrations with diseases and hereditary predisposition to various diseases and abnormal conditions had become a very fashionable field of inquiry.

In 1960 Nichols set up a laboratory to study human and animal chromosomes and started a concerted effort, in his words, "to determine whether chromosomal changes were involved in the production of cancer." By that time Levan had established the Cancer Chromosome Laboratory at the Lund University Institute of Genetics. Hoping to learn from one of the giants in human cytogenetics, Nichols asked his boss to invite the Swedish professor to stop by Camden en route to a fall meeting on human chromosome nomenclature in Denver, Colorado. Collegially and scientifically, the visitation succeeded beyond anyone's imagination. Prior to the meeting, two Philadelphia-area scientists—David Hungerford at the Institute for Cancer Research at Fox Chase and Peter Nowell at the University of Pennsylvania—had discovered how to make chromosomes from blood cells; specifically, how to add a particular substance to blood in order to get cells to divide. It is during this division, or mitotic stage, that chromosomes are visible with the aid of a microscope. Nichols had been working closely with the discoverers of this "hot" new technique and taught it to Levan during his brief visit. In turn, Levan shared some of his tricks for simplifying chromosome preparations from tissue culture cell lines. The mutually productive encounter would lead to a

Kromosomrubbningar kan lösa cancergåta tror internationellt forskarteam i Lund

Dr Rei Kato, *Tokyo, dr Warren W Nichols, Camden, USA, professor Albert Levan, Lund och docent Waheeb* **Heneen**, *Kairo — i sanning ett internationellt forskarteam! — samlade kring ett av Genetiska institutionens moderna mikroskop.*

The success of Drs. Nichols's and Levan's work on chromosomes in cancer tissue received coverage in Sweden, where Nichols earned his Ph.D.

long-term partnership and an international scientific exchange of consequence. Nichols would have a mentor on each side of the Atlantic Ocean.[5]

Levan readily accepted Dr. Coriell's offer to return to the Foundation in the summer of 1961. Together, Levan and Nichols perfected methods for visualizing chromosomes and for preparing mitotic chromosomes from the peripheral blood of several laboratory animals. This latter innovation made it easier to study the relationship of chromosome cytology to virus-induced cancer. The two institutions—one based in virology and the other in genetics—devised a collaborative plan to explore the connections between viruses and genetic mutation. In the spring of 1962, it was Nichols's turn to travel. Intending to spend the year in Lund, he stayed for fifteen months. The reason for the extended stay was a serendipitous discovery that significantly altered the course of cytogenetic investigation.

In Lund, the scientific partners set out to test several different viruses in cells in culture and make preparations of their chromosomes when an "*extra*

[5] Nichols would earn a Ph.D. in genetics at Lund University in May 1966. Dr. Coriell participated in his doctoral examination and witnessed the conferral ceremony.

vitro" event intervened. A measles epidemic was ravaging the city. Children with Down's Syndrome were long known to be at higher risk of suffering severe consequences of measles. Just the year before in Camden, Nichols had been investigating the chromosomal patterns exhibited in mongoloid children. Local health officials learned of that study and asked the visiting pediatrician to test the measles victims for this chromosomal abnormality. Unexpectedly, Nichols and his Swedish host found that, from the third to the fifth day after the clinical onset of measles, the blood culture of great numbers of infected children exhibited a large quantity of chromosomal breaks. Their results convincingly demonstrated that viruses could induce genetic changes.

Scientific publication of this discovery opened dozens of investigative pathways as researchers in laboratories around the world mounted hypotheses to explain the finding and as other viral diseases were tested to procure similar results. While the Swedish-American team was reluctant to draw firm conclusions from their findings, Levan announced that "if a virus can be shown to induce chromosomal changes, as we believe we have shown with the measles virus, it could also be a potential cause of later-occurring cancers in people." Nichols knew that, if the breaks were due to the direct action of the virus and not to an immunologic response or toxic reaction, it would not be difficult to devise tests to disclose concealed virus infections in tissue culture and even to detect the presence of human tumor viruses. The implications of the discovery could provide a career's worth of engaging scientific problems.

The avenues of research that Nichols had opened up as a result of his work in Lund in 1962 added to the Foundation's dynamic vitality. The publicity that resulted from his discovery and subsequent prolific output increased the institute's local and international reputation. His tenure strengthened collaborative and cooperative relations with other scientific institutions and scientists, brought genetics under the institute's canopy, and attracted a steady stream of grant funding throughout the period under consideration. With investigators such as Nichols on board, Dr. Coriell's call for expansion of senior scientific staff and facilities to house them became an easier sell.

The news from Sweden excited cancer researchers, aware of the manifest rise in leukemia incidence following a measles outbreak. Few investigators were as excitable as Ray Dutcher, who participated in science as though it were a contact sport. In fact, his choice of cattle over mice as experimental animals occasionally made his research resemble a rugby scrum. Convinced that a virus caused bovine leukemia, he frankly confessed his frustration that "most of the information we [scientists] get is negative information." Thus, whenever he obtained a positive result from his etiological studies, he would parade through the laboratories serenading his Camden colleagues with his saxophone en route to the lunchroom, where he would light up a celebratory cigar. Just months before Nichols's departure to Lund, he and Nichols had co-authored with other Foundation and Penn veterinary school sleuths an important article in the journal *Cancer Research*. Based on a study of fifty-nine leukemic cows, the article supported the etiological hypothesis that leukemia was transmitted along family lines by an infectious agent. Of course, the study did not rule out the possibility of cell mutation. Dutcher had nothing against the study of genetics. As a hobby, he bred rare budgerigars—a colorful alternative to white mice and brown cows—in the basement aviary of his Cherry Hill residence. But he was placing his bets on the study of virology as the disciplinary key that would unlock the causes of cancer. The findings of Levan and Nichols suggested that endogenous and exogenous theories of cancer's etiology were not incompatible, that viruses might explain genetic mutation.

Prior to the project's inception in 1960, most published work pertaining to causative studies in the general field of leukemia had to do with mouse leukemia viruses. To the extent that the strains of mice used for these studies were highly inbred, it was difficult to extrapolate conclusions for human leukemia. Dutcher considered the cow "a good median research subject between the mouse and man." Because bovine leukemia had received comparatively little scientific scrutiny, the project team was hopeful that a breakthrough in cancer etiology might emerge from its investigations. In 1962 Dutcher was preoccupied with the analysis of a variety of tissue cultures of leukemic tumors and tissues from leukemic cows. He had identified over two dozen viruses that had been isolated from the cattle and was attempting to recover a leukemia virus from them. The experimental herd was kept on the

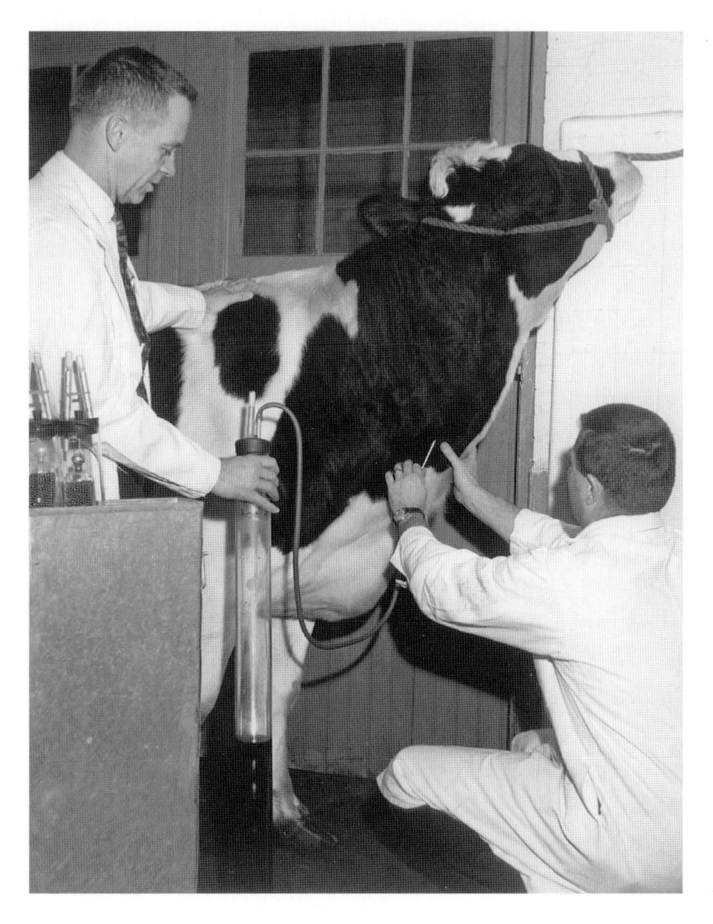

Drs. Coriell and Dutcher collect a sample of blood for a high visibility study of bovine leukemia at New Bolton, PA, in a collaboration with the University of Pennsylvania's School of Veterinary Medicine.

farmlands at the Veterinary School's New Bolton Center near Kennett Square, Pennsylvania, some thirty-three miles southwest of Camden. There researchers were trying to transmit leukemia to cattle by injecting them with the viruses and closely monitoring them. In April, Dutcher reported the project's progress at a national symposium and announced that pathological and clinical aspects of the diseased herd were exhibiting many similarities to human leukemia.

The conjunction of the ascendancy of viral theories of cancer causation and the discovery of the similarities between human and animal leukemia stimulated investment into bovine research. As with cytogenetics, the Foundation's investigations appeared to be at the epicenter of trends in biomedical science. By 1965, NCI had organized a Special Virus-Cancer-Leukemia program to coordinate a national long-range attack on leukemia. The Foundation's program in bovine research fell under its generous umbrella. Even the World Health Organization helped finance the project. Chemotherapeutic advances in the treatment of leukemia led to vastly increased public support of the Leukemia Society of America. That support helped fill the Society's coffers and its support of research. Dutcher served as president of the Southern New Jersey chapter of the Leukemia Society.

The bovine leukemia project was a microcosm of the Foundation's scientific strengths and strategy. Externally, it commanded the resources of a variety of funding sources. Like the cytogenetics laboratory, its director was involved in an inter-institutional collaboration. Internally, it could rely on a dynamic and symbiotic cooperation of disciplines and competencies. The project utilized the tissue culture expertise of Arthur Greene and the resources of the cell bank under his supervision, the genetic approaches of Warren Nichols, and the biochemical insights of Jesse Charney. This arrangement made financial as well as intellectual sense. Liberal funding of one hot project could help support several departments. In 1965, for example, a five-year $75,000 Leukemia Scholar Award supported Foundation research associate Edward P. Larkin's work in fluorescence microscopy. By the middle of the decade the institute's bovine research was extremely stable and full of promise. If Foundation trustees and staff celebrated achievement in the style of Ray Dutcher, the air outside the laboratories would have been filled with the sound of saxophones and the aroma of cigars.

The air inside the Camden laboratories, however, would soon set standards for purity. In 1965 Art Greene hired Gerald J. McGarrity to work in his cell biology group. Soon after his arrival, however, the John A. Hartford Foundation awarded the institute a $195,795 grant for a study of dust-free biomedical environments. Dr. Coriell asked McGarrity to take charge of what at the time was simply called "the cleanroom project." Born in Brooklyn, New York, and raised in Philadelphia, the new research associate had earned his M.S. from Jefferson Medical College and was working towards his Ph.D. in microbiology at Thomas Jefferson University's College of Graduate Studies. His job was to apply recently developed techniques for eliminating airborne and surface contaminants to the prevention of infection in various biomed-

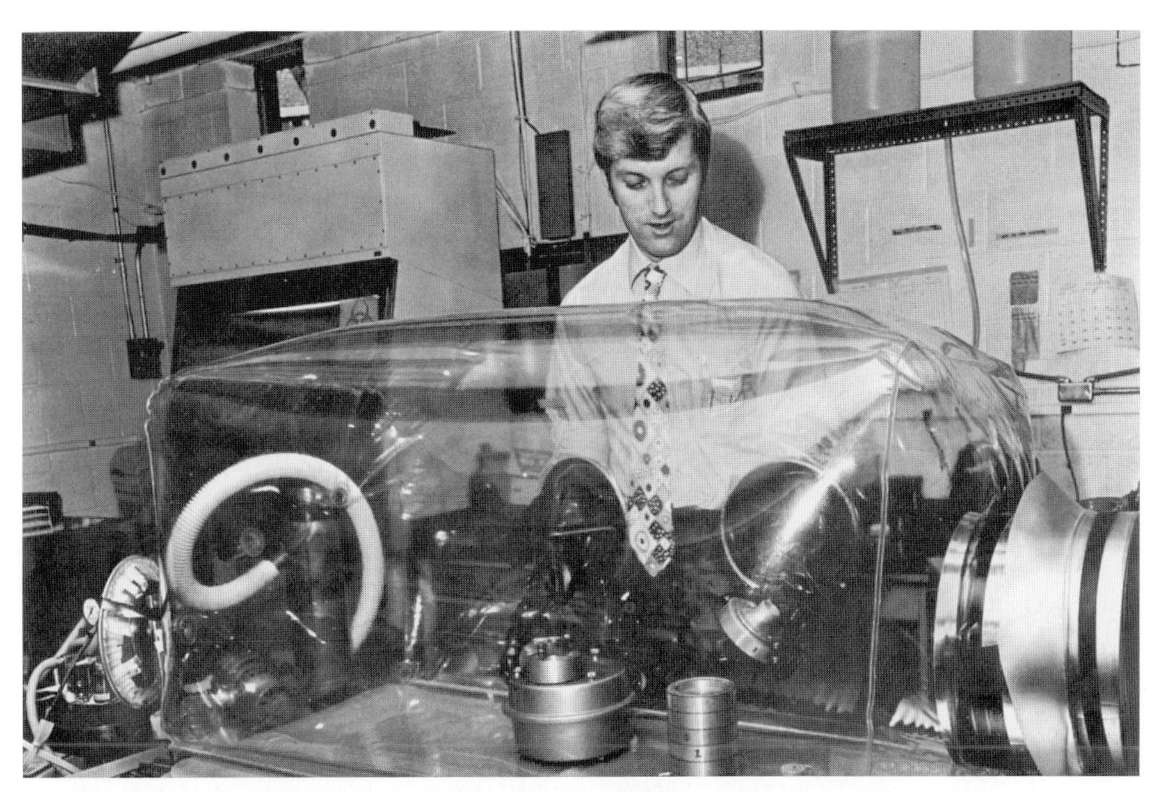

Dr. Gary McGarrity participated in the design of laboratory equipment used for infection control experiments.

ical environments. At first glance, the project seemed jejune. Testing the effectiveness of various brands of disinfectants, determining how best to mop a floor, taking endless air samples in different rooms and under varying conditions and times of day to monitor numbers of "colony forming units" of bacteria: these chores hardly resembled cutting-edge science. But McGarrity's findings proved alarming, and his solutions soon became part of standard armamentaria of well-equipped medical institutions worldwide.

For research laboratories everywhere, but particularly one charged with a national mission to certify and store uncontaminated cell cultures, the clean-room project was a critical initiative. Camden investigators had already shown the world that over half of all cultures used in cancer research were spoiled. Laboratory animals were frequently infected. Undetected contamination resulted in invalidated experiments and the waste of energy, time, talent, money, and animal lives. The lives of researchers themselves were at risk. By the mid-sixties investigators shuddered at the cavalier fashion in which they had handled deadly agents such as poliovirus in the past. Since 1945, over 2,700 laboratory workers in the United States were infected by the microbes they studied, and 107 died. In institutions intended to cure, the problem was worse. No one knew how many deaths were attributable to "hospitalism," but it was conservatively estimated that over one in every ten hospitalized patients acquired an infection that they did not have upon admission. Conceived in a quarantine hospital for contagious disease and possessing a growing cell bank and registry, the institute was a perfect environment for studies of imperfect environments.

Surprisingly, one of the first sophisticated tools tested at the Foundation for cleanroom application was laminar airflow control, a technology developed in the 1930s and 1940s for aeronautical purposes. Laminar airflow is a process in which the entire body of air moves at uniform velocity along parallel lines with a minimum of eddies. Flight researchers designed aircraft wings to achieve laminar airflow to reduce air turbulence that increased "skin-friction" drag and fuel consumption. Prior to 1965, the United States Air Force supported much of this research under the auspices of the National Aeronautics and Space Administration. In 1965, however, the strategic preoccupations of the escalating war in Vietnam, together with the low prices of jet fuel, caused the USAF to withdraw its funding. Simultaneously, NASA ended Project Mercury, its pioneering program of manned space flight. The Mercury capsules constituted NASA's first extraterrestrial biomedical laboratory where laminar airflow control was just beginning to be applied to tightly contained spaces to remove toxic air.

At the start of what would be a hiatus in lucrative government contracts for laminar airflow research for aeronautical and astronautical purposes, a local entrepreneur asked Dr. Coriell if his laboratories would test his own version of the technology in terrestrial biomedical environments. James Horneff managed a canvas awning manufacturing business, Horneff and Davis, in neighboring Collingswood. While installing his own product at a General Electric facility that was working under contract with NASA, he encountered laminar airflow devices and reasoned he could build soft plastic models that were just as efficient but vastly less expensive. He would install a few at the Foundation for free if the laboratories would test their reliability and explore their applicability. McGarrity soon found himself working with a prototypical Horneff unit in a small room behind the animal quarters. Soon units were being used in the tissue culturing labs.

Dr. Coriell knew that high efficiency particulate air (HEPA) filters similar to the ones he had encountered at Fort Detrick could clean the air in an empty room with amazing efficiency. The average size of a bacterium is approximately one micron, and HEPA filters could remove 99.97% of particles a third that size, including some viruses. Viruses are too small to be captured by filters, but since they normally travel on dust or water droplets, they are arrested with their vehicles. Thus, air supplied to a room could be rendered virtually sterile. Inside the room, however, humans and animals constantly shed bacteria and viruses. McGarrity found that contaminants generated in a room supplied with HEPA-filtered air could be decontaminated by laminar airflow control. In combination, these techniques essentially solved the problem of laboratory infiltration by microbes.

To protect researchers and technicians against infectious materials or inhaling infectious airborne particles, McGarrity and his colleagues devised a biohazard hood, an innovation that developed in collaboration with the Baker Company of Biddeford, Maine. The hood incorporated HEPA filtration, laminar airflow, and a high-velocity air curtain that allowed workers freedom of motion while separating them from cultures. The efficiency of the curtain was greater than 99.99%. Dr. Coriell's clinical orientation naturally propelled such advances beyond the laboratory. By 1968, the institute was testing its clean air installations with highly positive results in the operating rooms at Camden's Cooper Hospital, an intensive care unit of Philadelphia's Graduate Hospital, and elsewhere. A study was underway in the leukemia ward at CHOP to see if HEPA-filtered laminar airflow distribution systems could help to reduce or eliminate often-fatal infection during chemotherapy and after radiation required for bone marrow transplants.

The clean room project not only succeeded in its primary purpose of reducing contamination in the laboratory environment, but also provided important ancillary functions during the final stages of the building campaign. Investigations into cancer immunology and etiology were encouraging, but they provided few immediately practical offshoots. The immediate and im-

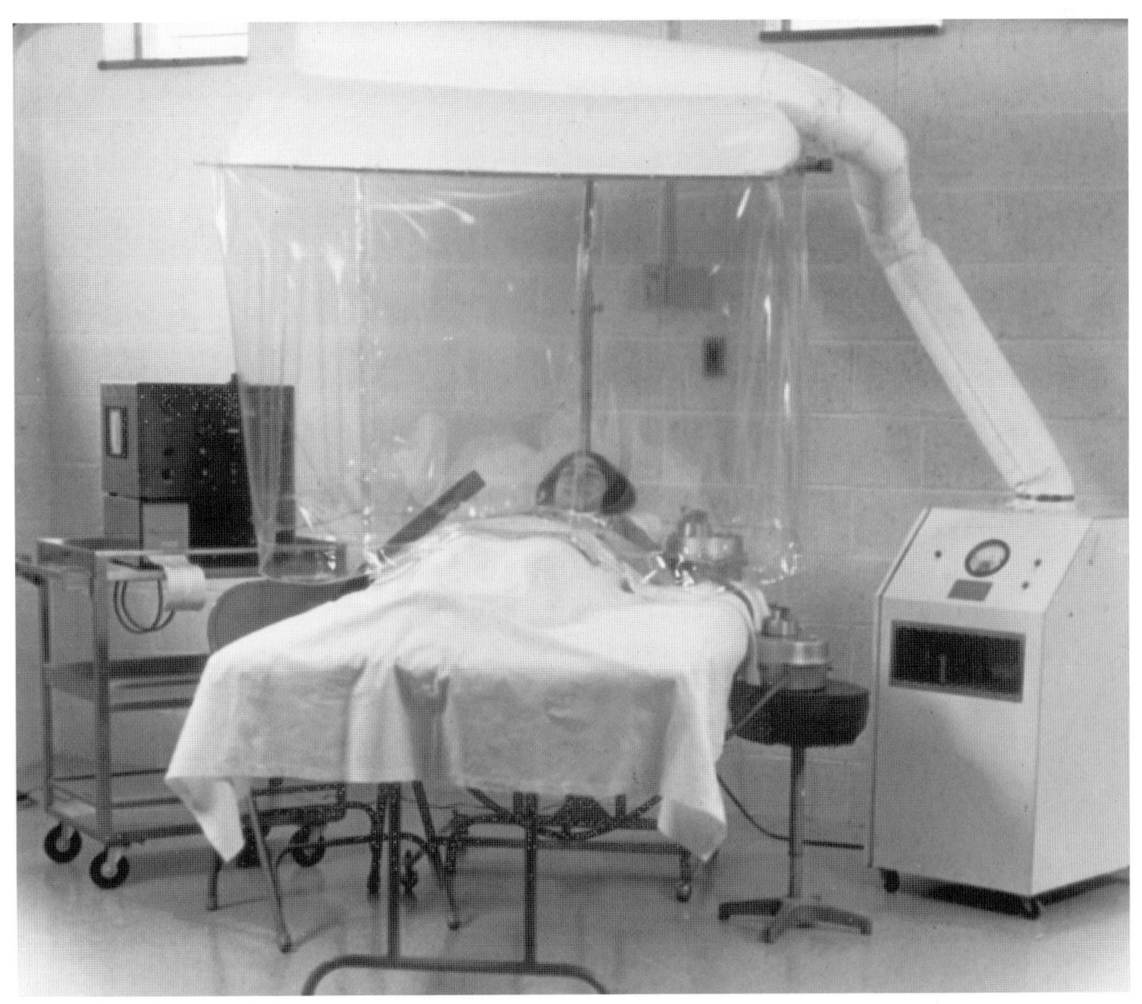

A laminar flow canopy in a clinical setting: one of several applications of infection control technology developed by Drs. Coriell and McGarrity.

minent applicability of the clean-room technologies wherever sterile environments were required showed supporters that the institute was actually improving human health and safety. Kicked off by the Hartford Foundation grant, the project seemed capable of sustaining itself. For trustees who advocated "an aware patent outlook," it appeared to be the enterprise that eventually could generate internal sources of income. Most of all, it allowed the institute to do its work better and enhanced its reputation as a research establishment that set standards for other laboratories to emulate.

Just as the clean room project helped improve the laboratory environment for Dr. Coriell and his co-workers, the ability of the cell bank to characterize cells that were of critical "in-house" interest provided the institute's researchers with an important fringe benefit. By 1967 the cell biology group headed by Greene had characterized, standardized, preserved, and placed in the national cell bank a total of thirty-five pure cell lines. Most of these cell lines were the ones commonly utilized in virus-cancer experiments. Their certification enhanced the reliability of such studies conducted on tissue culture. Several cell lines improved Nichols's ability to analyze chromosome abnormalities at the cellular level. Along with Dr. Coriell and other virologists, the cell biology group significantly improved techniques for growing cancer cells, standardizing culture media, identifying the species of various cell lines, and extending cell culture viability during prolonged storage in liquid nitrogen.

In the field of cell biology particularly, the slightest deviation from protocol could result in the contamination of cell lines. Tissue cultures were highly sensitive to the slightest breeches of laboratory etiquette, and the finely crafted experiment of a scientific genius could be destroyed by the failure of a lab assistant to wash a test tube properly. Laboratory technician Selena Dwight insured that the highest standards of environmental asepsis and procedural methods were maintained. Dwight mastered these techniques at Children's Hospital from 1953 to 1956 when she (and Greene) worked in the polio research division under Dr. Coriell's supervision. A technical perfectionist, she would impart her knowledge to scores of technicians and assistants until her retirement in 1993. One of the research director's great personal strengths was his ability to make each of his associates—from senior scientist to bottle washer—feel critically important to the institute's work. They were. Their leader created a democratic culture of mutual respect and interdependence at the institute. That culture was fundamental to its scientific success.

Another way to characterize a scientific community is by its attitude toward professional competition. Some researchers and research institutions tend toward secrecy and surprise in order to "scoop" the competition; others prefer to share as they learn in order to speed the progress of discovery. Dr. Coriell's instinct for cooperation and collaboration was widely acclaimed. Senior scientists of either stripe would find his openness congenial; younger colleagues tended to emulate their research director. As the Foundation began to assimilate Dr. Coriell's investigative style, it became an increasingly attractive place to work. In 1965, Daniel H. Moore, Ph.D., found irresistible Dr. Coriell's offer to come to Camden from the Rockefeller Institute for Medical

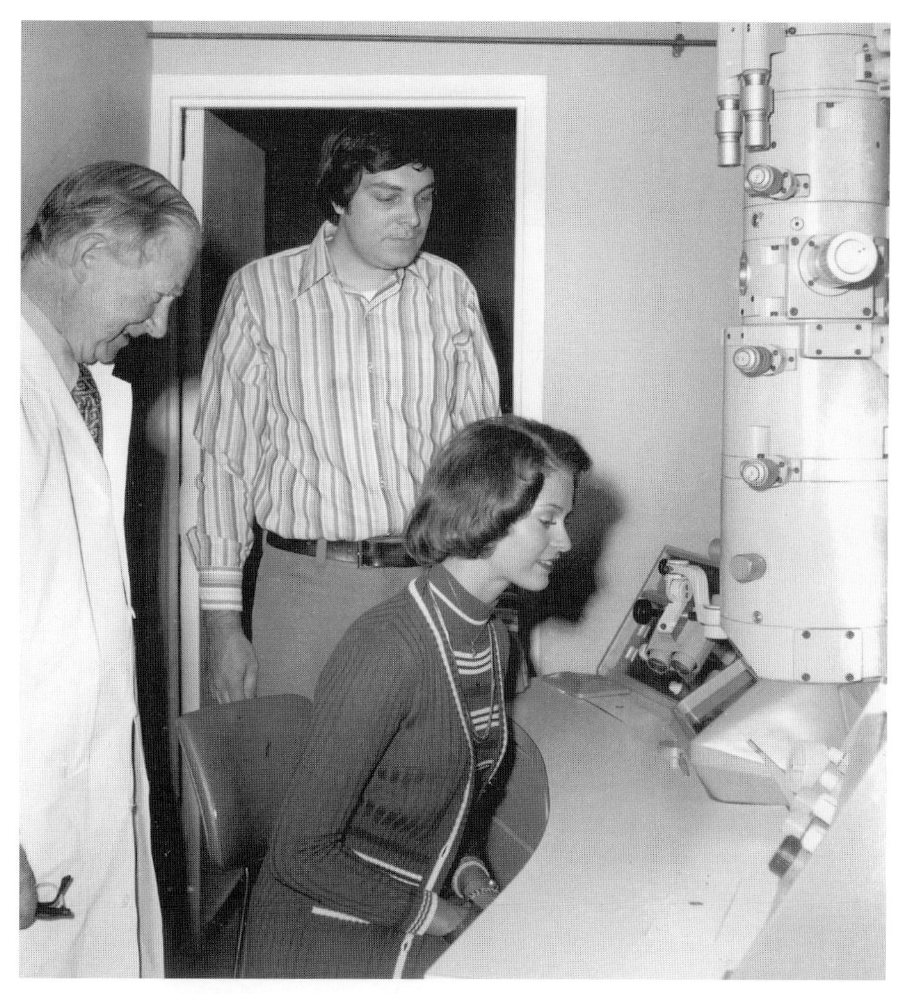

A well-respected scientist, Dr. Daniel Moore (left) also possessed the skills to communicate to the general public as well as to the many celebrities who visited the Institute during his twelve-year tenure. Here Dr. Moore explains the capabilities of an electron microscope to Rebecca Ann King, Miss America 1974.

Research to become director of the Foundation's new cytological biophysics laboratory.

Moore was a respected biophysicist, world-renowned electron microscopist, and perhaps the leading authority on breast cancer in mice. He first encountered the Foundation and its leader as part of a site visitation team commissioned by NIH in response to Nichols's initial grant proposal. Soon the two were collaborating. Thanks to Lavenia Taylor, a devoted institute volunteer, a division of the mighty New Jersey State Federation of Women's Clubs chose the institute as the beneficiary of its 1963–64 fund-raising project and contributed $30,000 for the purchase of an electron microscope.[6] But no-

[6] The scientific staff "rode the circuit" of Women's Clubs throughout the state lecturing about medical science and the Institute's programs. Mrs. Taylor served as New Jersey Federation president from 1964 to 1966.

Research associate Selena Dwight demonstrates the cell culturing process to Mrs. Thomas McKormick, membership chair of the West Jersey Federation of Women's Clubs, and Mrs. S. Herbert Taylor, the Club's vice president of its southern region.

body knew how to use one as well as Moore, and Nichols required a closer look at certain chromosomes. One day Nichols got a preparation of blood cells to a proper stage, and he and his boss set off for New York, processing chromosomes in the back of a bouncing bus in an attempt to time the preparation to drop in front of Moore's lens at just the right stage of processing. The attempt succeeded socially if not scientifically. Moore appreciated the gesture, but reasoned that the timetables of genetic experimentation required a calibrated precision incompatible with interstate bus schedules. He agreed to reciprocate the visit and to use the Foundation's microscope. Soon he realized nostalgically that the South Jersey Foundation resembled the Rockefeller Institute in its early halcyon days. Dr. Coriell made him an offer he could not refuse and announced to the trustees in April 1965 that Moore, his research team, and a colony of two thousand mice would make the move as soon as the new laboratory was constructed.

Biophysics endeavored to characterize biological structures using the tools of physical chemistry and physics. It was the "found" link that allowed the disciplines assembled at the institute to communicate optimally with each other. Not only did Moore's field complement Jesse Charney's biochemical expertise, but also their interests in breast cancer research and mouse mammary tumor virus (MMTV) intersected. Part of Moore's mouse colony was a highly inbred strain possessing mammary cancer. MMTV had been found in this strain. John Bittner of the Jackson Memorial Laboratory in Maine had concluded in 1936 that breast cancer could be transmitted from the mother mouse to her young in milk during nursing. Thirty years later, Moore proved that Bittner's "milk factor" was a virus that remained dormant until stimulated by hormonal factors in middle age. When baby mice would be foster-nursed by mothers who did not have MMTV, the babies did not get cancer. Moore's studies lent depth and breadth to the institute's concentration on cancer and viral oncogenesis.

Luring this eminent investigator away from Rockefeller—the legendary workplace of Lewis Coriell's boyhood heroes—was a major coup that signified to the scientific world that the research institute in Camden had come of age. Moore's research was well funded, his team talented and diversified. Staff members widely acknowledged that the advent of the Rockefeller group, which included Etienne Lasfargues, D.V.M., significantly stimulated intellectual intercourse and scientific productivity. Not long after Moore's arrival, his discoveries were attracting international attention and praise. For Dr. Coriell, Moore's commitment in early 1965 meant that he had finally assembled a complete scientific team. That achievement virtually insured the success of the building campaign—and more importantly of the central rationale for the expansion. It also helped catalyze a number of significant and even historic changes in the way the institute operated and the manner in which it presented itself to the outside world.

An Institute Matures

With the anticipated expansion of facilities and staff, Foundation trustees and director moved adeptly to "staff up" operations, rationalize administrative procedures, and reorganize scientific staff. In March 1965, as Dr. Coriell was successfully concluding negotiations with Dr. Moore, the Foundation hired its first full-time comptroller. The following month it retained the services of a professional auditing firm to work with the new financial administrator to revamp the organization's accounting methods, steward the gifts and pledges to the capital fund drive, and analyze overhead expenses. Correctly computing overhead was a critical concern. Grant income—particularly from the NIH—was increasing steadily. Analysis revealed that the institute's gross overhead expenditures approximated thirty-five percent, whereas the NIH's allowance to the Institute averaged only twenty-three percent of grant funds for indirect costs. Clearly, the situation was a "Catch-22," or in this case "Catch-23." The greater the institute's success in procuring grants to sponsor vital research, the more cash-strapped it became. In October the board authorized the comptroller to formulate a realistic overhead policy and attempt to renegotiate the NIH overhead expense allowance.

Another way to treat overhead expense was to reduce it. By October, Sheldon R. ("Bob") Wilson, as head of "buildings and grounds," was attending the meetings of the board's executive committee along with the comptroller. Wilson was trained by the Army as a laboratory technician and was working in Thack Read's laboratory at Cooper Hospital in 1954 when Dr. Coriell invited him to help with the Salk vaccine evaluation. Dr. Coriell had hired five young lab workers from the West Jersey Hospital to test the sera from children who had been vaccinated with either the polio vaccine or a placebo. They were not performing well, and Dr. Coriell needed someone to train and organize them. Wilson had just been selected at a higher salary and more job security as the chief "lab tech" at a Veterans Administration facility. But that laboratory was not yet constructed; Lew Coriell was a beguiling personality; and, besides, it was just a short-term grant. When Wilson retired from the institute forty years later as chief operating officer, he had left an indelible mark on it. And, yes, the five laboratory assistants shaped up.

By 1965 Wilson had become the director's indispensable jack-of-all-trades. In the early sixties, working with Selena Dwight in the cell biology group, he took on an additional title as maintenance engineer. Soon he would be the organization's purchasing agent. Whatever his title, his functions were always multi-dimensional. As a handyman, he could build what need not be bought; as a procurement officer, he could purchase at volume discount supplies that could not be built. He became the director's trusted sidekick, his operational eyes and hands. In the words of a former board chairman, "Wilson had his finger on the pulse of the institute from day one." Working with the architect and general contractor, he played a major role in keeping the expansion project on track. One senior scientist on the scene at the time called

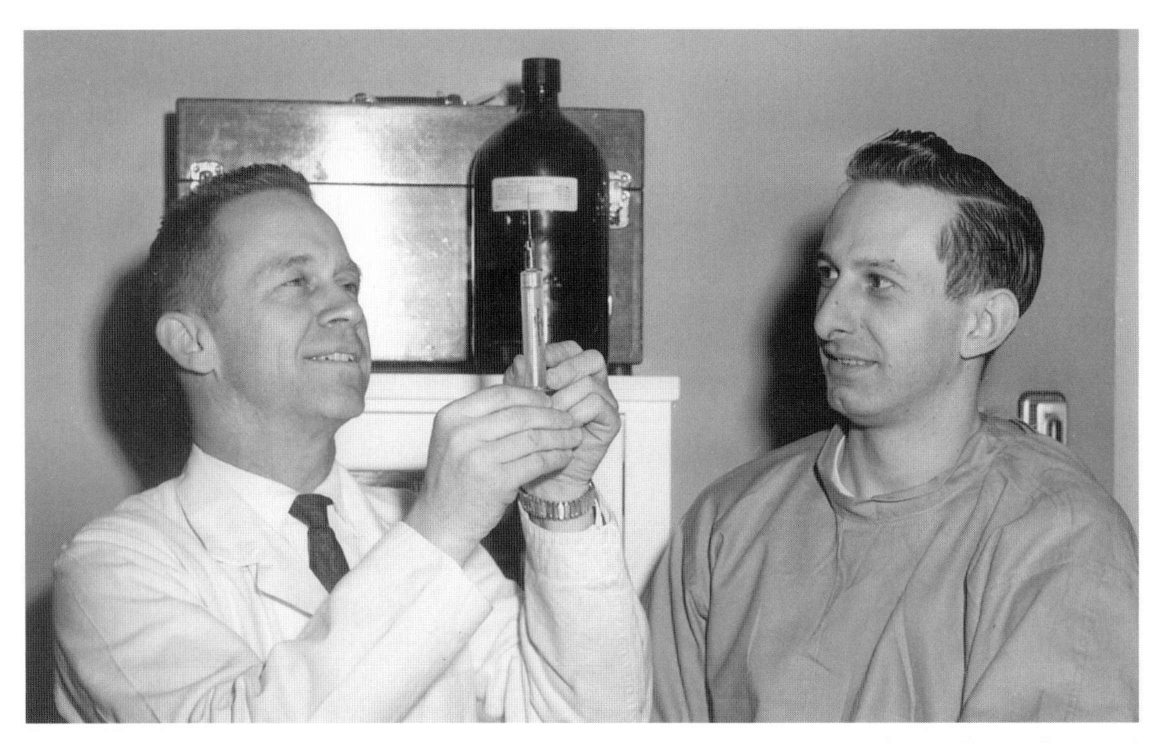

S. Robert Wilson (right): laboratory technician, supply sergeant, licensed plumber, monkey catcher, and eventual vice president of operations.

him "a diamond in the rough, but a genuine diamond." By October, the research director had hired an assistant to help organize the fundraising campaign. Differentiation of labor and specialization of function are hallmarks of a mature organization and were called for in the strategic plan. The new positions may have added to "gross overhead" in the short run, but they were essential to the ultimate economy of a smoothly running organization.

Dr. Coriell was a superb administrator who knew the value of surrounding himself with capable managers. At the same time, wary of bureaucratization, he was determined to invest every possible dollar in the scientific mission. He paid especial attention to the reorganization of his research staff during this period of transition and expansion. Sensitively, his first move insured that assistant director Nichols possessed salary and status commensurate to the incoming Moore. Moore had been promised "full membership," a salary-scale designation held exclusively by the research director. At the time all other senior scientists were designated as research associates. In view of Nichols's outstanding scientific achievements, the board unanimously approved his appointment as the third full member. With Moore's impending arrival as a department head and the actual and predicted enlargement of research staff, it was time to reorganize the interactive cohort of research associates into departmental groups. In 1966 biochemistry, cell biology, cytological biophysics, and cytogenetics became departments under the respective leaderships of Charney, Greene, Moore, and Nichols.

These internal alterations coincided with two momentous changes in the institute's public identity. On March 10, 1966, at a special meeting of the board, the trustees approved an amendment to the corporate charter that made cancer research the principal objective of the Foundation. On October 28, the board voted to change the name of the South Jersey Medical Research Foundation to the Institute for Medical Research. The chronological separation of these two historic events disguises the fact of their intimate interrelation. Indeed, the executive committee of the board had resolved upon these changes in principle in the early months of 1965 in response to two reinforcing events that involved the institute's capital campaign.

By April 1965, the Foundation had only raised approximately $214,000 toward its goal of $836,000. The Public Health Service had just approved the building program plans and the board nervously authorized Dr. Coriell to proceed with the preparations of detailed building specifications so that the construction could be put out for bid. If construction did not begin by the end of the year, the Public Health Service could withdraw its matching grant. The institute approached Julius A. Rippel, president of the Fannie E. Rippel Foundation, for help.

The Rippel Foundation president was the nephew of Julius S. Rippel, a Newark investment magnate who died in 1950 and bequeathed his residuary estate to the foundation set up to honor his wife's memory. The Rippel Foundation and the SJMRF enjoyed a relationship of some years. Both were incorporated in 1953, and one of Rippel's purposes stipulated in the founder's last will and testament was to provide funds to institutions conducting research on cancer. At the most critical point in the capital campaign, Julius A. Rippel suggested to Dr. Coriell that he consider specifying cancer as a research focus in the institute's mission statement. He also brought to Dr. Coriell's attention that the term "foundation" was more appropriate to a philanthropy that dispenses money than to an organization that requested it. Furthermore, he pointed out that the regional designation "South Jersey" did a disservice to the cosmopolitan mission of the institute and of science itself. Additionally, the geographic identity probably discouraged contributions from foundations headquartered and individuals residing elsewhere.[7]

The term "foundation" remained a legally correct term for the institute, and a corporate moniker was not something to be capriciously altered. Nevertheless, the Rippel Foundation's $25 million in assets certainly must have reinforced the wisdom of its president's recommendations. In May 1965, the executive committee resolved to change the institute's name and so informed the Rippel Foundation, which promptly pledged $100,000 to the building campaign, payable as an "over-the-top" finale. Wisely, the committee refrained from making the actual name change until the capital campaign was practically completed. The last thing the board wanted to do was to cause public confusion about its institutional identity at the critical juncture in the fund raising effort. The executive committee protracted its careful deliberations of alternative appellations while it carefully searched national and state registries of corporate names. In September 1966, when the fund drive was within $10,000 of its goal and the Rippel grant was received, the committee unveiled its recommendation for the new name: the Institute for Medical Research. Amazingly, while there were scores of independent, corporate- and university-affiliated laboratories with the name "institute for medical research" in their titles, all of them, like the Rockefeller Institute, had eponymous modifiers. On October 28, the board unanimously resolved to rename the corporation.

Amending the mission statement came more quickly. Unlike the change of name, the modification of the corporate charter to underscore the institute's commitment to cancer research possessed immediate, positive fundraising implications. Since 1962, funds directed to biomedical research on the causes, prevention, treatment, and cure of cancer had increased exponentially. Moreover, Dr. Coriell had been orienting research toward an assault on the causes of cancer for a decade and needed little encouragement to validate this pursuit with legal prose. On May 12, 1965, Fred Greiner informed Rippel Foundation vice-president Herbert Englert that he would be pleased to draw up for the philanthropy's consideration "a proposed modification of the Charter to include cancer research as one of the aims of the Foundation." An initial draft was ready by May 20. Following a June meeting with Rippel officials, the executive committee began to fine-tune the language of the amended

[7] When the board originally incorporated, the designation "foundation" was highly appropriate. The corporate entity was established to raise funds for a research institute. If it failed to found one in Camden, it could petition the courts for a ruling of *cy pres* to allow it to dispense the funds to an extant medical research institute.

statement. In October, Dr. Coriell prefaced his annual research report to the board with the declaration that the Foundation "is dedicated to cancer research at the basic level, seeking to explain the cause and mechanisms of cancer." In February 1966, the executive committee resolved to change the second section of the Foundation's certificate of incorporation to state that the organization—

> through conduct of medical research and related academic, diagnostic and clinical activities, independently and in cooperation with others, will seek to develop basic knowledge concerning the cause and control of cancer and other diseases and to promote better public health through application of this knowledge.

At a special meeting of the board held at the Walt Whitman Hotel on March 10, 1966, the trustees endorsed this amendment.

Historic participants often have recounted faithfully the story of the Rippel Foundation's role in the change of the corporation's name. It is associated with positive memories: the awarding of a major grant and the completion of the campaign. What had been forgotten was a previous, less fortunate episode that predisposed the board to accept the Rippel's overture. Just weeks prior to the SJMRF's approach to Rippel, the institute learned that it had failed in its bid to capture the resources of one of the great American fortunes. Shortly after Irénée Du Pont, direct descendant of the founder of E.I. Du Pont de Nemours and Company, stepped down from the chemical company's presidency in 1926, he began funding a scientific enterprise called the Cancer Research Laboratories, which operated in Philadelphia until 1940. That year he changed its name to the Biochemical Research Foundation (BRF) and moved the operation from Penn's Graduate School of Medicine to a three-story brick building in Newark, Delaware—adjacent to but independent of the University of Delaware.

Du Pont had established this not-for-profit corporation to funnel funds directly into the autonomous research unit, just as the SJMRF was incorporated to do. But there was a big difference: by means of a 1935 trust fund, Du Pont had substantially endowed his institute. When he died in 1963, the BRF assets approximated $2,000,000, but his will had not provided additional funds to the institute for its annual operations. Its trustees had a choice: they could "spend down" the endowment and go out of business in four or five years, or they could arrange for another biomedical institute to take over the endowment and continue the kind of research Du Pont had funded. The trustees reasoned that the former alternative was impractical because it would be impossible to sustain investigations with a doomsday clock ticking away above the heads of research personnel. They arranged to have other institutions petition the Orphans' Court of Philadelphia for a *cy pres*[8] award of the assets.

[8] The legal doctrine called *cy pres* allows courts the discretion to interpret the terms of gifts and wills when executing such terms would be impracticable or illegal so long as the general intent of the donors or testators is observed.

Here was the answer to the Camden institute's prayers for a windfall of available capital. On September 15, 1964, Lew Coriell and Jack Dorrance filed a court petition to have the trust estate awarded to the SJMRF. The petition clearly articulated the institute's intention to use the BRF assets as endowment "in order to give needed financial stability to a young and small organization." The court had appointed a Philadelphia attorney, Owen B. Rhoads, as "Amicus Curiae with the powers of a Master," which meant that his ruling had the force of law. In January 1965, Rhoads filed his preliminary friend-of-the-court brief to announce which of the nine claimants, in his authoritative opinion, most closely resembled the BRF in terms of mission, structure, and function.[9] The first criterion was institutional autonomy. By that measure, the brief argued, there were only three legitimate claimants: the Institute for Cancer Research (ICR) in Fox Chase, Pennsylvania, the SJMRF, and the Wistar Institute. Of the three, only Wistar and the ICR possessed a scientific advisory council. More saliently, of the three, only the ICR declared the conquest of cancer its principal objective. Owens filed his final report on July 27. Alas, the SJMRF narrowly lost the judicial contest and access to an endowment.

The experience was catalyzing. The following year the Camden institute possessed a scientific advisory council known as the "research advisory committee" and it had made the conquest of cancer its fundamental purpose. It had witnessed the absorption of a "foundation" by an "institute" and had changed its name accordingly. While it is historically conjectural, it seems quite likely that these two major modifications of name and mission would have occurred without the influence of the Rippel Foundation. Still, the two events were mutually reinforcing, and one can understand why one was recollected and the other neglected in the corporate memory of the new Institute for Medical Research.

While entertaining ahistorical hypotheses, it is tempting to consider the interplay of timing and choice. The *amicus curiae* brief argued that the ICR was best positioned to assimilate the BRF's projects and personnel into its organization in part because the success of the SJMRF's building campaign could not be foreseen. That argument provoked the SJMRF to file an objection on February 11 to the brief. Ultimately unavailing, the objection helped postpone the court's decision past April.[10] It was during this interlude that Drs. Coriell and Moore were negotiating. If Dr. Coriell had invited the BRF contingent to occupy the new space being purchased by the ongoing campaign, would the "friend of the court"—cognizant of the centrality of cancer research to the SJMRF—have inclined its opinion toward the Jersey organi-

[9] Joining the competitions were seven Philadelphia-area medical institutions: University of Pennsylvania School of Medicine, the Wistar Institute, Temple University School of Medicine, Fels Research Institute of Temple University, Albert Einstein Medical College of Yeshiva University, Hahnemann Medical College and Hospital, and the Institute for Cancer Research. The Damon Runyon Memorial Fund for Cancer Research—a supporter of the SJMRF—petitioned the court to use the BRF assets as endowment funds under its own management to be dispensed as grants.

[10] The court ruling was "confirmed absolutely" on November 26, 1965.

The search for the breast cancer virus led to the establishment of a mouse colony in the basement of the Institute for Medical Research's laboratory building.

zation and helped solve its financial problems? If Dr. Coriell had suppressed his scientific instincts, promised the space to the BRF researchers, and abandoned his cultivation of the Rockefeller group in order to "go for the gold," would the new financially viable Institute for Medical Research been scientifically vital? As sophomoric as such questions may be, they serve as a reminder that history is not predestined.

As soon as the campaign was completed, the Institute for Medical Research—reconciled to the unavailability of the Du Pont funds—moved decisively to remedy the defect of inadequate endowment by finding substitutes for it. Its first initiative was to petition for an annual appropriation from the

The rapid growth of the breast cancer project required the expansion of the mouse colony. Tens of thousands of mice were housed remotely in air-conditioned trailers.

State of New Jersey. On October 14, 1966, the executive committee, aided by the advice of two experienced executives from Campbell Soup Company, devised a strategy. The Institute would make an initial $300,000 request for the fiscal year ending June 30, 1967. Traditionally, such overtures would be made to one's assemblyman, who would introduce legislation on his constituent's behalf. But the executive committee decided to approach the executive branch of government directly. Perhaps the committee realized that Republican Assemblyman William Dickey was on the wrong side of the political fence, or maybe the strategists knew something about the transformation of state politics that was taking place.

Probably no time in the state's history was more auspicious for such an approach. Governor Richard J. Hughes had been reelected in a November 1965 landslide, and his coattails carried Democrats to power in both houses for the first time in half a century. Unlike his fiscally conservative predecessor Robert Meyner, Hughes had an expansionist view of state government. Even more important, the year 1966 was a watershed in the very concept of government in the Garden State. In 1964, the U.S. Supreme Court had dealt a deathblow to the archaic system of county-run politics in its decision in *Reynolds v. Sims*. It ruled unconstitutional the county-based organization of the state senate because it resulted in severe malapportionment and thus flagrantly violated the court's mandate of "one person, one vote." The state supreme court enjoined further legislative elections pending redistricting and constitutional revision. When the delegates gathered for the third constitutional convention in the state's history on August 10, 1966, it was clear that a genuine state politics was inevitable and that the governor (constitutionally the most powerful in the nation) would henceforth dominate it.

Such a sea change would take years to develop, but the court ruling emboldened Hughes in 1966 to seek a broad-based tax for the state. Although his bid to enact a statewide income tax stalled in the not-yet-altered senate, he was able to sign legislation for a three-percent sales tax in April. With two-to-one Democrat majorities in the senate and assembly, there was little doubt that the legislature would appropriate his budget request. Dr. Coriell had approached Roscoe P. Kandle, the state commissioner of health, in the fall, just after the board endorsed the commissioner's nomination to the board and invited the governor to speak at the building dedication ceremony. Kandle agreed to serve as an advocate in Trenton and arranged a meeting on December 29 between Foundation officials Langston, Stretch and Coriell and Governor Hughes, state treasurer John Kervick, and the commissioner. Accompanying the Camden contingent was the recently elected Democratic state senator from Camden County, A. Donald Bigley. Governor Hughes and Kervick were favorably disposed to the overture from this vibrant organization that aided the economic development of a Democratic city in a Republican county.[11] They sug-

[11] Senator Bigley rode Governor Hughes's coattails for a single term only. His seat reverted to a Republican.

gested that a formal request for state aid be made to the Council on Medical and Dental Education. This was good news to the petitioners; Kervick chaired the Council. Composed of several influential supporters of the Institute and "fans" of Dr. Coriell, the Council met in Kervick's office on January 18, 1967, and approved the application. The governor's budget request earmarked $100,000 for fiscal year 1968, the year the sales tax kicked in. A year late and a third of the amount anticipated, the appropriation was nevertheless an important recognition of the state's appreciation of the Institute as the most important independent biomedical research facility in New Jersey.

The Institute was also becoming an important statewide advocate for major alterations in the pattern of healthcare delivery in the state. From the day of his arrival in Camden, Dr. Coriell had been an impassioned, active campaigner for public health and an authority upon whom local and county officials learned to rely. As the Institute broadened its corporate title, it also expanded its range of advocacy. It would not simply petition the state for support; it would shoulder its responsibility for advising the state government on matters in which it had expertise and interest. One such concern was medical education in South Jersey. Dr. Coriell was a leading participant in a regional planning commission that was studying the need for a medical school and regional medical center in the southern end of the state. He and his Institute would become forceful proponents for both as the drama played out over succeeding years. Achieving the twin goals had important political ramifications for the Institute. The organization could take pride in the fact that its senior investigators held impressive faculty appointments at Philadelphia's prestigious medical institutions, but it could not reasonably expect annual appropriations from the Commonwealth of Pennsylvania. To Garden State officials, Philadelphia was the competition. A state-funded medical school and regional medical center in South Jersey would provide faculty appointments and avenues for fruitful scientific and clinical interaction that would bind the Institute closer to the state in which it was incorporated.

In calling for more medical education in South Jersey, the Institute practiced what it preached. In 1966 it co-sponsored with the Camden County Medical Society a series of public health seminars on prevention, diagnosis, and treatment of infectious diseases. During the 1967–68 academic year it conducted an intensive 32-week postdoctoral course in general virology that attracted nearly a hundred students from twenty-three Delaware Valley organizations. During that year, in order to encourage promising novices to consider medical research as a career path, the Institute entertained over five hundred high school students with guided tours of its laboratories. And in the summer of 1967, it sponsored a countywide science contest and awarded six winners Summer Fellowships to permit outstanding high school students to work alongside the research staff. These innovations in 1966–67 foreshadowed the Institute's longstanding commitment to professional and popular education. These and similar programs, such as availing other medical organizations of its new auditorium, were a way of thanking the community for

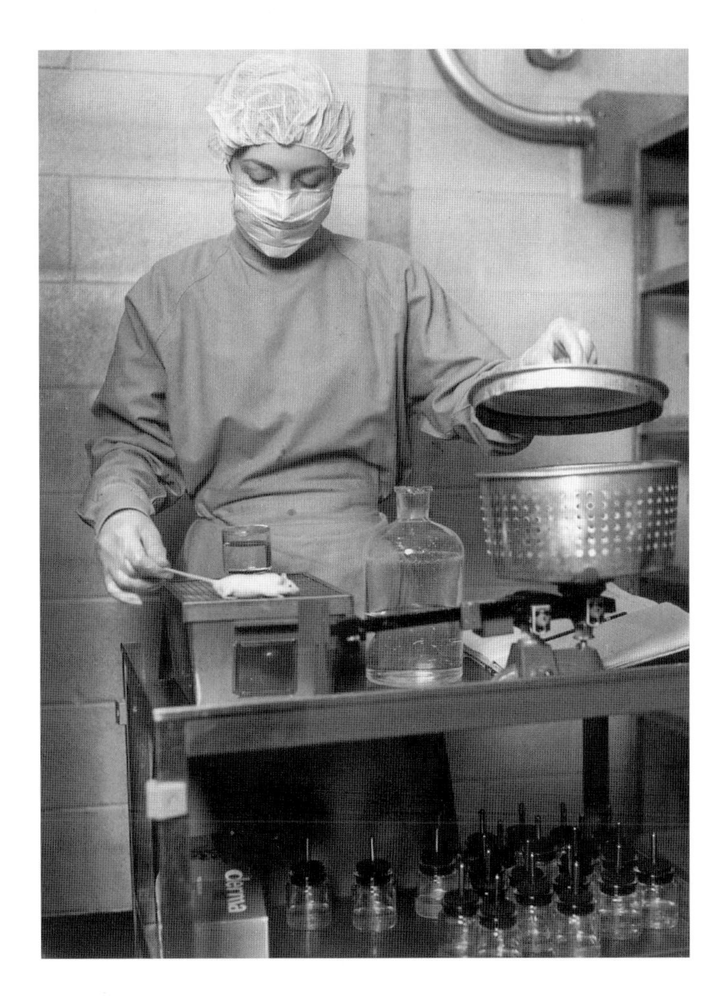

Long the mainstay of experimental science, the laboratory mouse became a critical tool at the Institute, and much effort was dedicated to ensuring its health. Here a mouse receives its daily weigh-in.

its support, promoting public awareness of the Institute, and cultivating city, county, and state resources.

Of Mice and Men

By the time of the tenth anniversary of the opening of its original laboratories, the Institute had achieved an international reputation as a research institute that did elegant science, especially in the application of cell culture techniques in biological research. The cell bank was in high gear. With the arrival of Dan Moore and his team in the summer of '66, the research staff was complete.[12] Its scientists were delivering keynote addresses at prominent scientific conferences worldwide. Outstanding investigators from around the globe were asking to collaborate on various projects and to become permanent or visiting members of the research staff. The institution with the new name had launched well-attended educational programs. Nationwide, cancer research

[12] His mouse colony arrived in October.

was being funded at unprecedented levels. The Camden investigators, biting at the heels of cancer's cause, boldly announced that chase as its fundamental objective. Indeed, by 1967, Dr. Coriell was calling the scientific hypothesis that viruses cause cancer "our conviction." Such confidence was undoubtedly fortified by the portending award in 1966 of the Nobel Prize in Medicine to Peyton Rouse on the fiftieth anniversary of his discovery of the first virus to induce solid tumors in animals.

Material growth complimented scientific development. The new additions—occupied earlier but not officially completed until June 12, 1967—provided a total of 42,000 square feet (nearly an acre) of state-of-the-art research facilities. Dr. Coriell and the trustees had built a reasonably effective administrative and resource development infrastructure. A dedicated volunteer organization helped bring annual gifts to an all-time high. The state itself had signaled its recognition of the Institute's arrival with an annual appropriation. Since 1962, when the board had set its long-term goals, total revenues from research grants had more than tripled, research and technical staff had more than doubled in number, and facilities had grown by a factor of two and a half. The scientific institute that Lewis Coriell had founded had grown rapidly, and—on the surface—the future looked bright indeed.

In retrospect, had the plan for growth taken the originally estimated full decade to unfold, it is possible that officials would have detected seismic changes that would soon shake the very foundations of the Institute. Perhaps they would have slowed the pace of development accordingly. In April 1967, as the new facility was being dedicated, the Institute's balance sheet was showing its first significant operational deficit. That shortfall would deepen the following year, when the Institute was beset by shocks followed by aftershocks of events and conditions that drastically altered its environment. The best-laid plans of mice and men, said the poet Robert Burns, often go awry. In 1962, Dr. Coriell elaborated a strategic plan to free his institution from the pains of what he called unplanned growth. He and his colleagues soon discovered that *planned* growth could also be painful. By 1968, trustees were frankly acknowledging a state of crisis. "Lew Coriell was a pretty stoic guy," recalled one department head. "But in 1968 he was scared."

CHAPTER SEVEN

THE PERILS OF PROSPERITY (1968–1977)

THE INSTITUTE FOR MEDICAL RESEARCH'S relative independence, sound institutional strategy, and scientific accomplishment could not isolate it from the larger political and social turbulence of the late 1960s or from the economic recession of the first half of the 1970s. The period from 1968 to 1977 dramatically juxtaposed internal promise and external impediment. Prodigiously productive, internationally renowned for its precocious contributions, believing itself on the brink of scientific breakthroughs, and supported in that belief by the pronouncements of peers and press, the Institute found itself victimized by larger forces and a consequent diminution of funding at the national level.

NIH AND THE PERILS OF PROSPERITY

The period of the institute's first great expansion (1962–1967) coincided with a period of general economic prosperity and of particular promise for biomedical research in the United States. In recognition of the twenty-fifth anniversary of the establishment of the National Cancer Institute, President John F. Kennedy designated 1962 as Cancer Progress Year. His declaration followed the report of a group of scientists that would eventually constitute the Presidential Commission on Heart Disease, Cancer, and Stroke—informally known as the DeBakey Commission. Consonant with Kennedy's election campaign commitment "to get the country moving again," the report called for a "massive tooling-up of our scientific potential" to prolong life and reduce disability. It called for extending research, educating scientists, and building laboratories in order to catalyze "a vast acceleration of the pace of medical research." The report concluded with the idealistic belief "that we are at the beginning of a biomedical revolution whose triumphs against disease and human suffering can only be dimly seen at the present time."

NIH, 1948

NIH, 1976

The phenomenal growth of intramural research at the National Institutes of Health in Bethesda, Maryland, between 1948 and 1976 mirrors the development of federally funded research institutes and academic centers across the country.
Air Photographics, Inc.

Congress liberally supported the expansion of this medical frontier. By 1967 the NIH budget had risen to nearly one and a half billion dollars. A thriving economy lubricated congressional largesse. Between 1961 and 1965 the economy expanded by one fourth, displaying a dazzling annual rate of growth. When the institute dedicated its new facilities in April 1967, the country was enjoying its sixtieth consecutive month of economic increase. Rhetorical calls for more science were answered with federal dollars and buoyed by rising national wealth. In other words, five years into the institute's strategic planning for development, it would have been difficult for its leaders to discern an impending, abrupt reversal of fortunes. Yet that is precisely what happened.

Events on the national scene decisively affected the fortunes of medical researchers in Camden and elsewhere. Within weeks of Kennedy's assassination on November 22, 1963, Lyndon B. Johnson declared before both houses of Congress "an unconditional war on poverty." Democratic legislative majorities and the emotional leverage exercised by Johnson in the wake of JFK's death provided liberals a rare opportunity to enact laws and sponsor programs devoted to economic opportunities for minorities and underprivileged groups. The success of Kennedy's economic policies enabled his successor to usher in the Great Society, but policy makers and politicians expected the cost of this huge endeavor to be funded by a "peace dividend"—the money saved by the shortly anticipated end to the Vietnam War. The unpopular protraction of that conflict undermined Johnson's political career and severely stressed the federal budget. Following the Tet Offensive in January 1968, the American government dramatically intensified its costly military buildup in Southeast Asia. It may have been impossible to wage winning wars on poverty, cancer, and Communism simultaneously. The sacrifice that medical research made to this multi-frontal crusade, however, was more directly the result of Medicare—the costly program designed to sell the middle class on the more liberal aspects of the Great Society.

While the American military forces were trying to contain Communism abroad, the American medical establishment waged a relentless civil war against national health insurance—its version of encroaching socialism. Acutely aware of the AMA's opposition to such proposals as Medicare, the administration of President Lyndon B. Johnson and the Democratic Congress took pains to insure that doctors and hospitals accepted the new program, which was signed into law in 1965 and implemented in 1966. More immediately concerned with the successful, cooperative launching of this far-reaching initiative than in the publicly esoteric aspects of financing it, the federal government resorted to what sociologist Paul Starr calls "the politics of accommodation."

In his magistral work, *The Social Transformation of American Medicine*, Starr cites two key decisions that set the stage for the eventual crisis. The first was the concession to the American Hospital Association (AHA) and other organizations to provide reimbursement to physicians and hospitals indirectly through "fiscal intermediaries." Blue Cross, the intermediary of choice, would reimburse the hospitals; the government, having surrendered direct cost control, would pay the bills. In other words, the more hospitals and their physicians charged for services and the more buildings they built, the more income they received. Rosemary Stevens, in *In Sickness and In Wealth*, said, "Medicare gave hospitals a license to spend."

Stevens is quick to point out that this license was not used capriciously or for institutional self-aggrandizement. Rehabilitation of non-conforming space and antiquated facilities, particularly in urban areas, was long overdue. Scientific and technological advances were leading to more effective and expensive medical procedures. Political and social calls for including increased numbers of economically disadvantaged people under the umbrella of modern medicine and healthcare encouraged the expansion of facilities. Hospitals were paying heed to the mandate society had given them. By the end of the 1960s what Starr calls "the politics of accommodation" had turned into what Stevens calls "the politics of debt."

Therefore, in the last half of the 1960s, thanks to Medicare and Medicaid, medical research began to compete for its share of the federal healthcare budget with massive hospital construction projects, proliferating third-party insurance reimbursements, and the extension of primary health care to the elderly and disadvantaged. Liberal social activism had its effect on the orientation of medical research itself as political forces began pressuring the NIH to focus on therapeutic benefits rather than on basic science. Within the Department of Health, Education and Welfare (HEW), laboratory investigation competed for dollars with anti-poverty programs. The deaths and departures from the Senate of champions of medical research, the election of Richard M. Nixon as President, and the retirement of NIH director Shannon spelled the end of the "golden years" of the NIH.

Had those halcyon days continued, the budget of the National Cancer Institute in fiscal year 1970 would have approximated $230 million, based on the average annual rate of increase for appropriations in the Sixties. In fact, the American Cancer Society recommended a $245 million appropriation for NCI in fiscal year 1970. In prior years, Congress tended to heed the ACS's advice. The Nixon administration's first budget request, however, allotted only $180.7 million to NCI.[1] On July 31, 1969, the House of Representatives approved the appropriations bill containing NCI's reduced allotment and promptly recessed for the summer.

When Congress reconvened after Labor Day, Dr. Coriell was on Capitol Hill to attempt to head off Senate approval of the House's appropriations bill and to press for more funds for cancer research. He succeeded in meeting with Senator Clifford P. Case of New Jersey. Case was an influential and sympathetic member of the health appropriations subcommittee. The Republican's arrival in the upper house in 1955 had coincided with James Shannon's ap-

---

[1] This constituted an actual reduction from the Johnson administration's inadequate "guns and butter" budget of the previous year.

pointment as NIH director. Dr. Coriell pointed out to the senator the ironic coincidence of the increasing incidence of cancer and declining federal support for cancer research. He labeled the approved package "paltry for a disease whose medical bills approach $2 billion per year" and asked Case to consider a ten-percent increase over the 1969 budget for NCI. His arguments were cogent but unavailing.

Simply put, within the federal government generally and the Republican Party particularly, the liberal agenda of the mid-Sixties that aimed at societal redistribution of medical services was giving way to grave concerns about the American economy.[2] Nixon had ordered an across-the-board reduction for health care programs. Dr. Coriell called this move a "hatchet cut" and complained publicly that it was made "without regard for the merits of the [research] program or the needs of the nation."

The need to control costs due to runaway inflation, however, was an urgent national imperative. By any measure—expenditures per capita, the rate of growth in the cost of services, the percentage of GNP, or of the federal budget—healthcare costs were spiraling upward far faster than the generally troublesome rate of inflation for the economy as a whole. The President imposed wage and price controls on the entire ailing economy in August 1971.[3] If he could resort to such draconian measures nationwide, he could undoubtedly endure the wrath of a few scientists protesting the curtailment of their pet programs within the NIH.

One way to curb such wrath was to politicize the biomedical research establishment. In 1970, Mary Lasker persuaded Ralph Yarborough, Democrat Senator from Texas, to form a "civilian" committee to see if the infusion of dollars into research could accelerate cancer's conquest. The recommendations of the committee—on which IMR trustee Jonathan Rhoads served—resulted in the 1971 passage of the Conquest of Cancer Act (S. 1828). Signed with great fanfare, the "War on Cancer" legislation did stimulate cancer investigation but at the expense of basic science. It soon became clear that most of the NCI's funds were directed to targeted research such as the development of specific chemotherapies, early detection, and rapid diagnosis. Medical schools and other training and educational centers, rather than independent research laboratories, were getting larger slices of the appropriations. More ominously, the legislation authorized that directorships of the NIH and NCI would henceforth become political appointments. In the words of the NIH's astute chronicler, "The longstanding fear of the scientific community . . . that government patronage of science would perforce lead to government control seemed menacingly evident in 1972."

---

[2] In any event, Case's opposition to Nixon's nomination as the Republican's presidential candidate diminished his influence upon the Nixon administration's policies.

[3] Nixon aroused the fury of the medical community in January 1973 by maintaining controls on the healthcare industry while lifting them for the economy as a whole. When healthcare industry controls were finally removed in April 1974, medical costs promptly jumped over seven percent by year's end to an annual rate of over twelve percent. For years thereafter, medical costs would exceed the rate of inflation for the rest of the economy.

Ironically, the Lasker forces and other cancer crusaders outside the scientific establishment had sought to use the recommendations of Yarborough's committee to wrest the NCI from NIH control. They perceived as detrimental to their movement's autonomy the facts that all major policy decisions and budget requests of the NCI had to be approved by the NIH director and five echelons of HEW bureaucrats. Now, in theory, such matters would be taken directly to the President. They grievously miscalculated. The President and his Office of Management and Budget were ill equipped and disinclined to view NCI policy and budgets in terms of their scientific merits. Economic recovery, political expediency, and reelection strategy dictated executive decision-making.

The Institute began feeling the effects of shifting administrative policies and priorities on federal support for biomedical research by mid-1966. Between 1970 and 1977 NCI support for basic research fell from 56.3% of its budget to 48.8%. Only one-third of all grant requests were being funded, and extant multi-year grants were being renewed at lower levels of support. Partially as a result of this downturn, the Camden institute's cumulative operational budget deficit between 1967 and 1977 amounted to over $650,000. A minuscule fund functioning as endowment in a declining market was eroded as it was employed as a tourniquet to offset steady hemorrhaging. By 1970 a physical plant, expanded in 1967 to accommodate some forty-five scientists, housed one-third that number. Dr. Coriell had simply ceased to replace resignees as a merciful method of reducing staff. In a morbidly ironic way, the research director's burden was lessened by frequent defections. A wave of resignations during the five-year period beginning in 1967 may have reflected something as troubling as the declension of federal support for biomedical research. Camden was an imperiled American city.

The Decline and Fall of Camden

In general, one might conclude that laboratory scientists might have been less affected by the civil and political unrest of the late Sixties than impoverished ghetto residents, draft-age males, and flower children. But not in Camden. The IMR was on the margin of an increasingly depressed and dangerous environment. On July 13, 1967, just months after the dedication of the institute's new facilities, race riots erupted in Newark, New Jersey, leaving twenty-three persons dead and large portions of the city in smoldering ruins. Two weeks later the shocking cover of *Life* magazine called the riots "The Predicable Insurrection." Often referred to as the Newark of South Jersey, Camden nervously awaited *its* spontaneous combustion of resentment over poverty, unemployment, racial discrimination, residential dislocation, and alleged police brutality.

Sparked by the assassination of the Reverend Martin Luther King, Jr., Camden's conflagration began in the heat of the following summer. Sniper fire punctuated weeks of rioting, looting, and arson. Tensions persisted into

New York Shipbuilding Company in its heyday. Courtesy of Camden County Historical Society

the early Seventies when Hispanics revolted against the police killing of a young Latino in perhaps the worst unrest in the city's history. These sporadic rampages exacerbated Camden's economic problems as businesses left the city in droves.

In October 1967, the nuclear-powered submarine U.S.S. *Guardfish* slipped from Camden's naval yards, sailed down the Delaware River, and silently submerged into the depths of the Atlantic Ocean.[4] A faithful supporter of the institute, the once flourishing New York Shipbuilding Company had launched its last vessel and closed up shop. It dismissed some 2,400 workers. The closure dealt Camden a harsh blow at a critical moment. Employees at surviving enterprises found it impossible to disappear beneath the waves of urban violence in the city's streets. Epidemics of muggings, burglaries, and vandalism intensified between bouts of civil disturbance. Those who could flee the city fled.

Less than a month after the Newark riots, Ray Dutcher announced that he was moving the bovine leukemia project from the confines of a potentially incendiary city to the bucolic pasturelands of Chester County, Pennsylvania. It was clear that the institute's distressed finances and threatened ecology had significantly exacerbated Dutcher's seven-year itch. For seven years, the pro-

[4] The boat was officially launched on May 15, 1965, but not ready for active duty until 1967.

ject had been conducted at two locations with no special hardship. Still, co-location of both aspects of the investigation under the University of Pennsylvania's auspices made logistical sense. Besides, Dutcher could be a difficult colleague and his personal departure was viewed with some relief. At the end of January 1968, he, Edward Larkin, four other scientists, and seven technicians left the IMR for Penn's School of Veterinary Medicine.

Their departure merited a chilly sendoff. The new facilities in Camden had just been configured to accommodate the special needs of the bovine leukemia project. The virological expertise at the Institute had helped make possible Dutcher's discovery of virus-like particles in the milk of leukemic cows. And then, just as the project team felt that they had in their hands the actual agent that caused bovine leukemia, it was pulling up stakes for literally greener pastures. With the project went some $200,000 of laboratory equipment and the support of the NIH, NCI, and Department of Agriculture. When the group petitioned the IMR for a partial termination of the pension plan on behalf of the departing researchers who were unvested, the executive committee of the board unanimously and summarily rejected the request.

Dutcher and his group took advantage of affiliation with a renowned school of a well-endowed university with an attractive venue. Those remaining at the institute had fewer options. Cords of historic loyalty and chains of economic necessity bound the center to the city. It had just opened a new facility on four acres of donated city land. It enjoyed free municipal services it would otherwise have to purchase. The 1961 opening of the Cherry Hill Mall, which was developed by IMR trustee Eugene Mori, signaled the start of rapid residential and commercial suburbanization of Camden County. Civil unrest in the city dramatically accelerated this trend.

Businesses could easily justify the transition to higher-priced real estate outside the city where their wealthier clientele had moved. Some not-for-profit institutions likewise found reasons to escape the urban tinderbox. A faction of physicians at Cooper Hospital, for example, battled furiously with the hospital's board of managers for a new suburban location. Their patients were simply refusing to enter the city for treatment. The IMR was deprived of such justifications. The ultimate consumers of scientific discoveries did not window-shop. Mercifully, the non-public nature of the research enterprise and its location beyond the center of the city provided IMR personnel with the physical security of a relatively protected four-acre compound.

Fiscal insecurity could be as frightening as physical threat. The Dutcher defection underscored the advantages of belonging to a large-scale, multi-functional organization during troubling times. Then as today, the strategic rationale for the small, independent not-for-profit medical research institute involved its ability to move nimbly to investigate promising avenues of research, resist encumbering bureaucracy, and concentrate dollar investment primarily on research and only secondarily though meaningfully on education, service, and administration. After the exodus of the bovine leukemia group, members of the executive committee began probing beneath the rhetoric of this fiat of independence for assurances that the Institute could realistically

While his scientific productivity had never been greater, Dr. Nichols's administrative role at the Institute was also increasing.

compete with the major universities in the region. Some dared broach the possibility of affiliation with the University of Pennsylvania. Drs. Coriell and Nichols convinced them that the IMR's "greatest appeal [is] for those who are primarily interested in furthering cancer research" and that "dollar-for-dollar there is a far greater return at the Institute than at a university."

The problem was that in recessionary times there were fewer dollars all around. Universities with big endowments and diversified sources of revenue could "carry" struggling but essential research programs through hard times. Individually, they could exercise disproportionate clout in state legislatures. Senators, after all, had alma maters. Collectively, they were represented in Congress by powerful lobbying groups and could voice their concerns for medical research through well-staffed organizations such as the Association of American Medical Colleges (AAMC). Independent research institutes often found themselves on unequal footing with major universities under federal laws and regulations and found it hard to compete with them when it came to purchasing everything from test tubes to liability insurance.

On rainy days it was useful to have an umbrella, but Lewis Coriell was not about to camp under someone else's tent. Unbowed, he set about to construct a canopy for his Institute by pushing for a medical school in South Jersey and leading the charge for the mobilization of state support for cancer research (a campaign that will be covered in the next chapter). Dr. Coriell's contributions to these struggles have been viewed as ancillary preoccupations of a dedicated humanitarian. They were also vital elements of an urgent strategy for institutional survival.

INDEPENDENCE AND INTERDEPENDENCE

In the fall of 1968, evacuated by business and industry, Camden was a decaying husk. Few individuals would see its desperate situation as an opportunity. Lewis L. Coriell did. In September he and six other members of a committee appointed by the Camden Board of Freeholders filed a report entitled "A Medical-Dental School in South Jersey." Before and since Benjamin Franklin described New Jersey as "a keg tapped at both ends" observers understood that Philadelphia and New York City siphoned off much of the Garden State's human and intellectual resources. Among the fifty states, New Jersey ranked eighth in population, seventh in per capita income, and sixth in national provision of medical students. Yet few states possessed fewer institutions for medical and dental education, and on a per capita basis none of them did. In 1965 Governor Hughes advanced the idea of a medical school in southern New Jersey. Until 1966 there was only one medical school in the state.[5] Students went elsewhere for training and often stayed away. As a result, the ratio of physicians to New Jersey's population was lower than the national average.

By the mid-1960s the American medical establishment had concluded that the national average itself was too low. Following the 1965 DeBakey Commission's contention that the benefits of modern medicine were unavailable to large numbers of American citizens, healthcare manpower became an issue of national concern. The AMA and the AAMC quickly issued reports calling for the construction of more medical schools. Ensuing federal legislation dictated that such construction be carefully coordinated within "comprehensive health planning regions."

Cognizant of the historical unwillingness of New Jersey's government to muster the political will to finance additional educational resources, the federal government created competing, overlapping planning regions. New Jersey would constitute a single region. But the federal program also established a Delaware Valley region, centered in Philadelphia and including the ten southern counties of New Jersey. A similar redundancy was created in the New York City vicinity. The message was clear. Unless New Jersey formulated its own satisfactory, statewide plan for delivery of comprehensive, demographically proportioned health services to its citizens by 1970, it would be in-

---

[5] By contrast, the city of Philadelphia alone accommodated five medical schools. Seton Hall's medical school was established in 1954 and became known as the New Jersey College of Medicine and Dentistry after it was acquired by the state in 1965. The following year Rutgers Medical School, with its two-year basic science curriculum, accepted its first students. In 1970, the two schools joined together to form the College of Medicine and Dentistry of New Jersey (CMDNJ).

eligible for federal funds. Furthermore, the responsibility for the delivery of such services within its borders would become the jurisdiction of other states. As Edmund Wilson described it in 1923, New Jersey would remain "a region one traverses to go somewhere else."

Dr. Coriell could not let that occur. He had seen the ease with which a university in another state could take an important undertaking like the bovine leukemia project "somewhere else." He had spent countless unproductive hours traversing highways to labor at the Wyeth labs in Lancaster County, Pennsylvania. It was time to make the mountain come to him. Commerce had virtually abandoned Camden. It was time to fill that void with a major medical center and school that could provide the sort of institutional insulation that the University of Pennsylvania afforded the independent Wistar Institute. The mere presence of such a center in Camden would contribute to institutional stability, civil security, and scientific community. Clinical collaborations would multiply in convenient proximity. Essential bibliographic resources would materialize. State support (already upped to $279,000 in 1968) would in all probability increase as officials recognized the synergies created by having a prestigious research institute "on campus." Interdependence would insure independence

The staggering complexity of competing and cooperating interests and institutions at the federal, state, and local levels guaranteed that the ultimate location, configuration, and "ownership" of the medical center would be indecipherable for over a decade. But getting a medical school in Camden was the essential first step. The Institute's director knew what he needed and was temperamentally disinclined to await someone else's determination of his organization's fate.

As with high-school sports, Lewis Coriell stepped into a "skill" position that optimized his chances of effecting victory. He became the chairman of the manpower subcommittee of New Jersey's comprehensive health planning committee and he obtained an appointment to the freeholders' committee. Early on, it was clear that Governor Hughes was exerting political leadership that would insure state entitlement to regional autonomy and federal funding. Sectional politics and demographics conspired to guarantee that the state's next medical school would be located in South Jersey. But where in South Jersey?

Dr. Coriell wanted it located as close as possible to the Institute, and the committee report he helped to write stressed Camden County's site superiority as a population core, transportation hub, and educational center. By far, however, the most critical consideration in site selection for a medical school would be the proximity of a major hospital with educational capabilities. There existed eight regional hospitals in South Jersey, six of which contained over 250 acute care beds. Those six were fully accredited. In terms of the Institute's strategic interests, Cooper Hospital was the *sine qua non*. With perfect objectivity, the committee report made clear Cooper's comparative strengths in terms of the numbers of acute-care beds, admissions, outpatient visits, and approved residency programs.

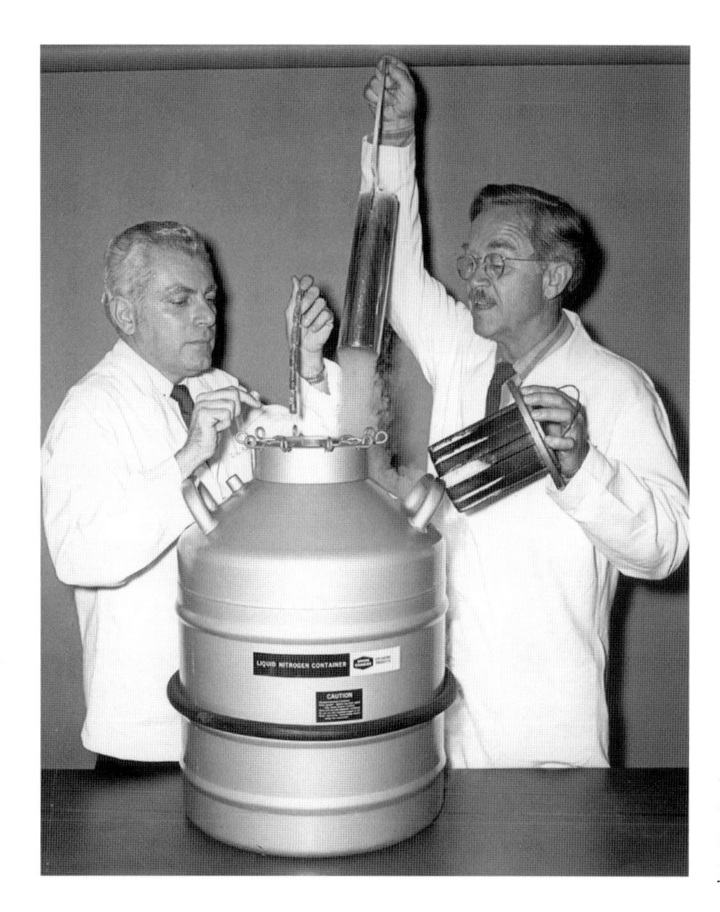

Having perfected the techniques of cryogenic storage, Drs. Greene and Coriell continually monitored the viability of frozen cells.

Having done everything possible to make the telescopic case for South Jersey, Camden County, the City of Camden, and—finally—Cooper as the logical process of choice for the ultimate arbiters of the state's next medical school, Dr. Coriell might have patently awaited the outcome. Atlantic City, Underwood-Memorial, and Burlington County hospitals had already expressed their desires to become clinical teaching centers for the new medical-dental school. There was only one problem. Cooper Hospital was not interested.

In 1968 the political geometry of Cooper Hospital's board of managers, administrators, physicians, and nurses (not to mention union organizers) resembled a billiard table the instant after a powerful "break." The facilities badly needed renovation and expansion. Faced with physical blight and civil turmoil, coalitions of entrepreneurial doctors argued for the construction of a proprietary satellite hospital in the comparative safety of suburbia. Conservative factions, backed by a majority of the board, adhered to the hospital's traditional mission as an urban community hospital. Meanwhile, discussions and rumors of mergers abounded. Municipal government sought to spur economic revival through hospital construction at the same time that regional business associations were demanding healthcare cost containment. In a stagnant economy, unions battled administrators for concessions as workers charged endemic mismanagement.

Cooper Hospital prior to the 1976 groundbreaking. Courtesy of Cooper Health System

Contention along multiple axes became acrimonious; litigation criss-crossed the institution's landscape like tracer bullets. In an effort to gain support for maintaining and improving the hospital's urban presence, a majority block of Cooper's board of managers forged a delicate alliance with predominately older visiting physicians. Tossing onto the bargaining table the incendiary issue of the hospital's possible attachment to a medical school might wreck that coalition. Jealous of their traditional hospital privileges, local physicians were reluctant to cede them to a carpet-bagging faculty of academic physicians. Cooper had enough controversies. Besides, it had a solid, albeit distant, medical school affiliation. Its historic relationship with Jefferson Medical College, many felt, sufficed.

There seemed no way to influence Cooper from without. Officers had assumed a bunker mentality. Entrenched positions on the board of managers resembled foxholes. Characteristically, Lew Coriell determined that, in order to win a battle, one must first occupy the battlefield. With his executive committee's blessing, he gracefully maneuvered himself onto the Cooper Hospital's board of managers in early 1969.

Dr. Coriell's inclusion on Cooper's board was a mark of the medical community's great respect for him, the first physician to serve as a manager in a dozen years. One of the hospital's venerable obstetricians, Frank J. Hughes, M.D. chaired the committee appointed by the county freeholders to make the case for a medical school in South Jersey. A senior staff member in no danger of losing his hard-won hospital privileges, Hughes was clearly committed to Cooper's participation in the medical school plan. It is possible, though conjectural, that he was able to convince influential proponents of the hospital's urban expansion that (1) a medical school in the city would weaken the argument for suburban construction and (2) that Dr. Coriell would prove a powerful persuader. In any case, the newest board member quickly gained membership on the two key board committees that best served to advance his objective: education and long-range planning. From those platforms he launched an effective advocacy for making Cooper the clinical teaching facility for New Jersey's next medical school.

Remarkably, through the continuing controversies that preoccupied Cooper Hospital during the early 1970s, Dr. Coriell was able to convince decision-makers of the wisdom of pursuing the hospital's role as a teaching center for the new medical school. In November 1971, William T. Cahill, Republican governor from Camden County, floated the idea of a medical school "without walls." Under Cahill's plan, graduates of the College of Medicine and Dentistry of New Jersey (CMDNJ) would gain their clinical training at a number of hospitals throughout the state. In September 1972, halfway through his single term, Cahill called upon Republican lawmakers to pass legislation to realize this idea.

"No walls" was a concept designed to save the state money by utilizing local resources for statewide educational purposes. It was also a convenient political dodge for Cahill, who was loath to appear to be awarding this prize to his home county, at least during his first term when he would have to face the electorate again. Dr. Coriell saw through the dodge as soon as the governor broached it in November and publicly denounced it as adverse to the interests of the people of South Jersey. "A medical school without buildings or a full-time faculty," declared Coriell, "would almost surely turn out poorly trained doctors."

Insiders knew that a new South Jersey medical center *with* walls was an eventuality. Harrison A. Williams, U.S. Senator from New Jersey, was pushing such a package in Washington at Cahill's urging. In 1972 Dr. Coriell adroitly recruited the CMDNJ's founding president, Stanley E. Bergen, M.D., to the Institute's board. In 1975 Bergen—who would remain a devoted trustee for a quarter-century[6]—designated Cooper Hospital the clinical centerpiece of South Jersey's medical education program. In 1977 New Jersey citizens approved a $120 million bond issue to expand CMDNJ, and Cooper became the

[6] Bergen's resignation coincided with his retirement and appellation as founding president emeritus of the UMDNJ.

Dr. Stanley Bergen. Courtesy of the University of Medicine and Dentistry of New Jersey

first hospital in South Jersey to affiliate with the College. It accepted its first students the following year.

This achievement is traditionally seen within the historiography of Cooper Hospital and of the CMDNJ, not as a central aspect of the Institute's history. Because the eventual official agreement between the Institute and the *University* of Medicine and Dentistry (UMDNJ) did not occur until mid-1980s, it has been difficult to appreciate the connection between that mutually beneficial relationship and Dr. Coriell's heroic proselytizing for the hospital's educational affiliation two decades earlier. It is clear, however, that the 1984 state appropriation to construct a medical center in Camden that included the IMR would not have been possible without the essential groundwork that the IMR chieftain perspicaciously laid in 1967, when he was sworn in by the county board of freeholders to survey the need for a medical-dental school in South Jersey. Likewise, it would have been difficult for him to have justified the painstaking, time-consuming leadership he imposed on that long-term decision making process had it not been for the more immediate economic hardships imposed on his own organization.

Threatened by the diminution of research funding at the federal level and the deterioration of Camden at the local level, the Institute found fiscal salvation at the state level. The strong probability of adjacency to a South Jersey medical center fortified the Institute's hopes for the future. Meanwhile the state's annual appropriation sustained the laboratories through hard times. But, between Governor Cahill's authorization of the new medical school in 1972 and the designation of Camden as its probable location in 1975, a series of events would interrupt New Jersey's support of the IMR and jeopardize the organization's viability.

The State of the State

State aid to the Institute would have been impossible without the imposition of New Jersey's first broad-based tax—a three-percent sales tax—enacted in April 1966. It must be remembered, however, that this duty was approved only after Governor Hughes failed to secure an income tax. Cahill's 1972 attempt to resurrect the levy earned him the resentment of his party and played a big part in his unexpected primary-election defeat the following year. Clearly, calling for an income tax was an act of political suicide. Just as clear, however, the lack of tax revenues was causing the state to abdicate its fiscal responsibilities. In April 1973, in its famous decision in *Robinson v. Cahill*, the state supreme court declared unconstitutional New Jersey's property-tax formula for funding public education. Cahill's gubernatorial successor, Democrat Brendan Byrne, was able to use the court decision to justify a crusade for a statewide income tax.

Even with large Democratic legislative majorities in the wake of the Watergate scandals, Byrne's campaign was divisive and protracted. Faced with a growing economic recession, the governor announced sweeping governmental program cutbacks and salary freezes. To illustrate the need for school funding in accordance with the court mandate, Byrne made certain that there was no "fat" on the educational budget. The IMR was a victim of "collateral damage" from the governor's budgetary bomb. By early spring 1975 it was apparent that the administration had cut the Institute's request from its 1976 fiscal-year appropriations proposal.

Ironically, the Institute's short-term crisis resulted in part from its long-term advantage. The CMDNJ legislation had reassigned the Institute's appropriation under the department of education rather than the department of health. The IMR's trustee roster reflected this new arrangement in 1972 when CMDNJ president Bergen, who reported to the state's chancellor of higher education, replaced health commissioner Kandle on the board. In fact, the IMR aid package became part of the College's yearly appropriation. The trustees were happy with this new arrangement. It was thought that this change would somewhat de-politicize the annual supplication and that an educational institution (thought to be locally based in the near future) would be somehow more appreciative of basic research than a huge public health bureaucracy. As it turned out, the Institute's appropriation was part of the $5 million cut from the CMDNJ's annual budget.

The timing of this curtailment could not have been crueler. For more than a decade, spurred by enlightened opportunism and scientific promise, the Institute's pursuit of growth had superceded its search for stability. As a result, the lion's share of raised funds was dedicated to bricks and mortar rather than to endowment. The 1962 strategic plan had called for a $3 million endowment by 1965. Yet, at the start of the 1970s the fund stood at a paltry $125,120, over half of which was contributed by board vice president John Dorrance. Fundraising in the early Seventies conformed to pattern as the prospect of imminent scientific breakthrough—as we shall shortly see—again prompted the organization to embark on yet another major construction effort.

The decision to authorize the building of a new animal facility was eased by awareness that the state's appropriation was tantamount to the annual income from a $6 million endowment. In 1975, however, with the real endowment fund struggling to surpass the half-million-dollar mark, the state's tax-supported "endowment" suddenly vanished. Like income from endowment, state aid was particularly valuable because it constituted unrestricted funds that could be used at the board's discretion. To make matters worse, just as the IMR prepared for an emergency appeal to private sources of support that fall, Cooper Hospital launched its $4.5 million Second Century Fund campaign. Weeks later the University of Pennsylvania announced a $5 million drive. These efforts severely reduced the pool of funds available to the IMR.

Restoration of state funding became the Institute's most immediate goal. The board of trustees invited to its spring 1975 meeting several members of the South Jersey contingent of the state assembly, the "lower" house from which the annual appropriations bills emanate. Burlington County's George H. Barbour, accompanied by three freshmen Democratic representatives of Camden County ("Watergate babies," as the Republicans ruefully labeled them), explained to the board that funds would be restored only after fiscal reform measures passed both houses. For the Democrats, that meant an income tax. Assemblyman Barbour outlined a strategy for the institute and promised regional, partisan support.

The legislature adjourned for the summer without resolving the state's fiscal crisis. In the fall, the Institute pled its case to the legislature and the governor's office and succeeded in having separate funding legislation incorporated into a $10 million supplemental appropriations act. Unwilling to let steam escape from the fiscal pressure cooker, Governor Byrne never "called for" that bill (a traditional maneuver tantamount to a pocket veto). Then, minutes after the senate failed to approve the income tax package passed by the assembly in the spring of 1976, he used his line-item veto to strike the Institute's $351,000 appropriation from the higher education budget.[7] The Institute prepared contingency plans to lay off nearly one-fifth of its workforce. Not until July, in the face of the state supreme court's order to close public schools if the legislature failed to produce an equitable mechanism for educational funding, did the income tax legislation finally pass.

When the state's crisis passed, the Institute's immediate problems abated. A bitter residue remained: an operational deficit of nearly $300,000, retardation of research momentum, and a scary realization that the center's margin of excellence was highly susceptible to forces beyond its control. But there were also silver linings. One salutary consequence of the ordeal was renewed commitment to endowment enhancement. Another was the solidification of state funding. Turn-of-the-century observers have ordinarily viewed state aid as a constant since 1968, the 1976 interruption but a blip on the graph of ever-greater governmental fidelity. Such an interpretation is mathematically correct but historically dubious.

Before 1975, otherwise sympathetic ears in state government primarily responded to a different political pitch. Governor Hughes earmarked funds for the Institute as part of a strategy to forge a Democratic coalition south of his Mercer County base in an effort to dilute the northern political hegemony of Hudson and Essex Counties. Governor Cahill, Camden County's favorite Republican son, eliminated state aid to the IMR in 1971 and 1972. Each time

[7] Ironically, in March he proclaimed the first IMR Week, extolling the research center for "contributing major milestones on the road to medical victory over breast cancer."

Drs. William T. Read and Lewis Coriell, Governor Brendan Byrne, and Assemblyman Walter Rand celebrate IMR Week. Assemblyman Rand was one of Dr. Coriell's most steadfast champions.

the legislature restored the funding. Both executives peripherally understood the worth of the IMR, but its fate had always been subordinated to "transcending" political objectives. The IMR's statewide significance was never fully appreciated until it was forced to justify its entitlement to jeopardized state funds. In 1975–76, the Institute had wonderfully legitimized its case before a governor who had neither political debts nor agendas. After 1976, thanks to the income tax, the state's treasury was equipped to cement this new corporate—as distinct from political—relationship between the Institute and the state.

The legitimizing case for state support involved convincing the state of New Jersey that (1) cancer was the state's number-one health hazard and (2) the Institute was uniquely positioned to advise the state about cancer risks and to devise solutions to them. Ironically, had it not been for a state crisis in public education the Institute might not have had the incentive to engage the state about its crisis in public health. The story will be pursued in the next chapter.

On January 12, 1977, Governor Byrne officially proclaimed the week of March 20–26 "Institute for Medical Research Week." The proclamation helped make amends for the Institute's exclusion from the previous fiscal year's appropriation. It also evinced an acknowledgment of gender politics. The mid-Seventies marked an era of militant feminism and women's rights. The nation began to understand that the traditionally male-dominated scientific establishment had consigned research on women's diseases to relative neglect. "IMR Week," as the proclamation's wording makes clear, was invented to bring attention to breast cancer, the Institute's efforts to combat it, and the governor's sympathetic support of that fight. "One-term Byrne," as the executive was labeled after his heroic championing of the state income tax, enjoyed the Governor's Mansion and was combatively seeking re-election. The proclamation was signed the day after the governor delivered his State of the State address, in which he touted "a remarkable record of achievements." Dr. Coriell might have said the same about the state of scientific research in Camden.

The State of the Art

In his preface to the IMR's 1973 annual report, Dr. Coriell echoed the opening lines of Charles Dickens's *A Tale of Two Cities*: "It was the best of times, it was the worst of times . . ." The director's observations encapsulate both his exuberance and frustration:

> It is ". . . the best of times . . ." because of significant and sometimes dramatic advances made during the last few years, including conspicuous progress toward understanding the basic molecular processes of life and disease. It is ". . . the worst of times . . ." because at the very moment when light can be seen at the end of many tunnels, the relatively low Federal priority on basic research frequently constrains investigators to a pedestrian pace when they are eager and able to run.

By 1971 the opening to major advances in breast cancer research appeared brightly illuminated. To the scientific community, the scientists at IMR seemed to be holding the beacon. In that year, exactly one-half of the Institute's entire 42-member scientific and technical staff was waging a concerted attack on breast cancer. Jesse Charney's lean team of biochemists and Dan Moore's ample department of cytological biophysics had conspired to produce a stunning series of inter-related discoveries and technical breakthroughs. Their collaboration validated the model of the small multidisciplinary, problem-oriented research institute and put the Institute for Medical Research on the map of public awareness.

The Camden researchers had gone beyond other laboratories in weighing the genetic, hormonal, immunological, and viral factors in the complex etiology of breast cancer. Moore had proved in 1966 that a virus caused mammary tumors in his highly inbred strain of mice. Finding viruses in mother's milk in a human population, however, posed enormous problems of logistics, detection, and experimental control. The search took Moore in 1967 to Bombay, India, to a group of Parsi women who suffered an extraordinarily high in-

Drs. Moore and Coriell examine a mouse in conjunction with Dr. Moore's research on breast cancer, for which he received national exposure.

cidence of breast cancer. Descended from Zoroastrians who fled Persia in the seventh century, the Parsi observed strict codes proscribing marriage outside the religious sect. In short, they presented biomedical science with a "strain" of humans close-bred for thirteen centuries and highly susceptible to breast cancer.

For five years Moore and his group studied milk samples he had procured from the Parsi women and compared them with those of American women and, of course, with those of his mice. In February 1971 the researchers announced the results of their findings in an article entitled "Search for a Human Breast Cancer Virus" in the prestigious British journal *Nature*.[8] The milk of women with breast cancer, they argued, contained particles that are morphologically identical to the mouse mammary tumor virus.

Further proof was more dramatic. Moore had mixed blood samples from five breast cancer patients with purified mouse virus. Injecting that sera into mice susceptible to breast cancer, he found that the inoculated mice pos-

[8] The article was co-authored by scientists from research institutes in Michigan and Bombay. See the "Notes on Sources" section for the full citation reference.

sessed a significantly higher incidence of breast cancer than the control group injected with a mixture of normal serum and viruses. They boldly concluded that "the similarities between adenocarcinoma of the breast in mice and women are too extensive to be coincidental and that human breast cancer may also be a viral disease." The implication of these findings was clear: the mouse model may well be a fruitful paradigm for the study of human breast cancer.

The American Cancer Society took note and invited Moore to address the Science Writers Seminar at the ACS's annual meeting in Phoenix in April. The seminar was the showcase the Society used to cultivate media coverage for the more promising cancer-related scientific discoveries of the past year. A week later Moore's work received near full-page coverage in *Newsweek* magazine. The article made clear that, while a cure for breast cancer might be a long way away, screening tests might be devised to discourage endangered women from breast-feeding, and vaccinations might eventually be produced to eradicate the virus.

Moore, Charney, Lasfargues, and the other Institute researchers cautioned against premature public expectations that their work continued to stimulate. In October, at the National Academy of Science's fall meeting, a

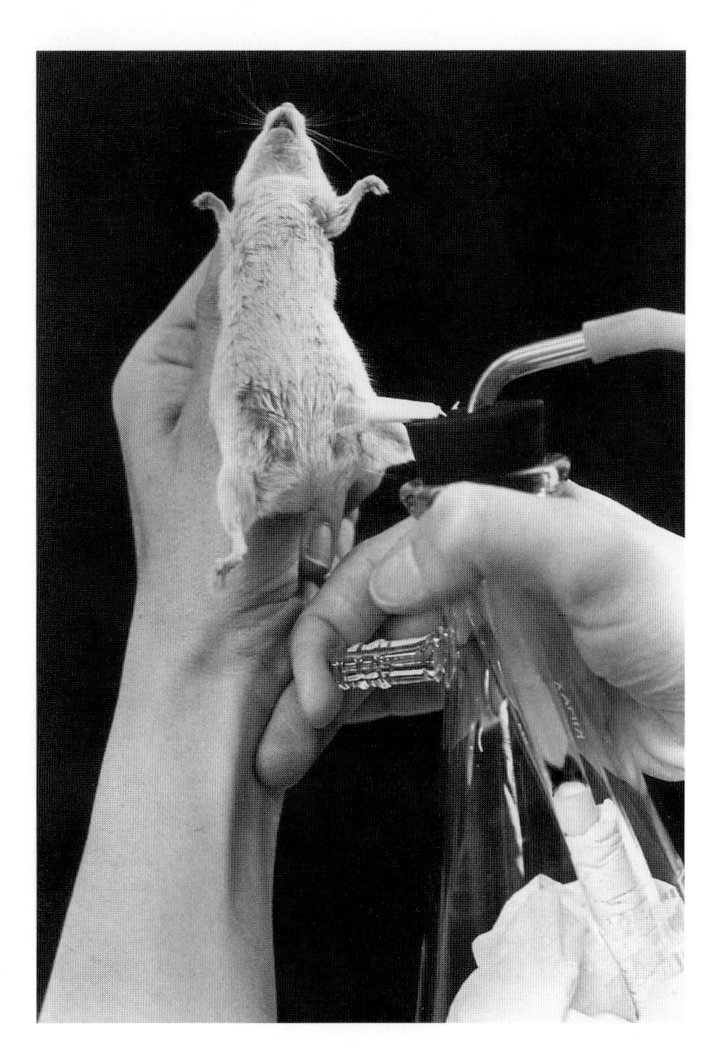

Isolation of the murine mammary tumor virus (the MMTV, or mouse breast cancer virus) required the milking of thousands of mice per day.

leading cancer researcher from Columbia University issued a warning to expectant mothers whose milk possessed the suspicious particles to avoid breastfeeding and potentially passing on breast cancer to their daughters. Other scientists, of course, voiced skepticism about such extrapolations. Most, however, acknowledged that the findings represented exciting progress and urged intensified investigation along the lines the Institute's researchers had laid out. Indisputably, the head of the department of cytological biophysics—and by implication the Institute—was the bellwether in the search for the cause of human breast cancer.

Under the spotlight of national attention, the Institute moved quickly both to encourage dispassionate scientific debate of the topic and to capitalize on its fame for fundraising purposes. With supporting sponsorship from NIH, Dr. Coriell arranged an international Symposium on Mammary Neoplasia at the Cherry Hill Inn on November 11–13. Nearly three hundred participants heard from forty-one panelists from four countries. The following Tuesday evening the Institute—conveniently reckoning from the opening of the first lab building—hosted its Fifteenth Anniversary Dinner. Its principal objective, nearly achieved, was to secure $1 million for the endowment fund. Featured speakers included U.S. Senator Harrison Williams and Dr. Anthony Bruno, the assistant director of NIH. To insure maximum public exposure of both events the Institute hired a media relations firm.

Scientific progress can attract financial support. It can also necessitate unanticipated financial investment to fulfill its promise. Scientific reportage suggested that the Institute had shown that it might be possible to prevent breast cancer in women. This was compelling stuff. It required more rodents; a small price to pay but an arduous row to hoe.

By 1972 Moore and his associates accommodated some 20,000 mice, compartmentalized into twelve pure strains, each with its own specialized experimental function. Cages filled hallways; the garage became a hotel for rabbits; some mice were moved to a renovated mobile home. Feed and supplies had to be stockpiled at a farm ten miles distant. The lack of environmental controls to maintain sterile conditions for these valuable colonies could trigger an episode that might severely jeopardize research progress. Moreover, Moore estimated he would require another 26,000 mice by 1974.

Extracting virus from mouse milk was a tedious pursuit that yielded very little of the precious commodity. To augment that meager harvest, Dr. Lasfargues had succeeded in culturing viruses in vitro, but the proportion of producing cells in the two developed cell lines was dramatically decreasing over time. And if, someday, there was the need to produce a vaccine, the Institute wanted to be in the forefront of development. That would demand a population explosion of mice in Camden.

Accordingly, the executive committee authorized planning for a new animal facility, a three-story wing costing over $4 million. NCI had entertained a grant proposal for the construction in the amount of just over $3 million. The Institute would have to foot the bill for the remaining million dollars. Given its strained financial resources, the center would be forced to borrow almost $700,000. The Bank of New Jersey and the South Jersey National Bank agreed to participate in a mortgage loan on a fifty-fifty basis. On September 28, 1972, with some reluctance and much courage, the executive committee resolved to authorize the indebtedness if the NCI proposal was granted.

The good news was that the NCI proposal was approved. The bad news was that the Cancer Act had kicked in. In an abrupt about-face, the NCI reversed its decision to give the project "high-priority" status and bowed to directives that assigned the highest precedence to construction projects that supported clinical rather than research goals.

Undaunted, the Institute pitched forward and constructed a temporary building, completed in May 1974, which allowed for cage washing and sterilization. Bob Wilson and his crew retrofitted five mobile home shells to accommodate four thousand mice apiece. The total cost was $315,355. The arrangement was not ideal, but it cost less than one-tenth of the originally envisioned project. The NCI magnanimously threw in $49,500 for racks and cages.

The economy was apt. In early fall 1976, the NIH informed Dr. Moore that it would not renew funding for his project beyond April 1977. The news was a devastating blow to Moore and a mixed blessing to the Institute. The scientist's growing reputation and deserved importance were complimented by

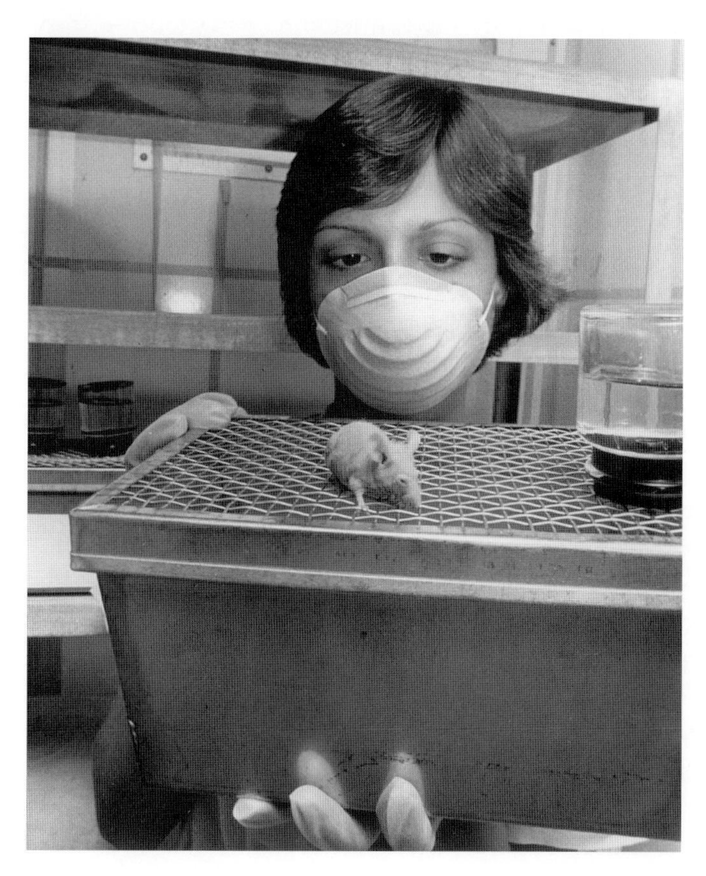

Technician Lucy Reed and one of her charges in the animal quarters.

an increasing imperiousness. The prodigious Jesse Charney and the renowned microscopist Nurul Sarkar left the Institute because of disagreements with their departmental chief. In September Moore was engaged in yet another imbroglio with Dr. Arnold Dion, whose premature promotion Moore had stubbornly insisted upon two years earlier. Colleagues confessed that the non-renewal of the NIH grant had left the brilliant researcher in a "highly emotional" state.

Moreover, an undercurrent of tension had developed between Moore and his boss during these precarious times. For five years at least, Dr. Coriell was announcing to the trustees that the Institute's attention was turning to human breast cancer. By 1974 Dr. Coriell was conferring with NIH officials to discuss the conduct of testing women with breast cancer. He saw affiliation with the CMDNJ as providing an important venue for such studies. Moore, however, was turning the corner into human research at a slower pace than the director deemed reasonable. With professionalism and mutual respect, both men treated the quarrel as a legitimate scientific disagreement, which remained largely beneath the surface. Ultimately, as a result of their different temperaments and organizational roles, their divergent opinions hardened into fixed positions. The bad news from the NIH shattered their *modus vivendi* by presenting new alternatives and an altered balance of power.

On September 29, the executive committee held a special meeting at Moore's request and with his attendance to consider the future of his project. Dr. Coriell excused himself from an October 13, executive session of the committee convened to determine Moore's fate. A letter dated October 4, from Moore's NIH contract officer, which invited the Institute to submit an alternative proposal, mitigated trustees' concerns that Moore's departure would involve serious financial loss. Moore had reached retirement age, and the executive committee had no authority to extend his employment without the recommendation of the director. He retired from the Institute in April 1977 and assumed a post at Hahnemann Medical Center in Philadelphia.

Moore's departure provided the Institute with an opportunity, as baseball scouts phrase it, to "put dollar on the muscle," to sign new talent at the positions best designed to help the team. Players were also repositioned. By the end of the year, renowned virologist/immunologist Anthony J. Girardi arrived to head up what would become a new department of virology and immunology. Arnold Dion became head of the department of molecular biology. Entienne Lasfargues was put in charge of the tumor cell biology laboratory. Warren Nichols, who had just shown that interferon could prevent chromosome damage caused by viruses, was able to recruit two new scientists. Researchers in the former department of cytological biophysics were reassigned appropriately. Interdepartmentalism was decidedly enhanced.

Organizational reconfiguration reflected an intellectual reorientation that had already occurred. Astute observers have noted the coincidence of the Institute's founding and the discovery of the "double helix" structure of DNA. By 1977 virology was no longer the discipline that characterized the Institute; it was now relegated to departmental status. The organizational chart mir-

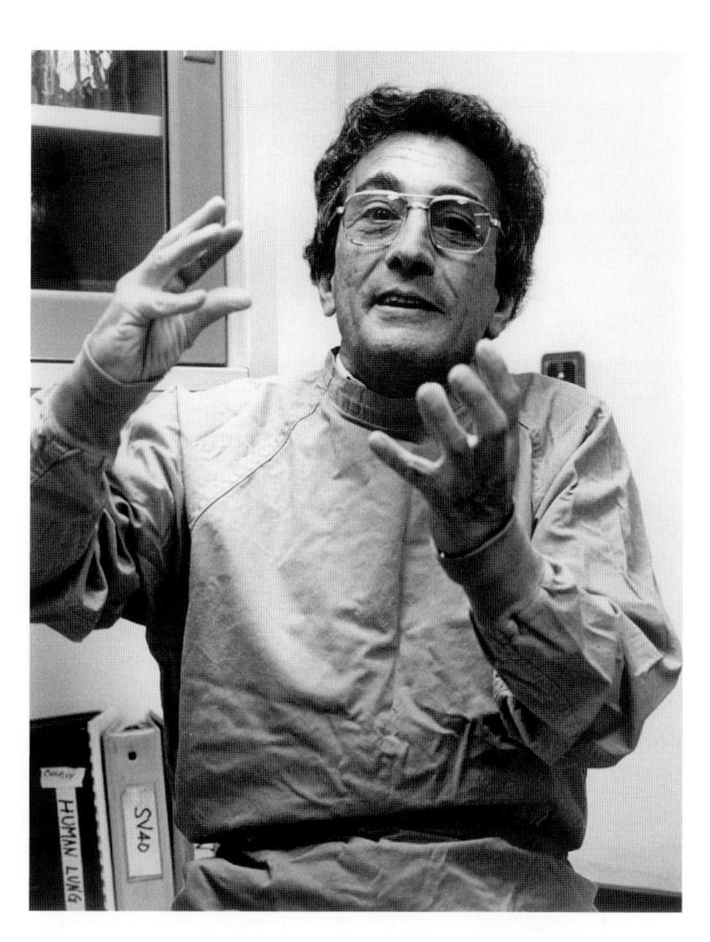

Dr. Anthony Girardi led the virology program and worked to develop a breast cancer vaccine for the mouse model.

rored the dawning awareness that viruses, if not the cause of cancers, may be implicated as triggers for other genetic, hormonal, or immunological changes. Nichols's work had alerted the scientific world to the relationship between viruses and genetic damage. Dion's ability to isolate and characterize reverse transcriptase in an effort to understand the relationship of MMTV to human mammary cancer testifies to the completion of that paradigm shift at the Institute. It seems almost miraculous that such fundamental intellectual restructuring could have occurred during a time of intense external challenge.

This same period witnessed a second major development that decisively shaped the Institute's future. As with the historical view of the state's aid package, it is convenient to look back to the creation of the NCI funded cell bank in 1964 and to infer therefrom its eventual significance and size. But as institutional strategists in the mid-1990s discerned, the NCI cell bank was a comparatively small operation. That operation expanded significantly in 1972 when the NIH's National Institute of General Medical Sciences (NIGMS) established the Human Genetic Mutant Cell Repository at the IMR.

Science's growing interest in genetic disease explained the need for such an archive. The Institute's internationally recognized reputation for excellence in cell biology, Greene's masterful stewardship of the NCI cell bank, and

Dr. Arnold Dion's work with breast cancer included the search for the human breast cancer virus.

Nichols's trailblazing work in cytogenetics (not to mention his heroic grantsmanship) predisposed the NIGMS to favor the Institute over seventeen other contesting laboratories. And it was dire financial need, caused principally by the redirection of NCI funds, that predisposed the IMR to seek the contract. Previously, revenue from the NCI cell bank accounted for about ten percent of the Institute's total annual revenue. By 1977—augmented by revenue from the National Institute on Aging for a small cell bank to assist Nichols's researches and those of other groups studying aging of cells in culture—cell bank revenue represented over forty percent of total yearly income.[9] In financially troubling times these new sources of revenue perhaps saved the Institute. But even salvation can have adverse, unintended consequences. The new repositories signaled a subtle shift from doing science to supporting science. The change was represented in 1977 by a symbolic contrast: silent diminution of the animal colonies after Moore's departure and festive dedication of an expanded cell bank facility.

The Best and Worst of Times

Like jagged bookends, Dutcher's departure and Moore's retirement bracketed an anxious decade. Between 1968 and 1977, the Institute for Medical Research endured assault. Not just events, but time itself was pulling the organization away from its roots in what already seemed like a distant age. With the sad harbinger in 1967 of Sidney Longmaid's death, the period marked the passing of other founding members of the board of trustees: Charles Carpenter, Bryant Langston, Eugene Mori, Wilbur Norton, and brothers Joseph and Emlen Stokes. Inspirational volunteer Lavenia Taylor died in 1974. She lived to see the board-commissioned portrait of Dr. Coriell rendered by artist Agnes Allen. Esther Coriell unveiled it in October 1973. The painting revealed a deception that the energetic, vibrant, physically fit, indefatigable research di-

[9] In science as opposed, say, to movie production, the quantity of revenue is directly related to the quality of product. In 1975, for example, Warren Nichols, Lorraine Toji and others at the Institute developed two cell lines, named IMR-90 and IMR-91, which continue to facilitate scientific research and enhance the Institute's revenue stream. Developed respectively from normal female and male fetal lung issue, these cell lines have been specially and thoroughly characterized. As a result, they have been used as normal control samples for a wide variety of studies reported in hundreds of scientific publications from around the world. Since the life span of these cells is precisely known, these cell lines have been widely used in studies of aging. But they are also germane to enzyme activity, gene expression and cancer studies, and have even been employed as a "tester line" for gene therapy vectors. The lines remain viable after more than a quarter of a century of storage.

rector naturally perpetrated upon those who met him in the flesh. The canvas confessed that he was no longer young. Time had passed so fast. Sixty-six years of age in 1977, Lew Coriell began to ponder the process of executive transition.

He and the IMR family could look back upon the past ten years with pride. Responding to the loss of institutional blood, the IMR had performed upon itself a lifesaving transfusion of ideas, personnel, and resources. Its scientific staff had achieved an outstanding reputation for its ability to conceive, fund, and execute research that could be replicated and confirmed by other scientists. It had compiled a prolific record of discoveries and applied contributions as evidenced by the volume and quality of their publications, invited lectures, affiliations, and positions of leadership among their peers. It had slowly expanded its focus beyond the central concern of cancer's cause to include aging, environmental hazards, and hereditary diseases. The center had strengthened its ties to New Jersey government, contributed to Camden's revival, positioned itself to capitalize on the changing state of medical education, enlisted new constituencies to its cause, replenished its board with individuals possessing wisdom, substance and fidelity, kept its technology reasonably up-to-date, and made sure its research remained scientifically *au courant*. Not bad for a small research institute in a troubled city in hard times.

Chapter Eight

Crossroads (1978–1985)

In 1978, twenty-five years after the establishment of the Institute, looking back with pride was easier than looking ahead with confidence. Typically, an annual meeting of the board occasioned more conviviality and larger attendance than quarterly business meetings. On the occasion of the twenty-fifth annual meeting of the board, however, Dr. Nichols welcomed seven trustees. Dr. Coriell was absent. The silver anniversary celebration seemed to capture that mood. For a major milestone it was a relatively low-key, albeit festive event. Its nostalgic tone was evident in the selection of the honored guest speaker, the distinguished Dr. Robert McAllister, the founder's former scientific comrade. One might even infer from its timing that the commemoration was an afterthought. It was not held until March 30, 1979, nearly five months after the organization's official birthday. Despite the Institute's financial predicament, no major capital campaign complimented the celebration. At least the event was extramural. On the occasion of the IMR's twentieth anniversary, Dr. Nichols had simply shown historical slides at the trustees' regularly scheduled board meeting in the Institute's conference room.

Bunker mentality was understandable. In truth, the Institute was preoccupied with its survival. It had spent the preceding decade reacting to crisis after crisis. By the end of 1980 the trends were ominous. Operating expenses were outpacing revenue; growth of revenue had been less than increases in the consumer price index. The cumulative operating losses from 1975 to 1980 approximated one million dollars and were forecasted to increase exponentially. That deficit did not include nearly $750,000 in cumulative unfunded depreciation expenses. Grants and contracts from the NIH constituted 74% of revenue in 1975 but only 66% in 1980.

The Institute found itself in a vicious circle of time when crisis management ironically precluded the long-range planning it so desperately needed. It had cultivated a sturdy resilience, an ability to recoil from assault quickly and remain intact. To use an automotive analogy, however, a shock absorber is not a car's most important part. The Institute's engine of scientific investigation was experiencing a fuel shortage. And, due to the vicissitudes of unpredictable funding, the fuel mix kept changing, requiring constant adjustment.

In 1980, for example, there were ninety employees at the IMR, just two fewer than the 1975 total. What appears as a negligible net loss (accountable perhaps to retirement) masks a pattern of tumultuous volatility. Twelve workers were let go in 1977, five in 1978, and nine in 1979. Such recurring instability severely hampered the training, productivity, and morale of personnel. Furthermore, the need to invest a declining and insecure stream of revenue in essential salaries caused the administration to cut corners on refurbishing the physical plant and replacing equipment, making the work of those salaried individuals less efficient and productive. The velocity of the downward spiral was increasing. Respected prognosticators of IMR's capacity to sustain critical mass in an increasingly competitive environment were not sanguine about its future. At the start of the 1980s, the Institute for Medical Research found itself at a crossroads.

TURNING POINT

In the grinding continuity of change it is risky to single out a crucial turning point in the life of an institution or individual. Nevertheless, it is clear that in 1981 the Institute found itself at perhaps the most dramatic intersection of political and economic events, personal and professional lives, and competing interests and institutions in its entire history. That year, four significant things coincided: (1) the IMR investigated the newly-named Cooper Medical Center's offer of land and building for possible relocation; (2) Ronald W. Reagan took the oath of office as the fortieth President of the United States; (3) Thomas H. Kean was elected governor of New Jersey; and, (4) Lewis L. Coriell turned seventy years of age and announced privately that he was contemplating retirement. Taken together, these four occurrences required the Institute to undertake discerning, sustained analysis and debate regarding its future as an independent nonprofit research institute.

Cooper's proposal alone would have stimulated mid-range feasibility studies and planning exercises. At the time, the Institute had no other means of moving closer to the vital center of the planned healthcare complex in Camden. Reagan's election, however, prompted IMR trustees to take a longer view of the organization's viability. The presidential candidate had campaigned against the bigness of federal government. He favored competitive, for-profit privatization of biomedical research. His administration immediately set out to cut back the budget of the department of Health and Human Services, including the NIH, and to consolidate federal health programs into "block grants" to the states. The state of New Jersey stood to lose billions of dollars of federal funds, a fact that might jeopardize the IMR's annual appropriation. Independent research institutes everywhere were questioning their sustainability. Relocation would involve costs that the IMR might not be able to incur under Reagan's "new federalism." As we shall see, Thomas Kean's election at the end of 1981 would ease those apprehensions.

Finally, Dr. Coriell's planned departure as CEO enormously complicated the forecast. From the board's standpoint, his retirement threatened to deprive the Institute of traditional sources of support. In the words of one trustee, the prospect presented "a major new hurdle" for the Institute. Yet from Dr. Coriell's personal vantage, he was going to make sure that his final turn at the helm would steer his vessel to safe harbor. In his illustrious career, he had devoted himself to both institutional and scientific advancement. Henceforth, the former occupation would become his primary focus. His professional situation, as well as the rapid pace of events, dictated that a long-range plan could not afford to be a long time coming. The Institute's leadership had to make momentous decisions decisively. The year 1981 was the beginning of a three-year reformation of strategic planning and progress.

Perhaps the most significant characteristic marking this transition to strategic institutional advancement was the IMR's novel commitment to investing "serious" money to it. It had come to the point where funds had to be diverted from the scientific enterprise in order to save the enterprise. Viewed retrospectively, the organization's original strategic plan was a pampered vision of a bright future with few impediments. Constructed in a time of economic boom and governmental largess, it lacked rigor. Now, faced with major obstructions that could block crucial, fleeting opportunities, the trustees realized the need to professionalize the functions of external relations and planning by retaining top-level administrative talent. The first step was to engage a professional strategist with knowledge of local, state and federal government, the medical community, and CMDNJ officials. The perfect candidate was just around the corner.

As a member of the board of managers of Cooper Medical Center, Dr. Coriell came to respect and admire David R. Kaloupek, the hospital's senior vice president. In November 1979, Robert L. Evans, M.D., Cooper's beleaguered and unpopular CEO, suddenly dismissed Kaloupek in what the hospital's chronicler calls "one in a string of abrupt terminations during Evan's tenure." When the board failed to persuade Evans to reverse his decision, Dr. Coriell—citing problems with Evan's management of the hospital—called for an evaluation of the executive's performance, which led ultimately to the hospital chief's departure. Highly regarded and well connected within the state, Kaloupek established himself as an independent consultant. Soon after Reagan's election victory in November 1980, Dr. Coriell sought him out to undertake a complete analysis of the Institute's internal and external situation. By mid-March 1981, Kaloupek had produced an objective, accurate analysis of the Institute's strengths and weaknesses and a comprehensive, workable preliminary strategy for survival and growth.

Kaloupek did not purport to draft the institution's long-range plan, though he did urge the board to structure itself to accomplish that goal. His recommendations were designed to build a secure platform from which to

With the restructuring of the board of trustees in 1982, Dr. Coriell assumed the new title of president and CEO of the Institute.

launch a concerted strategy. Having digested his near-term plan for the IMR's work, the leadership wisely retained the consultant to help them work the plan. Over the next three years, almost every tactic the Institute employed to stabilize that base was contained within the recommendations of the Kaloupek report. It is important, however, to recognize that the study was crucial, not seminal. As its author clearly recognized, the blueprint was premised upon the Institute's perceived strengths and would have proved ineffectual had those strengths not been real.

The Institute's first step was to fund immediate stabilization of operations and public and private development. The executive committee liquidated cash reserves in order to dedicate $350,000 over the following two years to acquire lobbyists and other professional counsel. The next step was to reorganize and expand the board of trustees to carry out those development efforts and to effect the third step, the formulation of a comprehensive long-range plan.

By the summer of 1982, the board welcomed five new trustees with a wider regional representation and experience in government affairs and strategic planning. William H. Bell, Jr., president since 1976, adopted the title "chairman of the board." Dr. Coriell became IMR president; and Dr. Nichols, vice president of research. Nichols's assignment freed his boss to concentrate on external relations and administrative command and signaled that Nichols was heir apparent to the presidency. Under Bell's leadership and Kaloupek's

Dr. Lewis Coriell, Mrs. Lydia Stokes, and Dr. Warren Nichols stand for a portrait on the occasion of Dr. Nichols's appointment as the S. Emlen Stokes Professor of Genetics, the Institute's first endowed research chair.

guidance, a rejuvenated board accelerated institutional momentum. Gabriel Danch became chairman of the new government affairs committee, and Frank Kelemen—chairman of Cooper's board—oversaw the new planning committee. In late 1981, headed by development committee chair Harold Shaub, recently retired president of Campbell Soup Company, the IMR launched the Research Advancement Program (RAP). A $3.4 million campaign, the RAP was the first phase of a two-part, decade-long development program.

Significantly, the Institute developed the RAP as an investment in its researchers, not in their improved quarters or relocation. It endeavored to endow the chairmanships of four departments—immunology/virology, cell biology, microbiology, and molecular biology—at the level of $750,000 apiece. In 1978 Lydia Stokes and other benefactors had established the Institute's first endowed chair in memory of her late husband, and Dr. Nichols became the S. Emlen Stokes Professor of Genetics.[1] The remaining $400,000 of the campaign's dollar goal was for new equipment.

In shoring up its scientific underpinnings rather than underwriting another expansion effort, the board was adhering to Kaloupek's recommendations. With finite resources, the board relied on its winning tradition of volunteer fund raising supported by a development director who also had responsibilities for community relations and public information. The difficulties the campaign faced reflected the increasingly fierce competition for private resources and exposed flaws in a strategy that professional consultation might have corrected.[2] By October 1982, the RAP had garnered pledges approximating $1.4 million. By mid-1983, gifts and pledges totaled $2.2 million. A year later, with the drive nearly a million dollars short of its goal, progress reports ceased but the momentum reemerged in the development program's second planned phase, the "Partners In Progress" drive of the late 1980s.

The RAP campaign succeeded in enhancing the IMR's endowment fund. Coupled with a rising market and prudent investment philosophy, the addi-

[1] Memorialization was an effective and meaningful door to increased philanthropy. Two years later donors successfully matched John Dorrance's $100,000 challenge gift to establish a memorial postdoctoral fellowship in Phil Scott's name. When Ken MacDonald died in 1982, his family selected the Institute through its RAP campaign as the beneficiary of a memorial fund in that founding trustee's honor.

[2] For example, the campaign was announced prematurely and its objectives were redrawn at least twice in its course. Major prospects such as RCA were solicited at the end rather than the beginning of the effort.

Dr. Etienne Lasfargues, head of the tumor cell biology laboratory, led a search for human breast cancer antigens in an effort to provide new diagnostic tools for the disease.

tional contributions helped catapult the investment portfolio to approximately $4 million by the end of 1983. That sum was sufficiently respectable to warrant the investment committee's decision to place the portfolio in the care of a professional investment management firm. Such readiness to contract outside expertise to accomplish specific external tasks was a sign of corporate maturity. In 1981, for example, the Institute engaged Ray Bateman, a powerful lobbyist and one of the most influential political figures in the state, to press the Institute's interests in the halls of the state legislature.[3] This newfound pragmatism at the Institute occasionally resulted in significant grants from previously uncultivated prospects, such as an Atlantic City gambling casino.

That pragmatism was also manifested in a series of tightly orchestrated special events designed by external counsel to cultivate the region's political, business, and labor leaders. Typically, a corporate sponsor would underwrite the event's costs, a carefully culled list of kingpins would be invited to subscribe as attendees, and a renowned keynote speaker—often not from the IMR—would provide the "draw." Of course, the speaker would relate the Institute's work to his or her own topic. On October 15, 1981, for example, some two hundred Delaware Valley executives gathered to hear U. S. Secretary of Health and Human Services Richard S. Schweiker talk about the importance of the IMR as a center "established by private individuals from the private sector for the public good." He called upon corporate charity to offset the diminution of federal funds to scientific research. Following him to the podium, Dr. Coriell, no proponent of the health secretary's new economic fundamentalism, publicly and politely agreed.

[3] A former state senate president, Bateman was the man Byrne upset in the 1977 gubernatorial election.

The tactically masterful juxtaposition of these two spokespersons showed that the IMR's external relations had developed a more sophisticated *realpolitik*. Five years earlier Dr. Coriell might have summoned a local reporter to take notes while he excoriated an administration's science policy. In 1981 the ancient tactic of "kissing the hand one cannot bite" had taken hold with positive consequences. The secretary of health was provided a bully pulpit from which to espouse Reaganomics. The Institute got a cabinet official to make its own case for increased corporate funding, but in the guise of patriotic public policy rather than hat-in-hand petitioning. Corporate executives from surrounding states learned of the IMR first-hand. And the Institute raised money at the same time.

This same smart realism infected the Institute's attitudes toward marketing commercial applications of its discoveries. For nearly two decades, the IMR advised its scientific staff to adopt "an aware patent outlook." Unfortunately, increasing competition for NIH funding provided sufficient "risk venture" for researchers who were increasingly forced to write grants to multiple sources of support in order to sustain fundamental research projects. In 1981, however, Reagan's Economic Recovery Tax Act provided incentives for private industrial investment in basic research. Soon thereafter the NIH changed its regulations to allow institutions to patent discoveries made in the course of government-supported research and to retain the royalties therefrom. In 1982 "Gary" McGarrity had entered into a licensing agreement to market a monoclonal antibody diagnostic kit to detect and identify mycoplasmas. Ranged in size and complexity between virus and bacterium, these persistent parasitic microorganisms infected about 15% of all cell cultures, invalidating experiments and diagnoses that used those cultures.

The incentives provided by the altered NIH regulations and Reagan's tax policy prompted the IMR in 1983 to revise its own patent policy to provide increased incentives to its research staff. The new guidelines awarded 25% of the royalties to the inventor instead of the previous 10%. Moreover, the inventor's department received an additional 25% of the commission. As the policy was being rewritten, two commercial firms approached the IMR with offers of financial support for research in exchange for the privilege of marketing rights to discoveries. Negotiations ensued, and the IMR soon reached an agreement with Human Medical Laboratory. The complexities of intellectual property and patent law presented the Institute with yet another need for external professional expertise.

Forward-looking commercial enterprises had reason to bet on the IMR's potential for profitability. By 1978 Arnold Dion's molecular biological incursions into specific immune responses to "foreign" viral proteins were bringing him and his collaborators closer to inventing a test to predict recovery rates and life expectancy of breast cancer patients. Etienne Lasfargues's tumor cell biology lab was testing for possible development of diagnostic tests for breast cancer. In 1980 Anthony Girardi's department of virology and immunology began rodent vaccination studies using extracts of human mammary tumor virus that might furnish a clue for prevention of breast cancer in

Dr. Richard Mulivor checks cells from a mother whose unborn child is suspected of being affected by hypophosphatasia, a rare hereditary disease which prevents normal bone formation.

women. The dynamic interdisciplinary interplay at the IMR seemed poised to harvest biotechnical applications from its basic research.

Now guided by a "*stimulated* patent outlook," the Institute was not going to "sell the store" to private firms. Since 1981 it had been exploring alternatives for developing complementary investor-owned enterprises. By 1984, the NIH had begun awarding small-business startup grants. In order to become eligible for such grants, the IMR established CytoTech International, Inc., as an independent for-profit corporation to manufacture and market products and services developed through its research. In 1984 it received its first grant to produce and explore the market for DNA from selected cells in the cell bank.

CytoTech was more directly the result of a stunning breakthrough in genetic research and the IMR's role in supporting it than of federal fiscal policy or changing trends in America's commercial and investment culture. On November 9, 1983, a team of scientists at the Massachusetts General Hospital (MGH) reported that it had devised the first genetic test for detecting a devastating hereditary disease known as Huntington's Disease.

Inhabitants of the remote village of Barranquitas on the southern end of Venezuela's Lake Maracaibo possess one of the highest incidences of Huntington's Disease. In 1979, Nancy Wexler, Ph.D., began to construct the family tree of one Barranquitas family with the disease, tracing the pedigree back more than a century to a woman who had died of the disease. Subsequently, the origins were attributed to a European sailor. Arthur Greene and his colleagues were on call to transport skin biopsies and blood samples of 570 of her living progeny from the Philadelphia International Airport to the IMR's cell biology department. There the cells from these sources were grown, harvested, catalogued, and stored until they became the experimental materials used by James Gusella's team at MGH to isolate and identify a genetic "marker" of Huntington's Disease.

The *New York Times* considered the discovery front-page news, and scientists correctly predicted that recombinant DNA techniques would yield tests for other genetic disorders. This expectation brought increasing national at-

Dr. Greene and Evelyn Goldstein examine the extended family tree that Dr. Nancy Wexler constructed for Huntington's Disease patients in Venezuela.

tention to the custodian of the "Venezuelan collection," the Human Genetic Mutant Cell Repository in Camden. The National Institute of General Medical Sciences renewed its contract with the Institute through 1988 for nearly $4 million. Before the year was out, IMR biochemist Richard Mulivor announced the development of a prenatal diagnostic test for hypophosphatasia, a severe metabolic disorder always fatal in infancy. Occurring in quick succession, these events signified to observers that the Institute for Medical Research in Camden was positioned to make increasingly significant and frequent contributions to the emerging revolution on genetic and molecular biotechnology. Such observations would have an impact on the ability of the Institute to relocate.

By 1984 the Institute began to realize positive results from its transformed external relations and to find reassurance in both its scientific achievements and its long-range planning. But back in March 1981 two pressing objectives remained in the foreground of the deeper strategic landscape. Most obviously, revenues were urgently needed to replenish cash reserves and sustain daily operations. Just as urgent was the unresolved question of the Institute's location. The president was convinced that proximity to the new medical center complex—in whatever form it eventually materialized—was essential to the Institute's future. Others were uncertain that a major capital project was essential to IMR's future performance and success, especially a project that might in precarious times drain precious financial resources from the research agenda. Realizing that the Institute could not possibly respond to Cooper Medical Center's offer of center-city quarters until architectural analysis, long-range planning, and fundraising feasibility studies were completed, the executive committee declared a moratorium on the issue of relocation pending the successful acquisition of a financial quick-fix. Kaloupek had an idea: the IMR would lobby the legislature and governor's office for the imposition of a one-cent tax on cigarettes to be devoted to research on cancer.

The consultant calculated that such a levy would produce about $8 million annually, and that—given its near hegemony in the field of cancer research in the state—the IMR might reasonably anticipate receiving a third of that sum. Ironically, the plan worked, but not as anticipated. The "sin tax" on tobacco products enabled the 1983 passage of the state's Cancer Research Act. The IMR's role in the passage of this historic legislation brought the research center such esteem in the state capital that, the following year, the legislature was rather easily persuaded to appropriate $6.2 million to relocate the IMR to the new University of Medicine and Dentistry of New Jersey campus in Camden pursuant to a formal affiliation between Coriell and the UMDNJ. To put the matter so succinctly, however, is to overlook the excruciatingly complex and painstaking efforts required to accomplish this coup and to depreciate the controlling force of chance events and coincidence in history. Kaloupek's wise-penny plan was rooted in the groundwork that Dr. Coriell had laid over the course of decades for the Cancer Research Act and for the capital appropriation that followed upon it.

Cancer in New Jersey

Just as the foundations for the UMDNJ affiliation agreement were laid in 1975, Dr. Coriell's fingerprints were revealed on another supra-institutional initiative. He began an ultimately successful campaign to get New Jersey's political leadership to acknowledge its responsibility for supporting, coordinating, and expanding cancer research, diagnosis, and treatment throughout the state. As with the call for a medical center in Camden, this effort, while established to play a larger, sorely needed role, was also designed to enlarge the umbrella under which Dr. Coriell sought to move the Institute while preserving its independence. Like the earlier undertaking, this one viewed the state government rather than federal and private institutions as its legitimating authority and primary support.

Dr. Coriell sought to capitalize on the statewide attention—which he himself had helped focus and amplify—on the troubling 1970 HEW study that analyzed cancer mortality rates by U.S. counties between 1950 and 1969. New Jersey's national reputation as "cancer alley" emerged from findings that it ranked first among all states in total deaths per 100,000 population. New Jersey's unacceptably high proportion of tumors directly related to industrial exposure prompted environmental legislation that, in turn, demanded more intensive epidemiological research.

The HEW survey influenced the passage of the National Cancer Act of 1971. Dr. Coriell understood that—as a result of that legislation—more federal dollars were available for diagnosis and treatment and less for basic research. Strategically, he could not fundamentally alter the Institute's mission, but he could position it at the center of a larger movement dedicated to improving the prevention and detection of cancer and the treatment and care of cancer patients.

Dr. Coriell's first step was to catalyze support for the endeavor. By 1975, he and others had garnered the cooperation of the CMDNJ, the state's health department, ACS chapter, medical society, and other germane organizations to form an organization called the Cancer Institute of New Jersey (CINJ).[4] He had no intention of creating a rival institution. Rather, he revived the idea of "institute without walls"—a concept he disparaged when it was applied to a medical center in Camden but which made sense when building a statewide coalition with the clout to petition the state legislature for support. In April, he became a charter trustee of the fledgling group.

The name of the new organization reflected an internal deliberation a year earlier. In March 1974, the IMR executive committee had enviously analyzed the televised solicitations of the Institute for Cancer Research of Fox Chase, only to realize that it could not emulate Fox Chase's fundraising success. Unlike its Philadelphia-area neighbor, the IMR possessed neither patients nor a role as a center for public health education. By creating the Cancer

---

[4] This CINJ should not be confused with the Cancer Institute of New Jersey established in 1991. (See footnote 11.)

Institute of New Jersey, Dr. Coriell hoped to attract the kind of public and private funding that a basic research institute found hard to cultivate and that came easier to centers of diagnosis, prevention, and cure. As the only private biomedical institute devoted to cancer research in the state at the time, the IMR felt certain that it could make the public case for its centrality to any state-supported endeavor. Its basic research would not only contribute directly to the ultimate cure for cancer but also could demonstrate its proven ability to transform laboratory discoveries into tests that contributed to early detection and other clinical applications.

The chance to make that case was improved in 1976 when the NCI published an updated survey of cancer mortality in the United States that showed that New Jersey continued to lead the nation in incidences of the types of cancer that most often proved fatal. Almost simultaneously, the CINJ and the CMDNJ's department of preventive medicine and community health published in the state medical society's journal an epidemiological overview of cancer in New Jersey. The review called upon the state legislature to provide secure funding for the creation of a statewide tumor registry. The article stalwartly warned that, "if these monies are not made available, then legislators will have no right to bewail the severity of the problem with fustian rhetoric."

Publication of these empirical findings and political jabs provoked several state lawmakers to introduce separate bills to finance cancer research. The drafted legislation recognized that the lack of a centralized strategy for coordinating research hampered the state's efforts to secure its fair share of federal funds and to attract scientific talent. Nevertheless, bills calling for a state cancer research institute with or without walls remained bottled up in committee. They repeatedly failed to reach the floor for a vote because the legislature was preoccupied with other issues. Democrats had ridden the coattails of Byrne's surprising reelection victory in 1977 into big majorities in both houses. Byrne now dictated the legislative agenda and pursued an ambitious legacy. Comparatively esoteric issues such as biomedical research could not compete with publicly controversial and popularly accessible initiatives such as casino gambling, Pinelands preservation, mass transit, and the Meadowlands sports and entertainment center.

THE STATE COMMISSION ON CANCER RESEARCH

As Byrne—his legacy established—entered "lame-duckhood" in 1981, Kaloupek persuaded Burlington County's influential state senator, Democrat Charles Yates, to introduce legislation to amend the 1948 Cigarette Tax Act by supplementing it with a penny surtax. It was not a hard sell; Yates had joined the IMR board in 1979. On March 24, 1982, the IMR hosted the South Jersey legislative caucus. At that seance, Camden County's state senator Walter Rand suggested to Dr. Coriell that the best way to insure passage of such legislation was to avoid language that suggested that one organization in one legislative district or county might reap windfall rewards. He persuaded the Institute to

Camden's favorite son, Congressman James Florio, salutes the Institute on the occasion of its 25th anniversary.

support legislation that called for the creation of a state commission on cancer research. After all, the next governor would have his or her hands full coping with Reagan's new federalism. The idea of a commission implied statewide inclusiveness and statesmanlike deliberateness; it bought votes and time. And, if properly worded, the bill could ultimately direct major funding toward the Institute. Dr. Coriell heeded the senator's shrewd advice. Meanwhile, the committee on government affairs christened a campaign to secure additional legislative backing, identify and cultivate citizen-group support, and sound out gubernatorial candidates.

The Institute had forged close ties with the Democratic candidate from Camden. Eyeing the run for the executive office, U. S. Representative James Florio had stopped by the Woodcrest Country Club on March 30, 1979, to toast the IMR's twenty-fifth anniversary. Two years later he conceded that he had lost the gubernatorial election by less than two thousand votes, the smallest plurality in New Jersey history. The victor was Thomas Kean, a patrician Republican from distant Essex County and an apostle of Reaganomics. Prospects appeared bleak. Looks, however, can be deceiving.

In fact, Kean's election was a fillip for the Institute for at least three reasons. First, unlike his predecessor, Kean needed South Jersey's support. Unlike Byrne who had never held an elected office prior to governorship, the new executive was a wily, experienced, and effective politician. In 1972 and 1973, he presided as Speaker over a state assembly that had thirty-nine Republicans, forty Democrats, and one Independent.[5] Thereafter, he served as minority leader. In order to move legislation in such circumstances, one learned how

[5] His Speakership was the result of an infamous deal with five Hudson County Democrats.

to forge bipartisan coalitions and to suppress sectional animosities.[6] Those skills were imperative for a first-term governor whose legitimacy was challenged by an electoral victory that represented less than one-twelfth of one percent of the total number of votes cast. To win reelection he would have to make inroads into South Jersey, an area that had overwhelmingly supported his rival and Camden's favorite son, Jim Florio.

It is often forgotten that in 1980, two years after the taxpayers' revolt in California led to Proposition 13, there existed a serious secessionist movement in South Jersey. Because secession faced insuperable constitutional impediments and because the rebellion began as a journalistic joke, the spontaneous uprising is recalled, if at all, as a curious historical footnote. But movements that fail to take off often constitute illuminating indicators of the temper of a time, and this one mirrored the deep-seated resentment many South Jerseyans felt for their region's purported treatment by the state government. The crusade was taken seriously at the time. Over forty municipalities approved secession; the Atlantic County Democratic organization adopted a secessionist plank; and officials in Cherry Hill vowed to support it if their community became the capital of the sovereign State of South Jersey. The Senate Judiciary Committee held public hearings on the issue, and the Byrne administration called the movement an "insurrection" and threatened to activate the National Guard if it continued. A fence mender by nature, the incoming governor was predisposed to be good to South Jersey and to Camden.[7]

The second factor that recommended Kean's victory to the Institute was his embrace of Reagan's "supply-side" economic policies. Kean was convinced that he could encourage sufficient economic development in New Jersey, particularly in the areas of science and technology, to offset fiscal pressures that would be caused by federal devolution and economic recession. He was committed to issuing sufficient general obligation bonds to fund the infrastructure for such development. The 1983 report of the Commission on Science and Technology for the State of New Jersey, which Kean empanelled as one of his first acts as governor, called for boosting support of basic biomedical research at UMDNJ and elsewhere in order to attract biotechnology and pharmaceutical corporations.[8]

Third and most significant, Kean championed environmental protection. As a state legislator, the Essex Republican had secured a deserved reputation as an environmentalist. His commitments to the environment and to economic development merged in his advocacy of legislation to protect natural resources from contamination. The federal government published its report of toxic waste sites in 1982. New Jersey topped the EPA's National Priority List with sixty-five of the nation's worst sites.[9] The state had four of

[6] As minority leader in 1976 Kean worked sympathetically for the restoration of the Institute's annual state appropriation.

[7] Attaching his name to the Thomas H. Kean State Aquarium at Camden is recognition of his success in that regard.

[8] IMR trustee Stanley Bergen served on the Commission.

[9] The state total was ten times greater than its nearest competitor, Michigan.

Dr. Lewis Coriell inspects the Cancer Research Act, signed into law by Governor Thomas Kean. Assemblyman Elliot Smith (left) and Senator Walter Rand (right) sponsored the legislation.

the nation's ten worst dumpsites and ten of the worst fifty. One hundred and twenty sites were located in South Jersey, including the country's worst contamination, a landfill in Gloucester County, adjacent to Camden County.

Embarrassed New Jerseyans were largely unaware that the Kean administration had aggressively fought to have the state head the list. Kean knew that, in order to attract business and industry to the state, he needed "Superfund" dollars to clean up toxic waste sites. He also understood that hazardous waste cleanup meant an interim infusion of federal funds and a rise in employment in New Jersey. By 1988 New Jersey had received about half of all the Superfund allocations.

The national notoriety accompanying announcements of New Jersey's unenviable status focused public attention on the health risks of living and working in the Garden State in a way that the publication of epidemiological statistics in medical society journals could not. The health risks had not magnified; Dr. Coriell and others had been warning about them for a decade. Nor did the incidence of cancer increase. But public anxiety grew. That electoral fact finally focused the attention of astute politicians on the scientific fact that cancer was a state problem. Kean amended Senator Yates's penny-tax proposal and penned into law in June 1982 a bill to increase the state surtax on cigarettes to a nickel per pack. On January 17, 1983, he signed into law the Cancer Research Act (S.390) sponsored by Senator Rand and established a Commission on Cancer Research, whose work would be funded by a $1 million annual appropriation from the state cigarette tax revenue.

The Act's preamble was an unprecedented acknowledgment of the state's responsibility for encouraging cancer research and a self-indictment for failures that deprived its citizens of the benefits of scientific research.[10] It urged prompt well-funded "corrective measures" be adopted "to make up for lost ground and to make the State competitive within the next 5 years." The responsibility for fulfilling the law's mandate would rest with the New Jersey Commission on Cancer Research, consisting of nine members including the commissioners of the departments of health and of environmental protection. The commission was empowered to authorize research projects, apportion funds, apply for federal underwriting, enter into contracts, accept private gifts, and employ an executive director and staff.

The commission's first executive director, former state Senator John J. Fay, Jr., credited Rand and Coriell for avoiding institutional parochialism and advocating a statewide solution to the cancer problem. "Had it been regional," Fay concluded, "it wouldn't have sold." Still, the law's wording systematically excluded research that was not a "biomedical research project at the cellular or molecular level." That phrase significantly reduced the field to the IMR, UMDNJ, Rutgers, and Princeton's new department of molecular biology. In 1984 the Commission, on which Kaloupek served as a member, awarded $1.3 million in seventeen grants, including a two-year award to IMR to support Dr. Dion's breast cancer studies.

Ultimately, the establishment of the commission on cancer research focused attention and helped coordinate New Jersey's fight against cancer.[11] On balance, however, the *direct* benefits of the legislation to the state and the IMR were minuscule. A one-million-dollar annual investment would never solve a problem that cost New Jersey over one-half billion dollars each year in cancer treatment alone. Not until 1988 was the annual appropriation increased to $3 million. By then, in response to protests from institutions doing behavioral, socioeconomic, psychosocial, epidemiological, and demographic research on cancer, the commission's mandate was vastly expanded and, from the Institute's vantage, watered down.

Such nugatory investment from an allegedly dedicated surtax that was securing annual revenue of approximately $45 million was inexplicable. When asked to explain the discrepancy, the chairman of the assembly appropriations

[10] The bill's language is so close in substance and style to some of Dr. Coriell's position papers on the subject as to suggest he played a part in the drafting of the legislation. The law's second paragraph reads as follows: "The Legislature finds and declares that although this State has the highest cancer death rate in the nation for many of the most frequently fatal types of cancer, it has provided relatively little encouragement for cancer studies at any of its local institutions involved in basic biological research; and that this failure has made New Jersey unattractive for the recruitment of highly skilled cancer investigators, has reduced the State's capacity to compete for its fair share of federal and private research dollars, and has been responsible for delaying the development of services and facilities necessary to conduct productive research. New Jersey's failure to make a concerted and intense effort in the war against cancer has deprived its citizens of the benefits resulting from the latest advances in basic cancer research."

[11] With the commission's help, the Cancer Institute of New Jersey was established in 1991 and opened its doors in 1997 as one of only 13 NCI-designated clinical cancer centers in the nation.

committee responded that research centers could not possibly absorb such an infusion of funds. He should have consulted the IMR. By 1987, the Commission had awarded the Institute four grants totaling approximately $340,000, far less than the $3 million dollars it had hoped for annually. Still, the role the Institute played in bringing the need for support of cancer research before the public and its elected officials reinforced its association with the state. Once again, this strengthened tie was originally knotted in the mid-1970s and exhibited in such new alliances as the Institute's contractual relationship with the state department of environmental protection (DEP).

The Environmental Research Laboratory

In 1975 the Institute's state funding crisis accelerated the development of the CINJ. In 1976 Dr. Coriell used the NCI and CINJ/CMDNJ studies of cancer in New Jersey as ammunition in the successful battle to restore the state's annual appropriation. Those developments—and, as we shall shortly see, the impact of a seminal publication by a national scientific organization—led to the Office of Cancer and Toxic Substances Research of the DEP to engage the Institute to identify chemicals in the environment (mutagens) that could cause genetic damage. Simultaneously, Governor Byrne's declaration of IMR Week and the public identification of the Institute as a center for breast cancer studies stimulated the IMR's Women's Auxiliary and six other women's clubs to lead a drive to build and equip an Environmental Research Laboratory at the Institute. Formally dedicated in March 1977, the new facility represented an investment in the work of the state.

The Institute's decision to engage in sampling the state's toxic environment was rooted in an ideology of public service, institutional self-interest, and scientific curiosity. Such work facilitated the IMR's political relationship with the state cancer commission and with those who controlled the annual appropriation. By the time the commission was formed, New Jersey's contractual support of the environmental research laboratory approximated the annual grant revenues secured through the commission for the Institute. Although the work involved the possibility of a risky distraction from basic research, scores of engaging questions for pure research were emerging from the applications of the environmental laboratory. There was also plenty of scientific precedent for such involvement. Since 1970, the Institute had invested steadfastly in studies of genetic toxicity, of the effects of chemicals and viruses on human chromosomes.

The organizational roots of the rapidly expanding field of environmental mutagenesis can be traced to the 1969 founding of the Environmental Mutagen Society (EMS), one year prior to the creation of the Environmental Protection Agency.[12] Governmental interest in this branch of research was

---

[12] The field's "spiritual" roots can be traced to the publication in 1962 of Rachel Carson's *Silent Spring*, which altered public consciousness about the environment by providing some of the

enormously stimulated by the EMS's first major position paper titled "Environmental Mutagenic Hazards," published in *Science* in 1975. The article stressed the importance of identifying potential mutagens *before* they were introduced into the environment, underscored the urgency of developing new and better test methods, and significantly influenced the eventual development of regulatory procedures within government and of testing within industry.

That the manifesto strongly supported the Institute's and the CINJ's position vis-à-vis the state would come as no surprise to the scientific insider. Warren Nichols served as councilor of the EMS since 1971 and as secretary of the Society from 1973 to 1977. He co-chaired the EMS's third annual meeting, which was held in Cherry Hill. McGarrity learned about mutagenicity analyses, or assays, from Nichols. In other words, the Institute was not simply following propitious scientific tendencies; it was directing them. Under the direction of McGarrity, chair of the microbiology department, the new laboratory was the only place in the state at the time equipped to conduct these environmental assays.

The laboratory's basic tool was the Ames Mutagenicity Test,[13] one of several rapid bioassays developed to detect the presence of mutagens in air, water, soil, leached contaminants, liquid wastes, and cigarette smoke. The Ames assay recorded measurable changes in the DNA of a standardized battery of five specifically selected strains of Salmonella bacteria after timed exposure to suspected carcinogenic chemicals. The advantages of such assays were remarkable. An assay would take two to four days to complete within a cost range of $500 to $1,000. In comparison, performing a laboratory test on mice might take two to four years to complete and cost between $150,000 and $500,000. Retrospective epidemiological studies took even longer. Moreover, such longitudinal studies can only be done after large populations are exposed to cancer and portions thereof subsequently develop it. Almost as reliable as the rodent bioassay, a short-term assay could be used to test a product such as hair dye before it was mass-produced and sold, or to assess a person's level of exposure to a dangerous chemical.

Scientists agreed that toxic chemicals played a role in the etiology of cancer. At the time it was estimated that at least eighty-five percent of human cancer was related to environmental exposure. In 1981, prompted by epidemiological studies that spotlighted New Jersey's dismal cancer mortality trends and tiring of newspaper headlines asking "Does New Jersey Cause Cancer?," the state's DEP published its own report that suggested the problem was regional and not confined to the Garden State. Airborne chemicals from Mid-

---

first public evidence of how pesticides were poisoning the earth. Published the year Dr. Coriell decided to devote himself completely to the SJMRF, the seminal work tops many lists as the most important book of the last half of the twentieth century. Dr. Carson died of breast cancer two years after its publication.

[13] Also referred to as the Ames salmonella assay, the test was developed by EMS member Bruce N. Ames in 1970.

As chairman of the microbiology department, Dr. Gary McGarrity oversaw the environmental toxicology program.

western and Canadian industrial sites and waterways contaminated with pesticides failed to respect geopolitical boundaries. Interestingly, this expanded view of cancer epidemiology mirrored the altered demographics of board development. In 1982 IMR board chairman William Bell announced an effort to attract philanthropic support from the Greater Delaware Valley and, accordingly, to expand the board to represent a broader geographical constituency. Calling the IMR a microcosm of the community it served, Bell argued that "the work of the Institute concerns our entire mid-Atlantic region, where cancer risk is among the highest in the nation."

On the surface, such a statement might be viewed as a rhetorical opportunism designed to cultivate financial help from a regional populace increasingly concerned about environmental health risk. At a deeper level, however, the assertion reflected an increasing scientific preoccupation with the interplay of genetic control of life processes and environmental assaults, with the relationship of biology and ecology. What were the effects of frequency, duration, and intensity of toxic doses on carcinogenesis? How did chemicals interact with viruses or within individuals with different genetic backgrounds? Indeed, how did they react with one another? At the time there existed some 70,000 commercially used synthetic chemicals. The idea of doing short-term assays of their permutations and combinations was logarithmically bewildering. Regional extension of environmental concern and growth of the field of mutagenics reinforced Dr. Coriell's call for an expansion of environmental research at the IMR.

The New Jersey State Department of Environmental Protection supported the Institute's environmental mutagenesis laboratory. The lab's director, Dr. Tom Atherholt, measures cancer-causing chemical contaminants from the Delaware Valley watershed.

The 1982 publication of the EPA's Superfund list and the ascendancy of environmental protectionism in Governor Kean's public policy agenda reinforced the good sense of Dr. Coriell's proposals for expansion. With seeming suddenness, the state's policy makers, regulatory agencies, and citizenry became urgently interested in scientific answers to such issues as containment and disposal of toxic wastes, establishment of minimal acceptable risk levels of exposure, and effects of chemical combinations on cancer incidence.

Deep down, Dr. Coriell deplored the chemical-of-the-month approach to toxicology. He knew first-hand that the conquest of polio did not result from building better iron lungs. Until basic research uncovered the precise mechanisms that caused cancer and the ways in which chemicals affected those mechanisms, he believed there would be little technical or clinical advance. While negotiating with the state for contract funding for assays, he was using a back channel in Florio's congressional office to investigate the possibility of obtaining funding for basic research directly from the federal Superfund. Doing assays was publicly important but scientifically unbeguiling work. By 1983, when the contract was renewed, several other collaborating institutions had joined the effort. Strategically, however, the work served to establish within the state's governmental bureaucracies the IMR's reputation for environmental research and to foster the state's receptivity to expansion of the endeavor.

Dr. Coriell's strategy of expansion also had an internal political purpose as he sought to convince the board of the need to move the laboratories. Skeptics asked their leader to show how a costly move would materially improve the IMR's performance of its scientific mission. Inalterably convinced that institutional presence on the future medical center campus was the key to vitality and growth, Dr. Coriell saw the enlargement of the environmental laboratory as a persuasive justification for moving. He argued that the environmental work represented a subtle change in scientific mission, which would be best served by a change of address. But until the DEP agreed to provide long-term or full-cost contracts for the mutagenicity testing, expansion of the environmental research laboratory was viewed as risky; relocation on behalf of that expansion, imprudent. Until the state found a compelling case for fuller commitment to the IMR, the prospects for relocation would remain dim.

Moving Uptown

Dr. Coriell instinctively understood two things about the IMR's location. From the standpoint of external relations, he knew that failure to relocate risked marginalization. The Institute needed to be co-located with the emergent medical center complex if it was to maintain its visibility in the eyes of state government. Intramurally, he knew that the easy interaction with academicians, clinicians, and students was vital to the IMR's ability to attract and retain world-class scientists. Saddled with the fiduciary responsibility of maintaining organizational solvency, the trustees struggled to reconcile Dr. Coriell's instincts with its own requirements of due diligence. Thus, it commissioned studies.

Cooper Medical Center's offer of a center-city site and building was the catalyst that had prompted the trustees to commission David Kaloupek's wide-ranging report about the IMR's institutional future in October 1980. Four years earlier Cooper had broken ground for its ten-story, $38 million pavilion that would rise facing Haddon Avenue. Across the street, the city had invested one million dollars to raze the Third Regiment Armory and adjacent structures in order to clear a site for the $75 million Veteran's Administration hospital, which U.S. President Gerald R. Ford had approved. The VA facility was seen as the cornerstone of a massive program to restore Camden's economic viability. Its construction would have assured the existence of the proposed medical center/medical school complex. In 1978, however, the Carter administration scrapped the VA plan in a budget-cutting measure, leaving city officials incensed and the long-range plans of many parties in limbo. As Cooper dedicated its new Keleman Pavilion in 1979, it offered a building to its new partner, the CMDNJ. When the College declined the consideration, Cooper approached the IMR.

Located on the southeast corner of Broadway Avenue and Stevens Street, the creatively named Broadway-Stevens Building had been purchased by Cooper in 1966, renamed the Medical Arts Building, and occupied by the hospital's nursing school. Built in the 1920s, the twelve-story facility encompassed about 55,000 square feet of useable space. An office building by design, its rehabilitation as a utility-intensive laboratory facility would entail expensive alterations. Organizationally, it possessed a dysfunctional verticality. Its size would not accommodate the needs of future growth. Also, it was four blocks away from a precious wedge of land known as Pulaski Park. Bordered by Haddon Avenue, South 7th Street, Benson Street and Washington Street, that was the territory the CMDNJ picked for its proposed Camden residence. On April 15, 1981, the noted architectural firm Wallace, Roberts and Todd (WRT), retained by the city on the Institute's behalf, recommended against consideration of Cooper's proposal.

Institute officials received the architectural study just as they were absorbing Kaloupek's sobering analysis of the IMR's financial status, which was delivered exactly one month earlier. The consultant doubted that the IMR had the resources to carry out a major capital project without compromising its financial integrity. The board agreed to accept WRT's recommendation and, as part of its long-range planning, asked the firm to study alternative locations based on its intimate knowledge of the Institute's requirements. With the fate of the VA project still in doubt, its site remained reserved for an urban ambition that would never be fulfilled. In August, WRT proposed for the IMR's future consideration three site plans on a parcel of land on Haddon Avenue, just south of the VA site opposite the future CMDNJ building.

WRT's holistic, exacting dissection of the IMR's site, space, and system needs not only provided a blueprint that the IMR could analyze for planning purposes, but also showed city and state officials that the organization was responsibly and professionally examining its options. Once again, the Institute's growing commitment to involving expert counsel in vital areas of resource development and planning paid off. The city apportioned this plot for the IMR and incorporated WRT's prototypical design into its master plan for future community development.

When the board accepted the WRT recommendation about the Broadway-Stevens building in the spring of 1981, it also suspended the IMR's explorations with Cooper and the CMDNJ about possible affiliation, which had been ongoing since 1978. One reason for the cessation of talks was the need to develop a long-range plan. Another reason was fear that the Institute's precarious financial situation made it vulnerable to possible loss of independence through merger with one of its larger partners. In a few critical years, however, the Institute had strengthened its posture through professional planning and analysis, improved fundraising, sophisticated government relations, an emerging biotechnological orientation, and a growing reputation for service to the state. When the affiliation negotiations were reopened in December 1983, the Institute was in an enhanced position to cut itself a more favorable deal.

The University of Medicine and Dentistry of New Jersey, 1984. Courtesy of Kim Sokoloff and the University of Medicine and Dentistry of New Jersey

The revival of talks with the newly titled University of Medicine and Dentistry coincided with the publication of the report of the Governor's Commission on Science and Technology on which Dr. Bergen served. Among the commission's five key recommendations were calls for the creation of a world-class infrastructure in biotechnology and an advanced technology center in hazardous and toxic substance management. Both of these recommendations referenced the kind of work in which the Institute was directly involved, and both referenced the UMDNJ as one of a number of appropriate institutional umbrellas for these initiatives. Inside observers knew that legislation would be drafted to include on the November 1984 election ballot a referendum to have the state issue a $62 million general obligation bond to promote these ends. A few months later it was understood that it would be an $80 million capital improvement issuance.

On February 1, 1984, less than two months after the Commission's report, Drs. Coriell and McGarrity unveiled a draft of a bold proposal to build an Environmental Toxicology Center (ETC) in Camden. The envisioned center would provide the region with a facility for research, education, consultation, and services having to do with detection and control of toxic chemicals on human health. It would translate findings from molecular and cell biology, microbial genetics, cytogenetics, recombinant DNA technology, and organic chemistry into information that could be rapidly utilized by government, industry, the scientific community, and the general public.

The center never became a reality, but no matter. The articulation of the *idea* of such a center at that precise juncture of events bore fruit. One of the most interesting latent functions of the proposal was the critical, palpable role it played in the Institute's relocation and affiliation with the UMDNJ. Institutions would be furiously competing for the capital funds the bond issues would make available. Dr. Coriell realized that the transformation of the environmental lab into a statewide environmental toxicology center would provide the vehicle for expansion and relocation to the medical center complex. In 1981, Kaloupek concluded that the proposal to relocate lacked, in his words, "a unifying rationale and valid factual case to justify the decision." Now in 1984 its rationale was also a bargaining chip. For the IMR's planning committee, the ETC proposal was the final piece to its strategic puzzle. In March the planning committee circulated its draft report to members of the executive committee as it prepared for the quarterly board meeting the following month. The latter committee declared that "it is time to get out of the 'talking' stage" and into action.

Previously, the planning committee had been talking *sotto voce*. Donald Meads had taken over the chairmanship of the committee the previous year upon his election to the board. President of the respected strategic management consultant firm Carver Associates, he had been handpicked for the role. On January 26, he communicated by private memorandum to Dr. Coriell and the members of the planning committee his summation of the committee's deliberations and preliminary conclusions. The report was not sanguine about the IMR's future as an independent research organization. It anticipated major obstacles to future funding, including the declension of governmental support for the kind of basic research performed at the Institute, an unfavorable forecast for grants for scientific training, lack of construction money, and furious competition for funds. The summary revealed that the committee questioned "whether IMR has the stature and breadth to compete in the environment which is emerging" and "whether [it] has the critical mass to meet this challenge." Bluntly, the committee concluded, "The preliminary answer is 'no.' "

By astonishing coincidence, Drs. Coriell and McGarrity presented the initial draft of their proposal for the creation of the ETC to the executive committee just six days after Donald Meads issued his challenging memorandum. The following month, the planning committee may not have reversed its dismal forecast, but it did provide a hopeful scenario for the IMR's independent future based upon the *deus ex machina* of the ETC's potential. With support from the UMDNJ, the Institute convinced Senator Rand and the South Jersey caucus to support legislation that would add $20 million to the pending bond issue to finance the IMR's relocation and the creation of the ETC under the auspices of the UMDNJ. These rapidly unfolding events and altered prognostications were presented to the full board on April 4. The board unanimously approved a motion to (1) negotiate and gain approval of an affiliation agreement with the UMDNJ;[14] (2) insure the IMR's participation in the proposed bond issue; and (3), pending the successful conclusion of the first two objectives, relocate the Institute to the medical center complex.

The four major events that converged in 1981, filtered through nearly four years of strategic transformation, had brought the Institute to this door of decision. The proposal to create the Environmental Toxicology Center provided the key to its opening. Once beyond the doorway of internal deliberation, however, the Institute would quickly find itself exposed to public debate over the best use of the bond funds and the ultimate configuration of the Camden medical complex. One hundred million dollars (the eventual bond issue was $90 million) backed by the taxing power of the state and subject to public referendum can marvelously focus the attentions of interested parties. A week later, at a special meeting of the executive committee to which the full board was invited as voting participants, the trustees learned of the real and

[14] In order to optimize the IMR's negotiating power, the motion endorsed the same participation with Cooper Hospital and Rutgers Medical School.

potential opposition to IMR's plans. Other interests would be lobbying strenuously for inclusion in the state and city's plans for the center, and the IMR could expect savage scrutiny and competition. The board authorized funds to retain a professional manager of the multi-faceted effort and steeled itself for an intensive effort to make a credible, defensible case for support of its plan.

The case for the establishment of the ETC was masterfully designed to reinforce the governor's policy agenda and to appeal to state and local political leaders and their constituencies. The précis of the proposal crafted for legislative eyes argued that the ETC and the relocation essential to its development

> . . . would do much to put New Jersey at the leading edge of the biotechnology boom. Also, it would address a major concern of its citizens: the environment. It would improve the quality of health care delivery and education and would enhance biomedical research. It would provide significant economic benefits now and in the future to Camden and the rest of the state. Finally, it would demonstrate the state's recognition of the needs, potential and vitality of southern New Jersey.

The fact that the state disbursed capital funds to relocate the IMR to the UMDNJ's South Jersey campus would seem to suggest that the lobbying effort, as lobbyists say, pressed all the right buttons. Yet, the ETC was never established, and the science-and-technology referendum approved by the voters in November did not fund the IMR relocation. The mystery is resolved by reference to another, less public "button." There was another important, less ostensible advantage to the relocation.

In 1975, when Governor Byrne signed into law the bill that established Cooper Medical Center as southern New Jersey's core teaching hospital, he inadvertently ignited a furious controversy. Aware of impending legislation to create a medical school in southern New Jersey, the osteopathic medical profession had quietly and effectively lobbied for insertion of language that insured that Cooper would sponsor osteopathic (D.O.) as well as allopathic (M.D.) educational programs. At a time when the theoretical and practical distinctions between these two medical persuasions were becoming blurred, uncomfortable proximity along Cooper's corridors exacerbated tribal prejudices. As a Cooper board member, Dr. Coriell vociferously opposed the conflation of allopathic and osteopathic training at the hospital. Crucible of compromise, the state legislature—understanding that an osteopathic vote equaled an allopathic one—ignored growing tensions and left the warring clans to resolve their differences. They did not. By 1984, lawmakers realized that the unscrambled conflict they had exacerbated could jeopardize the future of the new medical center complex. Before adjourning for summer recess, they introduced legislation to remedy the defects of their previous legislation.

The osteopaths were perfectly willing to surrender their claim on Cooper in exchange for a $9.45 million appropriation to build a facility for an osteopathic school of medicine at their Kennedy Memorial Hospital in Stratford. A bill to accomplish this objective was duly advanced. On June 18, Senator

Rand introduced companion legislation, Senate Bill 1890, to add $6.2 million to the Department of Higher Education's budget to allow the UMDNJ to retrofit the 50,000 square feet of space in its new teaching and research building—that would be vacated by the osteopaths—to accommodate the IMR.[15] The bill's statement gingerly suggested that the IMR was "currently *considering* [emphasis added] the expansion of its existing efforts to develop an Environmental Toxicology Center in Camden." It cited the IMR's scientific reputation and service to the state. It emphasized that the ETC "will create additional jobs in Camden and will contribute to a better economic climate in that city."

By signing both pieces of legislation on October 26, Governor Kean removed a potential source of controversy that might have diluted South Jersey support for the science-and-technology referendum at the polls the following week. In the process he built his political capital in a Democratic city he would carry a year later in his stunning re-election victory. At the fanfare signing of the IMR bill, Kean declared that both measures represented a "significant investment" in southern New Jersey. That was another way of saying that the region should not expect a share of capital funding for biotechnology.[16] Nevertheless, Bill 1890 provided for that contingency by allowing the funds to be dedicated either to new construction or to renovation of the teaching and research facility vacated by the osteopathic school. By spring 1985, the Institute had submitted preliminary design drawings for the retrofitting of the facility at the UMDNJ building to the state Board of Higher Education for approval at its June meeting. In the wake of a hard-earned achievement, IMR trustees reluctantly turned their attention to a topic that the rapid pace of urgent activity had allowed them to avoid. Its legendary leader was set to retire at the end of September.

The End of an Era

At the start of 1984, the IMR established a small, internal presidential search committee. Board chairman William Bell served *ex officio* with trustee Samuel Ballam, chairman of the board of the Hospital of the University of Pennsylvania and Drs. Rhoads, Coriell, Nichols, and McGarrity. The latter member was serving as staff representative. The intimacy of the grouping suggested an outcome that many people anticipated: a smooth transfer of the mantle of leadership to Warren Nichols, trusted trustee, eminent scientist, and vice president for research.

Nichols had earned the confidence of the president, board, and scientific staff, but his beloved boss's impending retirement and his indefeasible claim

---

[15] Burlington County Assemblywoman Barbara Kalik sponsored the companion bill in the assembly.

[16] In 1985 Rutgers University established the Center for Advanced Biotechnology and Medicine at its Piscataway campus in Middlesex County.

Dr. Jonathan Rhoads, an intellectual force from the Institute's early days, was a key advisor in the search for a successor to Dr. Coriell.

to the presidency placed him at a professional crossroads. As Dr. Coriell's lieutenant for a quarter-century, he knew firsthand the punishing regimen in store for the next president. Also, he understood that he had contributed to the Institute most significantly as a scientist and that the office of the presidency tended to distance its occupant from the bench. When the pharmaceutical giant Merck Sharpe & Dohme offered him an enviable position as senior director of genetic and cellular toxicology, Nichols determined to continue his service to the Institute as a trustee and scientific advisor. McGarrity became vice president. In the midst of intensive negotiations, lobbying and planning for the relocation, the Institute reacted to the late summer news of Nichols's departure by retaining a professional search firm to facilitate the hunt for a successor to the founder.

While Dr. Coriell's steadfast commitment to—indeed, identity with—his Institute reassured the board and staff that he would continue faithfully to support it as the trustees wished, he nevertheless worked hard at the difficult task of distancing himself from a role he had lived intensively for over three decades. It was necessary to show his colleagues as well as himself that a major transition was occurring. In early 1984 he accepted the nomination of the membership of the College of Physicians of Philadelphia to serve a two-year term as its president-elect effective July 1. That role placed exceptional burdens upon its occupant, whose succeeding two-year presidency would encompass the 1987 bicentennial celebration of the founding of the venerable and—alas—financially imperiled institution.

Finding a successor to Dr. Coriell was not an easy task. An inimitable combination of fierce independence, proprietary pride, and loyalty to community had helped him resist abundant offers of tenured positions at major institutions and corporations. Most senior scientists of his stature were either securely ensconced in such posts, heading up their own establishments, or close to retirement themselves. Promising investigators working to secure their reputations were reluctant to take on administrative responsibilities at critical stages in their careers. A new breed of scientific administrator had been recently hybridized at the NIH, but very few of its members had ventured from the pool were they were spawned. In truth, the Institute's presidency occupied a very special niche in the ecology of biomedical science.

By summer 1985, the search committee had settled on a respected geneticist with impressive credentials. Arthur Greene delivered the Institute's

Lew and Esther fondly remembered their trip to the Orient, which the board presented to them upon Dr. Coriell's retirement.

formal offer to the scientist at an international genetics meeting in Finland. But, less than a fortnight from Dr. Coriell's scheduled departure at month's end, the chosen successor abruptly reconsidered. Gary McGarrity learned the shocking news as he was preparing to depart from a scientific conference in Tokyo, Japan. When he returned to Camden, board chairman Bell asked him to serve as acting president. McGarrity understood that the Institute had few options and reluctantly agreed to assume a post that possessed lots of responsibility and little authority. He made it clear that he would assume the position as custodian; he had no wish to be a candidate for the permanent position. At the October annual board meeting, William Bell stepped down from eight effective years as chairman, William Kallelis succeeded him, and McGarrity was named acting president.

On November 8, the day after Governor Kean was re-elected by the greatest plurality in New Jersey history, the Institute unveiled the biggest and most festive celebration in *its* history. Chaired by trustee Sally Harral and fittingly entitled "A Tribute to Dedication," the gala honored Dr. Coriell, his family, and his accomplishments. Close to three hundred admirers celebrated the retiree's extraordinary life, imbibed, dined, danced and—in the process—financially contributed to research at the Institute. Tributes poured in from the President of the United States, Governor Kean, Camden Mayor Melvin

Primas, American Medical Association president Harrison Rogers, and other luminaries. Deservedly, Lew and Esther Coriell were presented with a deluxe eighteen-day cruise of exotic Asiatic ports of call.

Through toasts, proclamations, laughter, and tears, Lewis Coriell mounted the podium. Dutifully and nostalgically he recounted the early days of the Institute. His departing injunction, however, was characteristically forward looking. Thanks to his and his associates' efforts on behalf of the establishment of the cancer commission, the environmental research center and the relocation initiative, the Institute could courageously embrace its future. Expressing his appreciation for the opportunity for retrospection and for the contributions of his scientific and administrative associates, he cajoled his partners to continue the fight for federal support of basic research and for state support of basic research's applications. As he departed the presidency, he had succeeded beyond anyone's imagination save his own to position his Institute to fulfill its promise.

CHAPTER NINE

LOOKING BACK, LOOKING FORWARD (1986–1992)

JANUS, THE MYTHOLOGICAL Roman god of gates and doorways, is depicted with two faces gazing in opposite directions. In the month of Janus, 1986, the IMR board unanimously adopted two motions that reflected its awareness of crossing a threshold not just to a new year but also to a new era. Looking backward appreciatively to Lewis L. Coriell's distinguished service, unselfish sacrifice, scientific accomplishment, and inspiring leadership, the trustees resolved to rename the organization, effective February 1, the Coriell Institute for Medical Research.

Looking forward with increasing confidence, the board unveiled a new logo to replace the cartoon microscope that had nestled against the last letter of the IMR logotype since 1978. Like a ceremonial shoulder-sash, a stylized double helix was diagonally superimposed from upper left to lower right upon a circle composed of tightly alternating light and dark horizontal lines representing a sphere. Said to express "the Coriell Institute's position in this modern age of biotechnology," the altered iconography symbolized the Institute's embrace of the new science of molecular genetics. Juxtaposing macrocosm and microcosm, the logo suggested the organic complexity and yet unity of nature. The elegant precision of its design implied that the universe is ultimately ordered and hence knowable. Yet, the abstractness of the symbol suggested that scientific knowledge of the biological world is esoteric, elusive, and subject to multiple interpretations. Although less obvious than the preceding icon, the novel image suggested a shared intimacy. One step removed from scientific inquiry, the observer of the earlier icon was looking *at* a microscope. The new participant, it seemed, was looking *through* the instrument to the object of scientific interest.

Stocked with new corporate moniker and logo, the Coriell Institute still lacked a new president. Candidates mindful of the significance of symbolic change might astutely infer from the new logo a broad mandate and awesome responsibility to recruit scientific leaders, obtain state-of-the-art research tools, and implement cutting-edge techniques that would position the Institute in the forefront of the revolution in molecular biology. And they might soberly realize that the reverence, affection, and admiration for Lewis Coriell that inspired the institutional name change meant that the next chief executive officer had a very tough act to follow. The trustees were entering a new game holding some very good cards. How they selected their next president would determine whether they had a winning hand.

Inside Straight

Into late spring a reconstituted search committee chaired by Harold Shaub, who also chaired the executive committee, interviewed several candidates recommended by the scientific staff and professional headhunters. According to professed criteria, the ideal candidate would be an eminent scientist, a politically adroit and widely recognized leader, an experienced administrator, and a proven fundraiser. On June 4, a month after he received Jefferson University's Distinguished Alumnus Award, acting president Gary McGarrity was chosen to succeed Dr. Coriell. Board chair Kallelis and Shaub jointly issued the announcement that day immediately after the meeting of the executive committee.[1]

There were plenty of substantive justifications for choosing this particular insider. As a scientist, McGarrity had impeccable credentials. Growing out of his earlier efforts to eliminate the nemesis of mycoplasmas to cell cultures and culturists, his contemporaneous interest in these microorganisms extended to their involvement in a number of human diseases such as walking pneumonia. Often misdiagnosed, mycoplasmal diseases were resistant to penicillin and several other antibiotics. McGarrity was able to devise a rapid, reliable diagnostic test for walking pneumonia and had begun to investigate the involvement of mycoplasmas in cataracts, arthritis, and certain neurological diseases.

While McGarrity's publications on mycoplasmas—never a major area of molecular research—were respected and oft cited, it was his early work at the Institute that had secured his reputation in the scientific community. The laminar airflow hood he perfected became as common to laboratories as the electric toaster to kitchens. His contributions to the Institute's trailblazing research in air filtration dynamics and distribution systems transformed biomedical environments, refined tissue culture science, and established standards of reliability in cell characterization that predisposed the NIH to award the cell bank contracts to the Institute.

[1] Why this decision did not await the endorsement of the full board at its regularly scheduled meeting has not been fathomed.

A cell repository is a collection of living cells maintained indefinitely in suspended animation in liquid nitrogen.

Members of the executive and search committees were acutely aware of the importance of the cell bank contracts to the organization's financial stability and of McGarrity's connections both to the history of the cell banks and to the NIH. At the time, NIH support of the cell repositories represented approximately two-thirds of the Coriell Institute's revenue. Just prior to McGarrity's selection as president, the NIH's Institute on Aging renewed its underwriting of the Aging Cell Repository with a five-year, $2 million contract on which Dr. Greene served as principal investigator. And the National Retinitis Pigmentosa Foundation, in cooperation with the NIGMS, funded a cell collection at the Camden facility. Since 1972 the repositories had distributed over 46,000 cell lines and could point to more than 6,000 published and presented scientific papers resulting therefrom. By choosing McGarrity as Dr. Coriell's successor, the trustees knew they had secured a chief executive officer who would champion the collections.

The significance board members attached to the cell repositories played a major role in McGarrity's ascendancy. Past president of the Tissue Culture Association, which Dr. Coriell helped establish, he was in the process of organizing the International Association for Cell Culture, an alliance of European and Pacific Rim scientists who would elect him their founding president. By selecting a successor trained, as was Lewis Coriell, in the disciplines of virology and microbiology, the trustees paid homage to the illustrious founder. At the same time, however, the choice represented a conservative attachment to the cellular sciences from which the Institute emerged rather than a progressive embrace of the new robust pursuits of molecular biology and molecular genetics.

Given the immediate and intermediate range preoccupations of the board, the reactionary aspect of the presidential selection is easier to perceive retrospectively. After all, McGarrity belonged to a score of national and international scientific organizations and committees. From his first scientific presentation as vice president for research at the 1984 annual meeting of the board, he had shown the trustees that he could comfortably articulate the research of his co-workers across the disciplinary spectrum. Furthermore, his investigative outfit seemed suitably coordinated with the latest fashions. As the simplest form of self-replicating cells, mycoplasmas were becoming attractive vehicles for molecular biologists wishing to study the characteristics of DNA. McGarrity's researches—together with his ability to understand the effects of DNA released into the environment—had earned him a spot on the NIH's important Recombinant DNA Advisory Committee. He appeared very well positioned to identify, cultivate, and recruit the scientific talent necessary for the Institute's advancement.

A similar, urgent consideration recommended McGarrity for the job. The statesman in the great republic of science also had to be an effective operative in the political state of New Jersey. The trustees astutely understood that the devil was in the details of the imminent relocation to the medical center complex. Political savvy would be required in this delicate period of transition. McGarrity had acquired this trait, and it did not hurt that he was tall, personable, handsome, and well spoken. As architect of the plan for the Environmental Toxicology Center, which was still a possibility at the time of his appointment, the new president was an articulate and recognized spokesperson for the Institute within the state.[2]

Less practical motivations also played a role in the trustees' choice. For obvious reasons, members of not-for-profit boards are often drawn from the ranks of for-profit corporate leadership. Blessed with entrepreneurial temperaments, they are inclined to identify with the virtues of enterprise. When these chosen few in turn are given the opportunity to choose, they are inclined to select individuals who personify their strengths. An indefatigable champion of basic research, Gary McGarrity was nevertheless a consummate scientific entrepreneur. The stewards of a financially stressed institution protectively subscribed to the notion that the business of science was business. The cell

[2] Later that year, Rutgers and the UMDNJ jointly founded the Environmental and Occupational Health Institute.

New board chairman Bill Kalellis asserted that "the sights of CIMR are focused firmly in the field of medical biotechnology."

bank contracts with the NIH, the environmental assay contracts with the state, and even hard-earned royalties seemed more business-like and secure than the gamble of grantsmanship that underwrote basic research, particularly during the Reagan era.

Beyond this affinity lay a more deep-seated, cautionary impulse that recommended McGarrity to the Institute's leadership. Trustees discerningly looked outward to welcome its next president and had been rebuffed. The eleventh-hour defection of Dr. Coriell's anointed successor caused a subtle but decisive shift in the board's presuppositions about leadership. Parochial rather than cosmopolitan considerations began to dictate the logic of succession. While the prospective move to the medical center complex was generally viewed as salutary, it was nevertheless intimidating and even controversial. The affiliation agreement with the UMDNJ had not yet been negotiated and several trustees were unsure that the eventual covenant would guarantee institutional autonomy. A man of legendary stature had stepped down. Would it not be better to gaze inward rather than search outward in order to find a successor? Would an outsider of commensurate stature understand, appreciate and utilize the social organization that Lewis Coriell spent a third of a century developing?

The election of Bill Kalellis to chair the board during the presidential transition revealed the trustees' predisposition. No other trustee—not even Jack Dorrance—had as long, active, and varied involvement in the history of the Institute. Kalellis co-chaired the original campaign to raise funds to build the first laboratory and had served as treasurer since 1969. Senior vice president of the investment firm Janney Montgomery Scott, he had built his professional career in the Camden community. The consummate insider who retained much of the organization's corporate memory, he had come aboard the executive committee the year young McGarrity joined the Institute and had witnessed the researcher's scientific productivity and professional conduct for two decades. Announcing the new president's appointment, Kalellis declared, "Few people know the Institute as well as Dr. McGarrity." The comforting converse better explained the board's choice: the Institute knew few eligible scientists as well as it knew Gary McGarrity.

Finally, the board began to realize that Dr. Coriell's continued involvement in the affairs of the Institute could have an intimidating effect on some outside candidates. It would have been impossible to conceive that the trustees would not seek to retain Dr. Coriell on the board's executive committee, where Dr. Nichols continued to serve. Even in retirement, the historic leader's legendary status, continued access to resources, institutional memory, unflagging energy, and unstinting commitment made him an invaluable resource. Ordinarily, incoming CEOs do not have to adjust to such a strong presence. Choosing a successor that had been a loyal subordinate to Dr. Coriell for twenty years was not the board's stated intention, but it began to be seen as an inevitable alternative to ceaseless searching.

No trustee consciously acknowledged the force of this collective, unarticulated motivation. Rational justifications abounded for choosing McGarrity. His impeccable credentials and insider's knowledge assured the board at a crucial moment that change could be conservatively managed. Even had the search committee succeeded in recruiting an eminent scientific leader from beyond the local arena, valuable time might be lost in establishing new relationships and negotiating steep learning curves. Indeed, a sense of immediacy began to surround the decision. Viewed retrospectively, the announcements of the appointment seemed almost prophetic in their emphasis on the transitional role of second incumbency. Bill Kallelis called the newly appointed CEO "the best person to lead the Institute in what will be a very active growth period during the next few years." McGarrity's first public presidential statement reiterated that sentiment. "The next few years," he declared, "will be exciting and challenging ones for the Institute." Neither an experienced administrator nor a proven fundraiser, Gary McGarrity might not have been "the man for all seasons," but most agreed, as he himself reluctantly acknowledged, that he was the man of the hour.

"The Next Few Years"

In the summer of '86, McGarrity's reign began auspiciously. New and renewed contracts for the cell banks helped stabilize funding. The state had expressed its confidence in the Institute with the $6.2 million commitment for new construction, enlargement of its annual appropriation, and renewal of its environmental research contract. The RAP campaign had been finally capped off, permitting needed expansion of scientific personnel. Relocation adjacent to the Cooper Hospital/University Medical Center, as the institution was now officially called, would stimulate the application of basic research to clinical care and contribute to Camden's economic revitalization. Affiliation with the UMDNJ-Robert Wood Johnson Medical School[3] would enhance collaboration, education, and recruitment, while the sharing of services and personnel would help control operational costs. Even the difficult losses of Coriell, Nichols, and several associates had the temporarily positive effect of reducing payroll obligations and enabling a balanced operational budget. The new president comfortably began his honeymoon free of institutional debt.

[3] The UMDNJ-Rutgers Medical School was renamed the UMDNJ-Robert Wood Johnson Medical School on July 1, 1981.

Dedicated staff has always been the backbone of the Institute: Selena Dwight, Bob Wilson, Jeanne West, Dr. Art Greene, and Mel Spellman.

McGarrity was given unprecedented support in his new responsibilities. In order to expedite the complex negotiations and administrative requirements of affiliation, construction, and relocation, the executive committee hired former Campbell Soup executive William E. Harwick as administrative consultant, while Bob Wilson served as vice president for operations. The Institute retained a professional development consultant to insure the success of the upcoming Partners-In-Progress (PIP) fundraising campaign to equip the new facility, cover relocation costs, and endow the research and education programs that RAP-funded recruitment of new investigators would demand. The arduous planning of the past five years had positioned the new regime for success.

Of course, every silver lining has a cloud, and success would not come easily. By September, it was clear that negotiations with the UMDNJ had stalled. If truth were told, not every University official was happy with the decision to share campus property with an independent organization. One senior university administrator in particular was waging a rear-guard action to discourage the Institute's move by means of delaying tactics. Negotiations occasionally got prickly. As the senior party in the eventual bargained relationship, the University naturally sought to control as much of it as possible. Take, for example, one of the major benefits the University expected from affiliation: basic science enrichment for its clinical faculty. Such education would be enriching to the extent that it was relevant. Should not, therefore, the University have some say over the structure of the courses the Institute would offer? Coriell officials had to beware of the slippery slope. Could not the University logically extrapolate from such a concession the right to review drafts of Coriell grant proposals to external sources before submission in order to monitor and perhaps advise the Institute about its research agenda and its relevance to the University? Obviously, such incursions would abridge the Institute's autonomy and its board's independence.

Attempts to resolve issues significant to each institution's legitimate self-interest protracted deliberations. The Institute first anticipated occupancy of the new facility at the end of 1987; the revised forecast was for a year later and that, too, would ultimately prove optimistic. Stalemate produced two effects that placed the Institute in a troubling situation. On one hand, it made little sense to expend RAP funds on the immediate recruitment of scientists only to squeeze new investigators into retrofitted quarters and then disrupt their work by relocating them. It was better to await custom-built laboratories in a new facility. On the other hand, staff reductions, relocation delays, and the uncertainties of presidential succession had slowed the pace of research. In early 1986 the Institute had fewer scientists on staff than when it opened its first laboratory three decades earlier. It was essential to move quickly to recoup lost momentum.

Moreover, several donors to the RAP campaign (some of whom had made contributions as early as 1981) were troubled that those funds had not yet been invested in their manifest objectives. A feasibility study conducted in the summer and early fall for the upcoming PIP fundraising campaign revealed discontent among prospective donors (some of whom were still fulfilling the pledges to the RAP) who would be asked to make yet another gift to the Institute. It was a classic double bind. The latter campaign had to succeed before the former campaign coffer could be judiciously expended, but, until those sequestered funds were used, donors would be disinclined to give again. And the dilemma was compounded by prolonged negotiations, which not only dampened donor inclination but also inflated the costs of construction, thus potentially increasing the campaign's dollar goal. The inside joke darkly predicted that, since the first phase of the drive had gotten a bad "rap," the second phase would be a real "pip" to complete. If successful, the consultant would earn her retainer.

Gift stewardship conspired with the need to maintain scientific progress to make the recruitment of researchers McGarrity's first presidential priority. His selections reinforced the Institute's traditional emphases on cell biology, microbiology, virology, and immunology. They reflected the expanded scope of the cell repositories, the expectations of the trustees, and McGarrity's own scientific enthusiasms. As acting president, McGarrity had hired Hitoshi Kotani as a research associate in the department of microbiology to complement his own investigations on mycoplasmas. After receiving his Ph.D. from the University of Tokyo, Dr. Kotani developed a rapid diagnostic test for walking pneumonia. In his studies of a mycoplasma known as a spiroplasma, he found that by adding the organism to nervous system cells it produced the kind of change that occurs when normal cells turn cancerous.

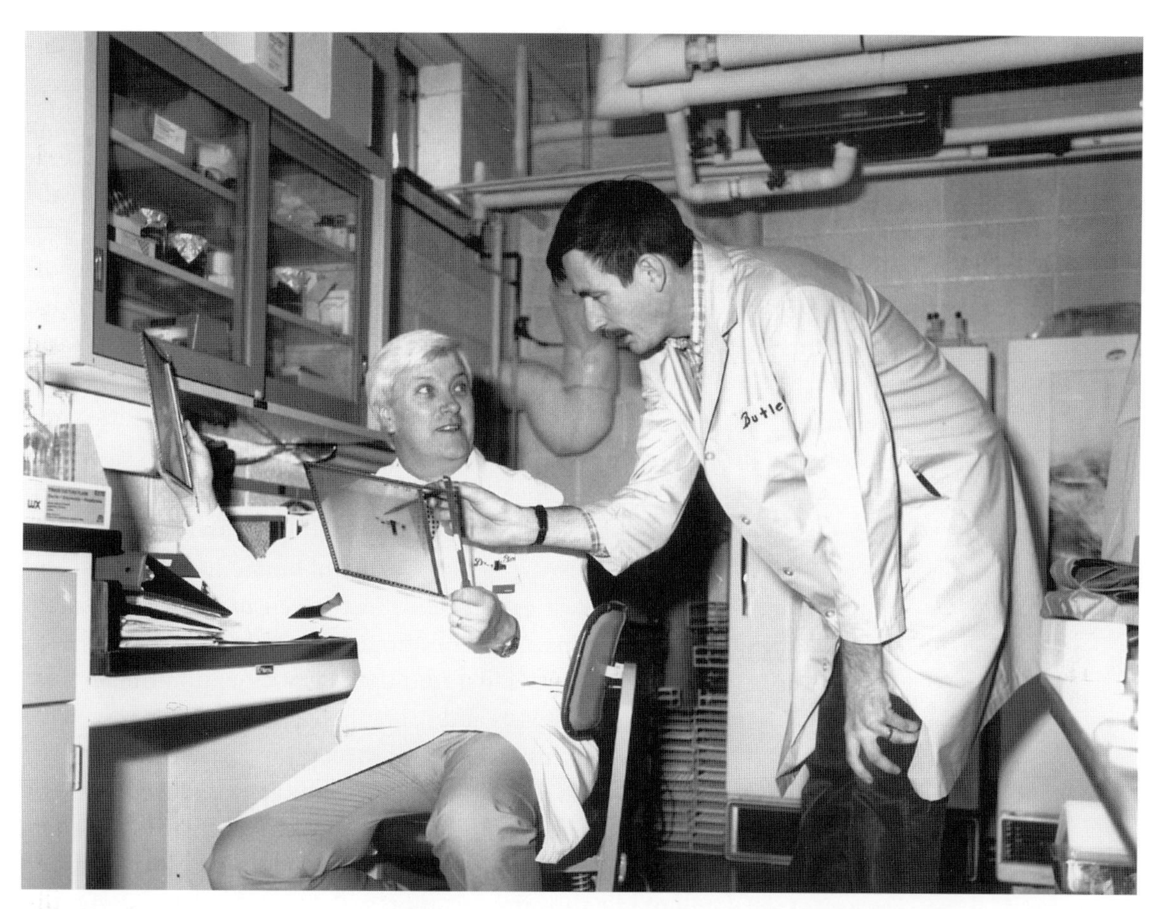

Drs. Gary McGarrity and Gary Butler examine a mycoplasma gel. Dr. Butler came to the Institute as Dr. McGarrity's postdoctoral fellow, remained as a member of the faculty, and now serves as the Institute's first quality assurance officer.

McGarrity's first hire as full president was a researcher who continues to make durable scientific contributions at the Coriell Institute. After receiving his Ph.D. from Cleveland State University in 1981, Gary Butler completed a postdoctoral fellowship with Eric Stanbridge, an illustrious mycoplasmologist at the University of California at Irvine. Butler arrived at the Institute in June 1986 to continue his work on those components of mycoplasmas that stimulate the immune system. Butler, Kotani, and McGarrity would collaborate on a range of studies that helped advance clinical diagnosis and treatment of mycoplasmal diseases.

Shortly after Butler's arrival, Dr. Jack Lipman, a pathologist, joined the cell biology department and helped manage the National Institute on Aging Cell Repository.[4] By the fall, Dr. Gary Ginsberg, a genetic toxicologist, joined McGarrity's department of microbiology to assist Thomas Atherholt, director of the environmental toxicology laboratory. The following year McGarrity

[4] Dr. Arthur Greene was its principal investigator until 1988.

lured Stephen Mueller from the Wistar Institute to join the cell biology department as an associate member and a collaborator with Lipman in the aging cell culture repository.

Mueller's appointment gave the Coriell Institute a focus on cardiovascular disease. Specifically, he studied the cobblestone-like lining of blood vessels known as the endothelium. Its cells control the movement of molecules in and out of the blood stream. It was believed that alterations in the functions of endothelial cells might be involved in a range of age-related vascular diseases. In 1988 the Archer & Greiner Foundation, a philanthropy established by the law firm Frederick Greiner founded, funded the establishment at the Institute of the Frederick P. Greiner Laboratory for Cardiovascular Research in honor of the former institute co-founder and board president.

Also in 1988, Helen Drwinga joined the scientific staff as assistant professor. She received her M.S. in medical genetics and Ph.D. in biomedical sciences at the University of Texas's graduate school of biomedical sciences. Her appointment as supervisor of cytogenetics in the cell biology department helped to reinvigorate the department of cytogenetics following Dr. Nichols's departure. In general, McGarrity's first round of scientific appointments supported the growing cell repositories and strengthened his own department of microbiology, particularly in his own area of mycoplasmal diseases. Even the short-lived attempt to build a department of neurobiology seemed to be partially premised on the connection between neurological disease and mycoplasmas. There were, however, other recruitments that increased the scope as well as the depth of scientific investigation at the Camden laboratories.

The Institute made an important investment in cutting-edge research when molecular geneticist Chung Kim joined the Coriell team in 1987 from the Dana-Farber Cancer Institute at the Harvard Medical School. After receiving his doctorate from the Albert Einstein College of Medicine in 1982, Kim completed postdoctoral fellowships at the Massachusetts Institute of Technology and the Harvard Medical School, where he was the recipient of the Amersham Award. The work of Subal Bishayee complimented Kim's work at the level of the protein. Bishayee received his Ph.D. in biochemistry from the University of Calcutta in 1975. He came to the Institute in 1989 as associate professor from the University of Pennsylvania School of Medicine, where he served as assistant research professor of pediatrics. For eight years he had been examining special proteins called growth factors. These growth factors, coupled with their chemical receptors, regulate cell growth in the body, including abnormal growth or cancer. Scientific staffing seemed to keep pace with the construction of its new facilities.

Scientific collaboration with researchers at Cooper Hospital/University Medical Center, also increased in anticipation of imminent proximity of the two institutions. In late 1988 the New Jersey Commission on Cancer Research funded a joint project pairing two Cooper researchers with Drs. Atherholt and Ginsberg to help determine the effects of radon gas on human cells. In 1989 Bruce Byrne, Ph.D., and Jack Goldberg, M.D., arrived in Camden to assume joint appointments at Cooper, Robert Wood Johnson, and Coriell.

After receiving his doctorate from Indiana University and completing a postdoctoral fellowship at Cornell, Byrne served on the Syracuse faculty before being invited to head Cooper's section of molecular biology. By mid-decade, human immunodeficiency virus (HIV) had been isolated as the cause of acquired immunodeficiency syndrome (AIDS). Byrne was an acknowledged expert in applying a complex DNA-based technology as a diagnostic device to search for AIDS. Goldberg left the SUNY-Upstate Medical Center to assume professorships in hematology and oncology at the hospital and the medical school. An appointment quickly followed at the Coriell Institute, where he investigated the capacity of lymphocytes to kill colon cancer cells. The two scientists' interests in immunotherapy symbiotically enhanced the Institute's acumen in immunological studies and tightened the connection between the two institutions and between basic research and clinical research.

Scientific education also intensified prior to the relocation due not only to the influx of UMDNJ students but also the establishment of an endowment fund that underwrote the Frank K. Kelemen Memorial Lecture Series. The fund was established immediately following the death in 1986 of the influential trustee who had played a significant role in securing the state appropriation that made the relocation possible. Since 1967 the Institute had sponsored annual postgraduate lecture series and continuing educational courses taught by a faculty of nationally and internationally renowned scientists, including several Nobel laureates. The 1986–87 course on "Molecular Medicine" was followed by "Cancer: A Multidisciplinary Perspective" in 1988. On October 26, 1989, while the physical transfer of the laboratories was still incomplete, the Institute undauntedly held a one-day memorial lecture series on "Genes, Genomes and Genetics" away from the organized disarray, in celebration of the relocation, and in honor of Frank Kelemen.

Ironically, the relocation that Kelemen had championed led to the disaffection of the greatest individual donor in the institution's history. In the fall of 1986, Jack Dorrance quietly announced that, at year's end, he was stepping down from the board of which he served as vice chairman for a third of a century. Effective the day following his official resignation, the board declared him an honorary lifetime trustee emeritus. In May 1987 Bill Kalellis and Gary McGarrity visited him to discuss his possible contribution to the PIP campaign, but the former chairman of Campbell Soup politely demurred. He had been skeptical about the necessity of the move to the medical center. He felt it would at least erode the Institute's separate identity and at worst jeopardize its independence. His departure gave the shocked leadership its first inkling of institutional life without Lewis Coriell at the helm.

The contours of the negotiations in the fall of 1986 convinced Dorrance that his fears might become realized. By December 1986, estimated construction costs approached $7.5 million, and the Institute pressed the UMDNJ to secure the extra funds needed and build the laboratory according to the specifications approved by the state's department of higher education. Collaterally, the Coriell Institute retained a small lobbying firm headquartered in Bridgewater to urge their legislative caucus, Mayor Primas, and Congressman

Florio to help break the impasse. In the meantime it appointed an attorney to draft and help execute affiliation agreements at the earliest possible date. Institute officials wondered aloud whether the authorized $6.2 million might better be turned over to the Institute to build its independent laboratory on another site, but such voiced alternatives may have been used primarily as bargaining chips. In any event, the Institute realized that it would be at a disadvantage at the bargaining table if the University began construction before an agreement was finalized.

By the end of January 1987, the two institutions had forged an agreement. The seven-page charter was executed on February 9, effective the following day. No *Magna Carta* of first principles, it was instead a cautious, generalized compact, a formalized legitimation of long-standing affiliation and intent. Basically it reiterated the publicly proclaimed benefits of programmatic interaction, provided academic privileges to Coriell scientists, set the terms of oversight, revision, and renewal of the agreement itself, and clarified the autonomous authority of the Coriell Institute as an independent, not-for-profit entity. In a word, it was a start.

The fact that both institutions delayed public announcement of the agreement until May suggests that the principals understood in February that any accord was moot until money could be found to cover the inflated costs of construction of the addition to the University's Education and Research building. By May, projected costs had increased another $200,000 to an esti-

The Institute's eighth expansion would not only provide 50,000 square feet of modern laboratory space, but also place the Institute on an academic and clinical campus.

The "new" Coriell Institute for Medical Research (1987).

mated total of $7.7 million, which was $1.5 million over the original projection. The state chipped in half of the overage on condition that the Institute raise the other half. Once the annual appropriations bill passed both houses before summer recess, Bob Wilson promptly re-bid the project. On August 5, topped with ceremonial hardhats and armed with shiny shovels, smiling officials broke ground on the swelteringly hot corner of Benson Street and Haddon Avenue. "All good things come to those who wait," proclaimed Senator Rand, "and we have waited a long time."

In a civilization that preserves fast-food restaurants as ancient monuments, "a long time" is a relatively foreshortened concept. When the Institute's first two presidents jointly and jubilantly cut the ceremonial ribbon at the official opening of the new facilities on November 1, 1989, celebrants—dating the project from Governor Kean's signing of the funding appropriation—joked that the move had covered two miles and five years. In fact, the move had begun over two decades earlier when Dr. Coriell began laying the groundwork for the medical center itself.

Mileage, as well as time, was a relative concept for a scientific laboratory relocating from space it had occupied for a third of a century. An unencumbered walk from Copewood Street to the brand new facility on Haddon Avenue might measure two miles, but trucking a two-story tall, seventeen-ton liquid nitrogen tank involved a 4.5-mile transit and enormous logistical and traffic challenges. Masters of logistical legerdemain, Bob Wilson and facilities director Thomas Ganor could undoubtedly write a chapter on the move itself. The delicate transit of cells from October 11 to 12 took months to choreograph. Virtually every member of the administrative and scientific staffs took an active role in the planning and execution of the relocation. Even before the move was completed, however, it was clear that location was not the only aspect of the Institute that had dramatically changed.

Power Shift

The unusual nature and process of executive transition at the Institute had subtly shifted the locus of authority and overtly reconfigured the apparatus of power within the organization.[5] During periods of presidential succession, particularly in situations where an interim executive possesses little administrative experience, it is not unusual for governing boards to exercise close managerial oversight. When confronted with the simultaneous challenges of finding a new home *and* a new leader, the Coriell board diligently committed its considerable expertise to insure controlled continuity. Like martial law in times of war, management by governance is supposed to be a temporary expedient. But a series of choices—each one of them reasoned, warranted, or unavoidable—ultimately led to a situation that could best be resolved by a second executive transition at the close of the decade.

The board had decided upon a "home-grown" candidate for president in part because it realized that Dr. Coriell's successor would inevitably inherit an office whose power would be attenuated by the board's and the staff's deference to the Institute's founder. Kalellis and Coriell knew that it was important to break that habit in order to legitimize the next president's executive authority. Accordingly, as soon as McGarrity was named to his interim role on October 3, 1985, Kalellis announced to the IMR staff that the acting president "has been given full and complete authority to serve in the same capacity with the same rights and privileges heretofore vested in Dr. Lewis L. Coriell."

Simultaneously, another official announcement revealed a subtle phrase that would eventually undermine the effect of the first. A media release indicated that McGarrity would be "*adding* [emphasis added] the administrative duties of Acting President to his international lecture and research schedule." Had McGarrity been offered the permanent presidency on the spot, the board might have exacted from him a consideration to *subtract*; that is, to moderate scientific travel and travail in order to concentrate on presidential business. Ever since Kaloupek's 1981 call for full-time administrative posts, the Insti-

[5] Power, in this context, is defined as the official capacity to shape institutional policy and to exercise control over the conduct of work and workers.

tute's board understood that the dual role of scientist-administrator, even as played by so capable a leader as Dr. Coriell, had become anachronistic. But in 1985 a national canvass had not been completed, and it was unreasonable to ask a productive, engaged investigator to interrupt the work to which, in all probability, he would shortly return.[6]

It is important to recall that the board's predisposition to look internally for the Institute's second president was originally premised on the expectation of Dr. Nichols's succession. When that expectation was dashed, the executive committee—on which Drs. Coriell and Nichols continued to serve—extended to McGarrity the same offer it was prepared to make to Nichols: the new (acting) president would be free to pursue his own scientific work. This concession created a problem. Most Institute scientists commonly confined their invitational presentations to the immediate region or within the eastern seaboard of the United States. McGarrity's lecture circuit, however, routinely carried him around the country and throughout the world. He had not sought the presidency and had agreed to devote fifty percent of his time to his presidential duties. That fact had important consequences for the Institute's "next few years."

Soon after the acting president was installed, the board restructured the chain of command to compensate for their concession. Typically the board's chairman served *ex officio* as chair of the executive committee. Kalellis smartly surrendered that job to the seasoned administrator Harold Shaub. The immediate past president of Campbell Soup was not the retiring type. With McGarrity's approval, Shaub immediately appointed consultant Bill Harwick, his former right-hand man at the company, to serve as executive vice president of administration. The designation "executive" meant that Harwick reported not to the president, but to the board through the executive committee, which is to say through the formidable Shaub. Intended as a provisional expedient, the arrangement became institutionalized. In terms of immediate practical accomplishment, it succeeded well; in terms of ultimate institutional affect, it proved a mixed blessing. The justifiable decision to select a successor from within, especially an ambitious scientific entrepreneur frequently abroad, resulted in the perpetuation of managerial oversight by governance. When the powerful do not exercise skills, the skillful accumulate power.

McGarrity's itinerary during the first eight months of 1987—a time of intensive institutional negotiation, planning, and fund raising—typified his schedule. He spent a week of otherwise chilly February in warm Havana, Cuba; several peach-blossoming March days in Atlanta, Georgia; and most of the temperate, dry Asiatic month of April in China and Japan. Bordeaux, France beckoned the new president for almost the entire perfect month of

[6] The board's appreciation of the potentially deleterious effect of administrative onus on scientific productivity was also reflected in its original plan to have Drs. Greene and Dion alternately share vice presidential duties. Dion left the Institute shortly after McGarrity was named president.

July. He returned to humid Camden for the ceremonial groundbreaking on August 5 and then promptly departed for a weeklong conference in the cool Canadian Rockies. The Institute could be justifiably proud of the high international profile of its new president. At the same time, however, its trustees understood that one could not bake the bread, tout the recipe worldwide, and still mind the store.

The unintended consequence of the necessary administrative intervention of Shaub and Harwick was the bifurcation of institutional authority. Ideal leadership is indivisible because one person is accountable to the fiduciaries for the success or failure of the enterprise. The peculiar transitional circumstances of the Institute dictated a different arrangement: management by adroit administrators who were quick to acknowledge that they knew more about soup than science. The entire operational side of the Institute was accountable to Harwick who reported, not through the president, but directly to Shaub and the executive committee of the board. McGarrity's presidency was essentially confined to the role of scientific director and institutional spokesperson. Even in 1990, when Harwick resumed his role as consultant, he continued to report directly to Shaub, as did Wilson on the administrative side and McGarrity on the scientific side. It was difficult for the Institute's operational staff to remain loyal to a president to whom its managers did not report. It was hard for the scientific staff to defer to a former colleague preoccupied with national and international activities. The arrangement confused allegiance and undermined morale.

Lowered morale was an ironic, unexpected consequence of a decade of progressive change. In the half-decade from 1986 to 1991, thanks to the strategic planning and progress of the preceding five years, the Institute enjoyed new facilities, new investigators, new equipment, new sources of support, and new notoriety. Dr. Coriell's presidency of the College of Physicians of Philadelphia from 1986 to 1988, punctuated by that institution's bicentennial celebration and a visitation by the President of the United States, significantly increased the Coriell Institute's visibility in the Delaware Valley. Mrs. Brooks J. (Sally) Harral spearheaded the formation of the Friends of Coriell, founded in 1990 to raise funds for and to increase the visibility of the Institute. That same year, Nobel Laureate Stanley Cohen received the first Coriell Medal.

Behind the posh glitter of riveting fashion shows and fashionable ribbon cuttings were substantive accomplishments that strengthened the Institute's foundation. Effective January 1, 1989, the NIGMS renewed its contract for the Human Genetic Mutant Cell Repository to the tune of $6.9 million over five years. On December 14, 1990, newly elected Governor Jim Florio announced that the National Institute of Mental Health (NIMH) had awarded the Institute a five-year $5.7 million contract to establish a national cell repository for the study of psychiatric diseases. The award was a tribute to good management as well as good science. Earlier in the year NIMH psychiatrist Elliott Gershon had made Art Greene aware that a contract for a genetic cell repository was imminent. For some reason, the NIMH failed to alert the Camden organization that the contract had been announced. Greene's persistence in checking in with NIH officials uncovered the oversight just days before the proposal deadline.

Trustee Sally Harral organized the Friends of Coriell in 1990.

Already the largest cell bank in the world for the study of human genetic diseases, the Institute would double holdings by virtue of the NIMH contract and become base camp for an assault on the genetic causes of schizophrenia, manic depressive illness, and Alzheimer disease. Exhibiting its political maturation, the Institute publicly touted the award not only as a step towards the eventual cures of devastating diseases but also as a boost to Camden's economic revitalization, an infusion of federal funds and jobs, and an ultimate savings for taxpayers and consumers of medical services.

Private support followed this public vote of confidence as local charities intensified their support and major philanthropic foundations of national scope made first-time grants to the Institute. Shortly after the NIMH announcement, for example, facilitated by Dr. McGarrity's superb cultivation, the highly selective Los Angeles-based W.M. Keck Foundation awarded $285,000 to the cell repositories. Within weeks, the NIA renewed its contract for the Aging Cell Repository to the tune of $6.3 million over nine years, and the PIP campaign successfully completed its $2.4 million final phase. Nineteen-ninety and 1991 was a cork-popping time of congratulatory testimonials and champagne toasts. The accomplishments of that pressurized period in the Institute's history burst to the surface like effervescent bubbles that disguised a deeper volatility.

The ferment of lowered morale was perhaps inevitable during this singular transition. Inevitably, to succeed Dr. Coriell was to invite invidious comparison. One might ahistorically speculate that the board bifurcated institutional authority in an unconscious effort to alter the presidential role so as to prevent such direct comparisons to McGarrity's illustrious predecessor.

Regardless, the new organizational structure changed institutional culture. Dr. Coriell's open-door management style had given employees direct access to the ultimate decision-maker. Now leadership became diffuse, more remote, and less accessible. In response, employees organized a "Crusaders Committee" to represent staff grievances to management. In broadening its jurisdiction, the executive committee of the board resembled regency. Often necessary, regencies are seldom popular. And while a king breathes, his heir remains a prince.

An unfortunate sequence of financial downturns, largely beyond the Institute's control, contributed to internal dissatisfaction. First, in the fall of 1990, the state was delinquent in paying the first half of its $790,000 annual appropriation, leading to significant cash-flow problems. Second, the state cancer commission announced that the department of health was threatening to suspend awards for cancer research in 1991. Third, the University, which had promised to match $500,000 of funds to secure the NIMH cell repository contract, reversed its decision. Ultimately, the situation was resolved when the UMDNJ agreed to forgive an outstanding $375,000 construction debt, but it left the Institute with a $125,000 shortfall, strained a tenuous relationship between administrative officials, and put undue pressure on legislators to intervene. Finally, three senior members of the research staff were without grants and were informed that they would likely be terminated in December.

To the executive committee, the first three challenges seemed to call into question the president's cultivation of state and university officials; the fourth problem, his selection of scientists. In fact, larger forces accounted for the diminution of state and federal largesse. Governor Kean had left Florio with a $550 million deficit gap in the 1991 fiscal year budget and mounting public anger over property tax increases. Likewise, national trends partially explained the difficulty Coriell researchers faced in obtaining grants. In an effort to reduce the national budget deficit, the federal government made drastic spending cuts. The NIH budget in fiscal year 1990 had fallen nearly $1 billion below the previous year's funding levels. It would support 688 fewer competing grants than it had in 1989.

Congress was not the only body intent on deficit reduction. The executive committee was aware that low award rates at NIH contributed to Coriell operating deficits for three years running. During that time, several researchers were subsidized by the staff development fund, which by the fall of 1990 was depleted. The decision to eliminate three research programs by the end of the year was unusual in the history of the institution, and it provoked an unprecedented response. The Crusaders Committee organized an "all employee" meeting on November 19 to question management about the Institute's finances and staff support. Clearly the transformed culture of the organization precipitated this confrontation.

Architecture as well as organization explained the altered relationship among scientists and between staff and management. Accommodating the organization's space needs on the compact footprint abutting the extant university structure involved a skyward design of five stories of laboratories, three more than the former facility possessed. Architectural verticality enforced a physical distancing among the scientific staff with negative implications for social commerce and intellectual exchange.[7] Discourse with the wider scientific community was also impaired because the Institute had abandoned in its relocation a spacious auditorium that seated large audiences for its celebrated lecture series. The organization also left behind a large car lot and the salubrious effect upon scientific enlightenment of free parking. After the move, attendance at these series markedly declined.

Even among those who enjoyed the new facilities and central location were ambivalent about the human consequences of the alteration. Particularly unfortunate was the need to segregate the central administrative offices in the original building, a temporary expedient made permanent by the $125,000 shortfall in the University's NIMH match. The grand hallway separating administrators and scientists captured in concrete the organizational divide charted on paper. The partitioning reinforced a growing sense of alienation. Despite the added value and cost saving associated with the conflation of two libraries, Coriell investigators regretted that their book and journal collections, which librarian Dorothy Gruber had devotedly and single-handedly acquired and organized, were now reposited across the great divide in the University's library. Long-time employees began to reminisce nostalgically about the long-gone camaraderie of the "good old days": the lunchtime ice-skating parties in the 1960s; Friday afternoons at the local pub in the 1970s.

Significantly, there were fewer "old timers" among the researchers to chronicle the institution's past to the new cohort of employees. Collective memory, the thread that secures an organization across time, was becoming attenuated. Rapid staff turnover at the precise time of corporate relocation and presidential succession obstructed the normal transmission of lore and exacerbated feelings of insecurity. In 1988 Arthur Greene, who had served the Institute for twenty-seven years, announced his departure from the post of principal investigator of the two major NIH cell repositories.[8] Retaining his position as vice president for research and scientific affairs on a part-time basis, Greene surrendered supervision of the repositories to Richard Mulivor, who had joined the Institute in 1978 and served as Greene's co-investigator since 1983.

The loss of corporate memory affected trustees as well as staff. In 1990 Mulivor would inherit the title of director of the newly titled John T. Dorrance, Jr. International Cell Science Center. Jack Dorrance died on April 9,

---

[7] In his engaging *Lives of a Cell*, Lewis Thomas notes that sociable termites, when sequestered in smaller assemblages, change their behavior abruptly. "As soon as they are removed from the group," Thomas observes, "and the touching from all sides comes to an end, they become aggressive, standoffish; they begin drinking compulsively, and abstain from touching each other. Sometimes, they even bite off the distal halves of each other's antennae, to eliminate the temptation" (pp. 53–4). Advisedly, the famed medical researcher was not drawing an analogy to the conduct of scientists in similar circumstances.

[8] Director of the Institute's vivarium since the early '70s, Jane Holben also retired in 1988 after twenty-two years of service.

Dr. Richard Mulivor directed the John T. Dorrance, Jr. International Cell Science Center.

1989. In January, thanks to Bill Harwick's ministrations, the most important philanthropist in the Institute's history came to recognize the advantages of relocation. He toured the new facilities in August 1988 and expressed his satisfaction with the building and what went on inside it. In January 1989 he helped orchestrate a timely $200,000 Campbell Soup Fund challenge grant that matched dollar for dollar gifts and pledges to the PIP campaign. Dorrance's passing terminally punctuated a five-year period that witnessed Coriell's retirement, Nichols's departure, and Greene's resignation. It was truly the end of an era.

A succeeding era was powerless to be born under the prevailing organizational rubrics. When Harold Shaub's close friend, Samuel Hudson, became chairman of the board in October 1989, Harwick relinquished the executive vice presidency so that Hudson could return more administrative responsibility to McGarrity. Soon confronted with the series of financial problems cited above, Hudson also demanded that McGarrity place an increasing emphasis on fund raising. Both management and governance understood that these steps were critically needed, but they also realized that they would require altering the original compact under which the new president had agreed to serve. Throughout this period, McGarrity was becoming increasingly interested in the applications of gene therapy and was receiving many attractive offers from industry. Renegotiating his job description in a manner that would further distance him from his research interests was not an attractive option. He and the board's leadership agreed to restart the process of executive transition.

Gary McGarrity presided over one of the most consequential periods of the Coriell Institute's history. Its accomplishments, however, had been secured by the reluctant involvement of governance into the affairs of management. That crucial half-decade had also served as a time for the Institute to learn how to live without its founder at the helm. Now it was time for governance to relinquish its provisional role and to search for a third leader, one who could command the allegiance of scientists and administrators, comfortably inhabit both worlds, and unite them within a single vision "as two eyes make one in sight," as the poet Robert Frost put it.

The Third President

In the late spring and early summer of 1991, Coriell officials sensitively began to gather from outside its borders expert intelligence and opinion about the state of the scientific enterprise at the Institute. Arguably, no one in the country possessed a more knowledgeable understanding and balanced perspective of the Institute than David P. Beck, Ph.D. As the former NIH program officer of the genetics program of the NIGMS, Dr. Beck managed the Institute's contract for its Human Genetic Mutant Cell Repository. It had been his duty to direct the collection development policy of the cell bank according to the needs and opportunities of genetic specialties and researchers throughout the country as well as within the Institute itself. On behalf of that objective, another of his responsibilities was to recruit and coordinate a nationally and disciplinarily diverse advisory committee of scientists. A prerequisite for that task was nothing less than a holistic comprehension of the directions of science, medicine, and research funding in the United States. To perform his role successfully, Beck had to scrutinize the Institute's management capacity and research competency with ruthless objectivity, yet develop a collegial rapport with its administrative and scientific leadership.

His familiarity with and fondness for the Institute did not end when he left the NIH in mid-1984 to assume the associate directorship for administration of the Public Health Research Institute (PHRI), an independent research institute in New York City. Nor did the reliance of Bob Wilson, Art Greene, and Richard Mulivor on his counsel. On March 26, 1985, on the occasion of the annual IMR Week celebration, he was invited to Camden to lecture on the future of research and the cell banks at the Institute. Thereafter he and his Camden colleagues kept in touch. So regular was the pattern of interaction

Dr. David Beck shakes hands with outgoing president Dr. Gary McGarrity.

that Beck attributed no special significance to Bob Wilson's phone call in the summer of 1991, asking if they might have lunch together in New York.

A few weeks later, Bill Harwick accompanied Wilson to the Beck's favorite Mexican restaurant near 26th and Lexington. With characteristic clairvoyance, Wilson and Greene had suggested to Harwick that the Institute would be wise to sound out Beck not only on his views of the Institute but also on his interest in leading it. Mealtime discussion ranged from the future of biomedical research at the Coriell Institute to Beck's mission to rebuild the scientific organization at the PHRI. It quickly became apparent to the former program officer that he was being scouted. When the parties left the lunch table for their respective institutes, each began to more fully appreciate that a more serious consideration of the possibilities intimated over coffee could lead to a perfect match.

Communication continued throughout the summer. Mutual admiration and anticipation blossomed. The Institute's board was sufficiently impressed with the candidate's suitability for the office that it disbanded a formal search committee before it was fully impaneled. The second time around, the board knew exactly what the Institute required in a leader. The trustees made clear that the new chief executive officer would possess successful and progressively responsible leadership and management experience, and would be accountable for the development and supervision of both the scientific and the administrative sides of the house.

On September 4, those responsibilities and qualifications were written into a revised job description, as Bob Wilson hopped a flight to San Antonio, Texas. The Association of Independent Research Institutes (AIRI), over which

Dr. Coriell had presided in 1977–78 and David Beck would preside in 1995–96, was holding its annual meeting there. The Institute's vice president attended only one function: a walk with David Beck along the San Antonio River's Paseo Del Rio. There, on behalf of the board, he offered Beck the Coriell presidency. At the annual meeting of the board in October, Samuel T. Hudson passed the chairman's gavel to James E. Palmer, and the trustees unanimously ratified the union. As of New Year's Day 1992, the Coriell Institute would have a new leader.

CHAPTER TEN

SYNTHESIS (1992–2002)

A PHOTOGRAPH ANCHORING THE LEAD, front-page article in the summer of 1986 issue of the Coriell newsletter *Discover* showed new executive Gary McGarrity exuberantly shaking hands with the outgoing president. Five years later, an almost identically composed image—albeit before a new building—portrayed David Beck clasping the hand of a departing Gary McGarrity. McGarrity resigned on October 31 to accept the vice presidency of Gene Therapy, Inc., in Gaithersburg, Maryland. As chairman of the NIH Recombinant DNA Advisory Committee since 1987, he had presided over that group's approvals of the first experimental applications of gene therapy in humans. His new position in the private sector suited his experience and entrepreneurial temperament.

For David Beck, the presidency of the Coriell Institute must have seemed like a destination for which his professional life had been preparing him. The third president arrived at the Institute almost forty years after Dr. Coriell founded it. In those two score years the scientific enterprise in the United States was vastly transformed. Lewis Coriell was a trained scientist who perforce became an administrator. Beck was a scientist who became formally trained as an administrator. Lewis Coriell missed being born in New Jersey by two centuries and two thousand miles. David Beck was denied the same experience by about two hours. En route northward to join her husband at his wartime duty station, David's mother stepped off a train in Wilmington, Delaware, on August 3, 1944, to deliver her first child. That original deviation apparently imbued her son with a distaste for detours. Once embarked upon a scientific track, he would not be derailed.

A LIFE OF SCIENCE

David Beck grew up in Owings Mills, Maryland, some twenty miles northwest of Baltimore. Now a charming suburban development redefined by highway interchanges, in his youth it spread forth as bucolic countryside.[1] Nature, as exhibited in the waters and woodlands of his rustic environment, constituted Beck's first laboratory. Hikes were scientific expeditions; biology, a backyard profession.

On winter evenings or during inclement weather, organic chemistry became an indoor pursuit anchored by Beck's trusty chemistry set and amplified by provisions ordered through the Edmund Scientific catalog. The catalog was a catalyst of his scientific imagination, a cornucopia of chemicals, test tubes, rubber hoses, motors, magnets, and microscopes. David Beck was as elated in boyhood as he was appalled in adulthood about the age's innocent ease of ordering substances: a pound of mercury here; the ingredients for gunpowder there. One could tap the *Guinness Book of Records* to determine the world's most stinky substance and order the chemical ingredients forthwith.

The manual accompanying the classic chemistry set moved David Beck's apprehension of objective knowledge from the empirical to the experimental. An experiment may denote inquiry into the unknown or demonstration of the known. Chemistry sets were composed for the latter purpose. Their recipes reiterated predicable chemical reactions, celebrated ritualistic reenactments of classic experiments, and inculcated scientific values among an impressionable novitiate. And, yes, they would occasionally result in a "controlled" explosion. Science, after all, had to be fun.

Policy makers worked hard to make science appear as play. On October 4, 1957, the United States' cold war nemesis, the Soviet Union, successfully orbited the satellite *Sputnik*. Viewing the technological achievement as propagandistic insult, the United States scrambled to redirect national educational priorities toward science. A best-selling book revealed to Americans "What Ivan Knows That Johnny Doesn't." Never before or since has America so purposefully imbued its children with the ideal of science as a noble vocation.

The Baltimore County high school system in which David Beck was educated responded to that challenge with superior curricula in mathematics, physics, and the biological sciences and with a project-oriented philosophy that emphasized learning by experimenting. The methodology suited Beck's intellect and temperament. In his senior year, the young investigator won the American Chemical Society's prize at the Baltimore regional science fair for a project that determined the amount of fat that could be extracted from various foods. The ACS awarded him the 1961 edition of the *Chemical Rubber Handbook*, a cherished compendium of data, laws, and relationships of inexhaustible range and biblical proportions. Winners at the Coriell Science Fair have been known to take home the most recent edition of the handbook as a trophy.

---

[1] The year Beck left Washington for New York, Baltimore's professional football team abandoned the city for Indianapolis. During a dark snowstorm on March 23, 1984, the Colts secretively stole away from their Owings Mills headquarters and training facilities, dispersing empty moving vans in several directions to camouflage the franchise's ultimate destination. Beck's departure from the NIH would be more forthright.

"All the News That's Fit to Print"

The New York Times.

LATE CITY EDITION
U. S. Weather Bureau Report (Page 39) forecasts: Cloudy and cool today and tonight. Mostly fair tomorrow.

VOL. CVII..No. 36,414. NEW YORK, SATURDAY, OCTOBER 5, 1957. FIVE CENTS

SOVIET FIRES EARTH SATELLITE INTO SPACE; IT IS CIRCLING THE GLOBE AT 18,000 M. P. H.; SPHERE TRACKED IN 4 CROSSINGS OVER U. S.

HOFFA IS ELECTED TEAMSTERS' HEAD; WARNS OF BATTLE

Defeats Two Foes 3 to 1 —Says Union Will Fight 'With Every Ounce'

Text of the Hoffa address is printed on Page 6.

By A. H. RASKIN

MIAMI BEACH, Oct. 4—The scandal-scarred International Brotherhood of Teamsters elected James R. Hoffa as its president today.

He won by a margin of nearly 3 to 1 over the combined vote of two rivals who campaigned on pledges to clean up the nation's biggest union.

Continued on Page 6, Column 7

IN TOKEN OF VICTORY: Dave Beck, retiring head of the Teamsters Union, raises hand of James R. Hoffa upon his election as union's president. At right is Mrs. Hoffa.

FAUBUS COMPARES HIS STAND TO LEE'S

Says He Will Remain Loyal to People of Arkansas—All Is Quiet at School

By HOMER BIGART

Continued on Page 18, Column 2

Flu Widens in City; 10% Rate Predicted; 200,000 Pupils Out

By ROBERT ALDEN

Continued on Page 8, Column 1

ARGENTINA TAKES EMERGENCY STEPS

State of Siege Proclaimed in Buenos Aires Region —Arrests Reported

Continued on Page 4, Column 5

City Sifts Charge That Schupler, Brooklyn Councilman, Sold a Job

By PAUL CROWELL

Continued on Page 15, Column 2

COURSE RECORDED

Navy Picks Up Radio Signals—4 Report Sighting Device

By WALTER SULLIVAN

WASHINGTON, Saturday, Oct. 5—The Naval Research Laboratory announced early today that it had recorded four crossings of the Soviet earth satellite over the United States.

Continued on Page 3, Column 6

The approximate orbit of the Russian earth satellite is shown by black line. The rotation of the earth will bring the United States under the orbit of Soviet-made moon.

Device Is 8 Times Heavier Than One Planned by U.S.

WASHINGTON, Oct. 4—Leaders of the United States earth satellite program were astonished tonight to learn that the Soviet Union had launched a satellite eight times heavier than that contemplated by this country.

Continued on Page 3, Column 7

SATELLITE SIGNAL BROADCAST HERE

Impulse Carried on Radio and TV—First Reported by Long Island Station

By ROY SILVER

Continued on Page 2, Column 4

Ex-Premier Mollet Accepts Bid To Form a New French Cabinet

Socialist Leader Agrees With Reluctance and Without Giving Much Hope

By ROBERT C. DOTY

Guy Mollet

Continued on Page 5, Column 4

Warsaw Crushes New Protest; Clubs, Tear Gas Rout Students

By SYDNEY GRUSON

Continued on Page 5, Column 2

560 MILES HIGH

Visible With Simple Binoculars, Moscow Statement Says

Text of Tass announcement appears on Page 3.

By WILLIAM J. JORDEN

MOSCOW, Saturday, Oct. 5—The Soviet Union announced this morning that it successfully launched a man-made earth satellite into space yesterday.

Continued on Page 3, Column 5

An inspiration for a young David Beck.

Convinced that science fairs can catalyze youthful interest in science, Dr. Beck committed the Institute's name and resources to the regional science fair in 1996.

Mapping comparative routes by which individuals arrive at similar destinations is a potentially frivolous but occasionally instructive endeavor. John Adams, whose reputation was misfortunately affected by his occupation of a presidency between the first (George Washington) and the third (Thomas Jefferson) heads of state, said that he practiced the arts of war and politics so that his children could practice engineering and diplomacy so that their children could cultivate music and literature. The generational progressivism implicit in that statement measured the distance the Institute—and American society—had traveled between *its* first and third presidents.

Lewis Coriell came to science through the pragmatic ideology of medicine and the omnipresent exaction of diagnosing and treating illness. David Beck came to science through unencumbered fascination with nature. The young Coriell had hunted in high country; his quarry, his sustenance. Beck was raised not far from "hunt country," where the recreational pursuit of the inedible fox enlivened fallow pastures with ritualistic chase. Where Louis Coriell labored to put fields under plow, mid-century Easterners profited by putting them under sprinklers. In those twentieth-century fields, the hazards

Dr. Beck's support of the establishment of the Coriell Auxiliary Golf Classic won enthusiastic support from his family. Beck's brother-in-law Martin Hoban, father Frank, brother Tom, and David Beck make up a 1996 Classic foursome.

were not ice storms but sand traps. Lew Coriell walked behind teams of horses as a farmhand. David Beck trailed golfers to putting greens, earning caddying wages to support his depredations upon the warehouses of Edmund Scientific.

The game of golf helped shape the contours of Beck's life of science. His father, a self-employed accountant, had been an amateur champion, born fifty yards from the first tee of an exclusive golf course where his son David would caddie as soon as he was able to carry a bag. The experience ignited David's appreciation of the game and introduced him to a host of wealthy and influential clients in a way that gave new meaning to the term "golf links." Few, if any, sports offer as much time between strokes or shots or plays than the walking, talking pastime of golf. Club members found it easy to take an avuncular interest in the prospects of the polite attendant with a seven-days-a-week work ethic. One such golfer was Sewall Watts, scion of one of the founders in 1900 of Ferris, Baker Watts, an investment bank headquartered in Washington, DC. A Princeton graduate and the university's local alumni representative or "interviewer," Watts determined that Beck would become a Tiger.

Another golfer had a different view of the aspirant's collegiate destination. Albert Lehninger, who resided in the neighboring village of Garrison less than a mile from the elder Beck's birthplace, once asked Beck about his academic interests. Beck's reply prompted the gentleman to confess that he was the director of the department of physiological chemistry at the Johns Hopkins University School of Medicine. Dr. Lehninger had come to Hopkins as DeLamar Professor in 1952. He was then making fundamental contributions to the

David Beck's scientific mentor: Dr. Albert Lehninger. Courtesy of Alan Mason Chesney Medical Archives

field of bioenergetics, the science that investigated how nutrients were metabolized into biochemically useful forms. He was the author of three classic textbooks, including the internationally touted *Biochemistry*. And he was offering this promising lad working access to his renowned laboratory during the summers, by far the sweetest stroke David Beck had ever witnessed in his rapidly expiring career as a caddie.

With the prospect of summer research in Lehninger's laboratories at Hopkins, Beck chose Princeton as his alma mater. In 1962 Princetonian science resembled its theology. Organized in a presbyterial manner, the science curriculum featured no formal offerings in biochemistry, but each academic soul was free to pick and choose within classical synods of biology and chemistry. Beck majored in biology, took courses in chemistry, and fashioned for himself a program in biochemistry that reinforced his summer work at JHU. Graduating *cum laude* in May 1966, he remained an additional month in New Jersey to complete work related to his senior thesis and took up formal residence as a graduate student at Hopkins in July. In 1967, Beck co-authored with Lehninger, who had become his mentor, his first published article, which appeared in the *Journal of Biological Chemistry*.

Lehninger's apostles inhabited a group of laboratories examining in various media his favorite subcellular entity, the mitochondrion. This organelle possessed genetic material and enzymes responsible for the conversion of food into useable energy. Working from separate vantages, researchers nevertheless shared equipment. Beck soon found himself more than willing to loan his gear to a shy, second-year student named Jeanne Crawford. He proposed marriage to her in August, and they were wed in November. Jeanne Crawford Beck received her Ph.D. in 1970 and completed a post-doctoral fellowship at Johns Hopkins as her husband completed his doctoral studies the following year.

The couple spent their next three years as post-doctoral fellows at Harvard University, where much of what would become molecular biology and molecular genetics originated. Cambridge provided an exciting intellectual and cultural environment for newly wedded researchers who rubbed shoulders with James Watson and other fabled investigators. The fascination of laboratory work insulated them from the social turmoil of the times. There was, David Beck admitted, "not a whole lot of the rest of the world around us." Unlike Lewis Coriell, David Beck was never torn between basic research and clinical medicine. He preferred the former because it was, in his word, "tractable," governed by predictable laws and subject to experimental controls. Dealing with human behavior and conduct, by contrast, was a "messy"

Taking a break after midterm exams on Friday at the Johns Hopkins University School of Medicine where they were graduate students, David and Jeanne were married on Saturday, November 19, 1966. They returned to class on Monday.

pursuit. A comforting conservative impulse flavored the scientific quest for certainty. Yet the longer one pursues that quest, the more complex it becomes, and the less "messy" human behavior appears in comparison.

This epiphany dawned in the years following the couples' return to the Baltimore area. They had pledged a mutual covenant to follow the best job, whoever landed it. In 1974 Jeanne accepted a position on the faculty of the department of obstetrics and gynecology at the Hopkins School of Medicine. David continued his education as a research associate at the Maryland Psychiatric Research Center in Catonsville, where the couple resided. As they established roots in the community, they became actively engaged in civic pursuits, were introduced to local and state politics, and became committed to a range of social policies. David established a reputation as a forceful advocate for an improved park system and a vocal opponent of psychiatric deinstitutionalization. He began to enjoy considerably the "messy" give-and-take of negotiating, opinion shaping, and consensus building.

It did not take Beck long to find an opportunity to sharpen these newfound skills. In 1977, he entered the NIH's Grants Associates Program, a training regimen that resembled an MBA course for science administration. Having been trained in science from the bottom up, he was now studying it from the top down. His virtual classroom was nothing less than the national scientific establishment, and he made the rounds of the NIH, National Science

Foundation, National Academy of Science, and halls of Congress. He became enamored of science policy and the ways in which it was shaped. A newer historiography and sociology of science informed the program's syllabus. It conceived of science not simply as accumulated objective knowledge produced by emotionally detached investigators but as a human endeavor, a social system penetrated by economic forces, social and political change, cultural values, and the widest range of human motivation. Science was messy after all!

In 1978, David Beck applied his new learning to his world of science as a program administrator at the NIGMS, where he would spend the next six years. He was responsible for a portfolio of grants in biochemistry within the Cellular and Molecular Basis of Disease Program. Three years later, while continuing to administer that program, he became chief of the molecular and medical genetics section of the Genetics Program. Without relinquishing those duties, he became deputy director of that program in 1982. During his tenure the program awarded approximately $130 million in grants and contracts annually, seeding research that led to the revision of many textbooks, including the discovery of the catalytic properties of RNA. That finding earned its discoverers the 1989 Nobel Prize in Chemistry.

Selection of scientific talent is one of the most important functions of a research institute president. The criteria for awarding grants do not differ fundamentally from the standards for furnishing employment. As in surgery, practice makes perfect. In his multiple capacities at the NIH, David Beck reviewed more talent than any dozen institute heads during the same period. Likewise, few institute chiefs possessed his insider's appreciation of the qualities NIH program administrators looked for in a researcher, a proposal, or a sponsoring institution. The experiences Beck gained at the NIGMS would add considerable value to the two estimable outfits that would subsequently retain him.

In addition to his administrative responsibilities at the NIGMS, Beck served as its director's special assistant for legislative affairs from 1981 to 1984. In that capacity he tracked and analyzed legislation that might affect the organization, formulated position papers, prepared and coordinated testimony, and responded to congressional inquiries. The post provided a bird's-eye view of the politics that shape policy and affect funding and sharpened his skills in government relations.

Within the scientific community, Beck's position at the NIGMS Genetics Program afforded him national vision and visibility. He came to know personally the country's leading geneticists and their endeavors. Part of his responsibility to them was to develop cell bank projects to support their programs, and it was during this period that IMR officers and scientists became acquainted with Beck as the program officer for the repository contracts. Among his many duties, this involvement with the Camden organization was the most exciting and satisfying. That involvement officially ended in early 1984 when another independent research institute made Beck an offer he could not refuse.

Established in 1942, the Public Health Research Institute was devoted to basic research and solutions to public health problems, especially in the area of infectious disease. The sizeable operation featured a hundred-member staff, a $7 million budget, and a director—three years into his tenure—who wanted to devote his energies to his laboratory. Richard Novick proffered a position that essentially allowed David Beck to function as executive vice president, not only overseeing operations but also rebuilding the scientific organization. The challenge appealed to Beck, and the salary allowed him to leap the chronic gap between noncompetitive NIH pay scales and those of private research institutes and universities. Jeanne Beck had little trouble landing a position on the medical faculty of the Mount Sinai School of Medicine. And, so, it was off to New York City.

The PHRI seemed like a small city in itself, and Beck effectively found himself running it. Internally, he was responsible for the management of finance, accounting, personnel, space, safety, and countless other functions. Externally, he handled government relations, grants and contracts, private and public fund raising, labor negotiation, technology licensing, patent prosecution, and academic collaborations. While he proved himself an effective and respected administrator, he had really been recruited for his strategic acumen. Novick wanted him to develop the institute's strategic plan and to recruit the appropriate scientific talent to accomplish that plan.

David Beck's training as biologist and NIH administrator sharpened his understanding of institutions. He left the NIH just as its scientists had isolated HIV and arrived in New York just as AIDS raised the specter of uncontrollable massive infection of populations. AIDS patients flooded the Bellevue Hospital, across the street from the PHRI laboratories. Traditionally committed to the conquest of the bacterial scourges of mankind through the development of antibiotics and prophylactic immunization, the PHRI was not focusing on the redrawn battle line. Etiologically, the diseases were vastly different; culturally, the terror was the same. Beck understood that government funding would eventually follow society's fears and that microbiology and cell biology had to give way to molecular biology and molecular genetics. By reorienting scientific approaches, reorganizing scientific personnel, rationalizing operations, and stabilizing finances, he would help the PHRI more fully accomplish its historical mission. Eventually he would duplicate that success in Camden.

In 1990 the institute in Camden had finally accomplished something David Beck had begun to consider for the research establishment in midtown Manhattan: its relocation. Like Dr. Coriell, he understood the importance of venue. The PHRI was housed in facilities belonging to the NYC Department of Health's Bureau of Laboratories. The arrangement dated back to 1941, when Dr. Coriell's friend and colleague Tom Rivers, then a member of NYC's Board of Health, suggested the establishment of the institute to extend and deepen the research capacity of the Bureau. So long as the PHRI received substantial municipal support, the relationship proved mutually beneficial. Once that support ceased, the relationship, like the ambiance itself, grew uncomfortable.

Beck was in the process of trying to arrange with the UMDNJ in Newark, New Jersey, a similar sort of affiliation that the Coriell Institute had achieved in Camden, when the South Jersey organization invited him to lead it.[2] Coincidentally, just as he was presented with the opportunity to relocate to a brand new building, so too was Richard Novick, who elected to depart for the New York University School of Medicine. The trustees of PHRI determined that Novick's successor would be drawn from the ranks of the captains of commerce. And, in the midst of that executive transition, Beck realized that his urge to relocate the PHRI was as personal as it was institutional. Appreciative partakers of the city's cultural riches, he and Jeanne never achieved what one popular songwriter has called "the New York frame of mind." Besides, the presidency of the Coriell Institute was a prestigious plum of a job. And, he was fairly confident that he knew just what it needed.

SYNERGY, SYNTHESIS, AND SUSTAINABILITY

When Dr. Coriell retired, he entrusted his colleagues with unfinished business: completion of the capital campaign, construction of state-of-the-art facilities, relocation, affiliation with the university and medical center, executive search, and expansion of research staff. With David Beck's advent, thanks to the sedulity of many trustees and administrators, the first four of those five challenges had been met in overlapping, sequential order. The new president arrived with a clear mandate to accomplish the fifth and final objective.

Within weeks of his arrival in Camden, Beck articulated an action plan designed to build new scientific programs at the Institute. The new president moved resolutely yet sensitively to call for essential transformations, making certain that his analysis respected traditions and achievements and that it built on historic and current strengths. The task ahead, he knew, was not a simple matter of augmenting staff; the Institute required a sustained, critical restoration of scientific momentum. Despite the tangible progress of the past five years, the Institute's central purpose had been losing ground. Relocation, fund raising, affiliation, and organizational ambiguity following Dr. Coriell's retirement had been interruptive and enervating; they had distracted institutional energy and focus from its *raison d'être*: cutting-edge science.

It was clear to Beck that a reformation was necessary for the Institute to achieve its next renaissance. He saw an urgent need to cross-fertilize and build critical mass around the evolving fields of human molecular and cellular genetics and the investigation of human genetic diseases. He sought to rebuild essential intellectual connections between ongoing research and cell bank activity, enhance infrastructure, and enhance endowment. That meant recruiting new faculty, reconfiguring and filling lab space, acquiring advanced research equipment, developing cutting-edge technologies, expanding col-

[2] On May 2, 2002, the PHRI cut the ribbon on its new home, the International Center for Public Health in Newark, New Jersey.

Drs. Coriell and Beck enjoy an evening together when, in 1998, the Coriell Institute hosted an event for nine visiting Nobel Laureates during an international science fair competition in Philadelphia.

laborative interactions, improving inter-institutional relationships, and developing new financial resources. In calling for such a reconstruction, he was recapitulating the scientific vision and historic achievements of the Institute's founder.

At the core of Beck's assessment and subsequent strategic conduct was an articulated understanding of the critical *internal* need to reintegrate the research program and the cell banking enterprise in terms of new genetic paradigms and technology. That reintegration implied a reassertion of the primacy of research at the Institute. The cell repositories originated as an ancillary service, an offshoot of the basic research progress pioneered by Dr. Coriell. The dissemination of well-characterized, uncontaminated cell cultures facilitated and helped authenticate the investigations of researchers worldwide. As cell banking activity began to flourish in response to international demand in the early 1970s, its derived income helped sustain the Institute's other scientific programs.[3]

Unintentionally but unavoidably, the repository began to divert institutional energy and resources from the pure research programs that had originally created it. Especially during the immediately proceeding five-year period, the cell repositories carried the Institute's reputation and pocketbook. By the time Beck arrived, the cell banking and related activities constituted

[3] By the mid-1980s, the repositories were annually mailing out more than 5,000 samples priced at $60 per flask.

In the cryogenic storage laboratory, where the world's largest collection of living human cells is stored, Thomas Schneider opens a tank of cells. Courtesy of The Courier-Post

over two-thirds of the organization's total income. The industry had become essential to the Institute's financial viability.

Moreover, in the public's mind, cell banking became the feature that separated the Institute from competing research establishments. From a media perspective, the repositories represented a comprehensible accomplishment that was easier to exposit that other esoteric biological investigations. More poignantly, portrayals of hibernating human cells, languidly alive, bathed in mysterious vapors, frozen in time in waist-deep stainless steel vats at minus 316 degrees Fahrenheit, and awaiting scientific resurrection held a peculiar popular fascination.

Over time, the income and attention bestowed upon the repositories subtly, seductively altered the way the Institute came to view itself. Public attention persuaded trustees and stakeholders to view the repositories as the Institute's most precious resource. The historic record of ripe fundability made it easy to conclude that institutional viability was largely a matter of discovering new diseases, representing them in cell cultures in the Center's repositories, and posting applications for automatic federal underwriting. In order to counter this complacency, Beck issued a powerful warning.

The new president warned an attentive constituency that progress in molecular biology and molecular genetics could rapidly transform the cell banks from a white hope to a white elephant. The Coriell Institute's fundamental research and cell repositories had enabled the progress of the human genome initiative, the international effort to map the location of each of the approximately 50,000 genes found on human chromosomes. Ironically, that project demanded new technologies that obviated the need for the kinds of materials the cell repositories were producing and disseminating. Beck foresaw the apocalyptic possibility that rapidly accumulating DNA sequence information and computer-based modeling could supersede frozen cells as a research resource.

Federal and private funding of the cell banks was a function, not simply of the Institute's past achievements, but of the contemporary, constantly changing demands of the research community. The cell banks needed, in Beck's words "to find, adapt, and adopt" new technologies that maintained demand for services. That imperative demanded the development of new technologies to insure that the repositories remained relevant to cutting-edge advances in the fields of cell biology, molecular genetics, and human genetics. That process had begun in 1990 with the extraction of DNA from selected cell lines, and it had to be made increasingly proactive. The only way to *react* to demands of those on the frontiers of human genetics was to position the Institute's research programs at that forefront.

When Beck arrived at the Coriell Institute, he found too few researchers and programs focused in the area of human genetics. While its science was first-class and its scientists productive, the Institute was simply too small, in his view, to sponsor research programs that did not dynamically and synergistically interact. Scientists competed fiercely for resources, but the victors, ironically, were the researchers who most effectively cooperated, who were able to share the latest technology and intellectual property.

Deprived of a common syntax, disciplinarily diverse Coriell investigators were unable to subject their colleagues' grant proposals to rigorous internal review prior to submission to granting agencies. Lack of cross-fertilization, critical mass, and shared best technology dampened the enthusiasm of NIH reviewers for Coriell grant applications. When the new president arrived in Camden, only three NIH grants supported an organization that had seven research programs. The Institute had to concentrate its resources in areas where it could provide focused intellectual leadership.

Curiously, when one breaks down the new administration's strategy for renovation into discrete objectives, Beck's calls sound like echoes reverberating across the Institute's progressive past. Almost every aspect of his plan had been adumbrated: recruitment of the best and brightest, interconnectivity between the research programs and the cell banks, professionalization of management, diversification of sources of revenue and philanthropic support, enhancement of endowment, nurturing of state support, commercialization of technology, products and services, development of new products, enhanced management of portfolio, continuing education of staff, cooperation and collaboration with other institutions, educational service to the community, development of an ever more influential and insightful board, enlistment and

Touring students from Dr. Brimm Medical Arts School. An enthusiastic supporter of the City of Camden's efforts to strengthen its educational programs, the Coriell Institute provides tours, internships, laboratory equipment, and scientific lectures to schools throughout the city. Courtesy of The Courier-Post

involvement of high-level scientific advisors, enlargement of space, and other solid initiatives.

The difference was that David Beck was able to synthesize these aspects of institutional advancement and embody them in a gestalt in which the whole was greater than its parts. He appreciated the need to synchronize and interdigitate these activities to the extent possible. He articulated succinctly and persuasively the reasons why the Institute should embark on each activity, showed how these activities did and should interact, and established their relative priorities. Most importantly, he was able to move beyond advocacy of strategy to hard-driven implementation of enabling tactics.

Plans are easier to write than to implement. Successfully executing a workable strategy requires discipline, determination, and decisiveness; fortitude, patience, and adaptability; achievement of consensus and cooperation; creation of earned mutual respect among the plan's shareholders; building of morale; and real leadership. In the case of the institution's strategy of the 1990s, concrete accomplishment accompanied polite pronouncement, action invigorated action plans, and shareholders participated in the translation of rhetoric into reality.

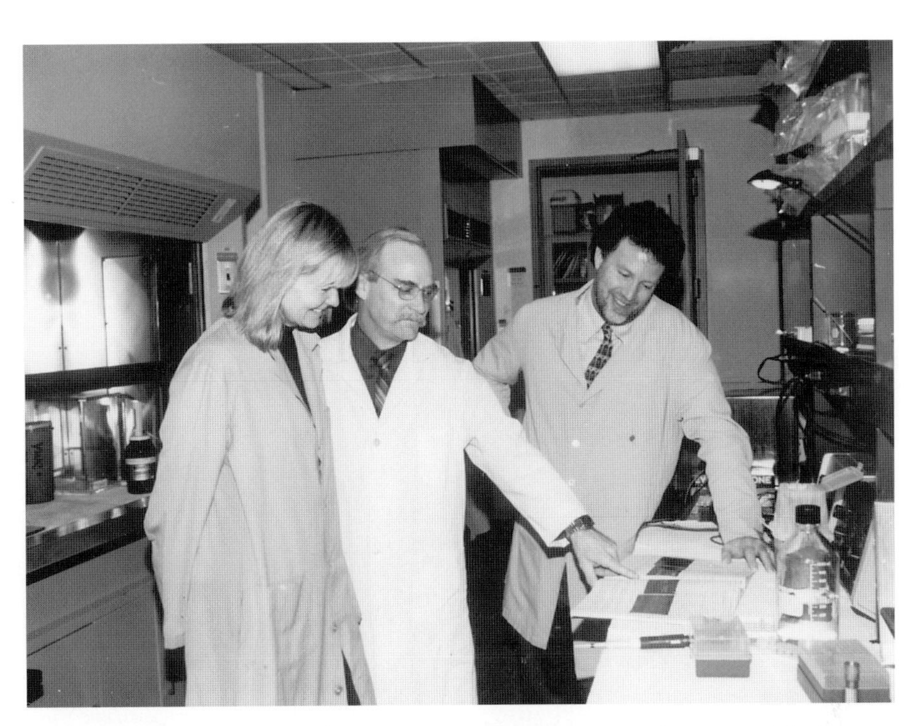

Dr. Beck began an ongoing effort to focus research programs and create a critical mass to encourage scientific dialogue. Drs. Kerri Smith, Patrick Bender, and Joseph Lorenz study samples from non-human primates and ancient DNA from human mummified remains to understand human origins better.

THE LAST DECADE

Expansion of the research program remained Beck's first priority. Equipped with only a modest staff development fund, he fulfilled his plan to recruit by 1993 two new principal investigators to help the institute make significant contributions to understanding the cause, transmission, and cure of genetic diseases.[4] In February 1993, Dr. Honghua Li joined the Institute following his doctoral work at the University of Southern California and his post-doctoral apprenticeship with Leroy Hood at the California Institute of Technology, where he held the Beckman Fellowship. Li had already established himself as a developer of sensitive methods of gene mapping and an expert analyst of human immunoglobulin genes. His development of a method of studying genes from a single cell increased the efficiency and reliability of genetic research worldwide. His work at the Institute formed an integral part of the national human genome project. He and his research associates were studying the range of genes that encode the human immune system in order to map and sequence individual genes and to discern the immune system's ability to generate myriad immune responses.

[4] His first recruiting priority was to retain a senior scientist of national repute capable of serving as scientific director. This remains an elusive objective and in all probability will await attainment of even greater critical mass and financial endowment.

Drs. Marcello Siniscalco and Renato Robledo investigate the population of Sardinia, Italy, to understand genetic variation.

In July, Marie Hoover came to the Coriell Institute as associate professor to continue her decade-long quest for the gene or genes involved in juvenile-onset (Type 1) diabetes with the continuing support of the Juvenile Diabetes Foundation International. Hoover earned her Ph.D. in 1984 at the University of Mississippi Medical Center. Following her post-doctoral training, she joined the faculty at the University of Louisville School of Medicine. She was searching human chromosomes to locate one of the genes held accountable for an individual's susceptibility to the disease and additionally to discover what gene or genes confer protection.

Recruitment efforts immediately thereafter were restricted for financial reasons to cost-saving collaborative projects. For the new CEO, that posed no problem. He viewed collaboration as a way to empower Coriell punch, stimulate cross-fertilization of ideas, cultivate potential recruits, and enhance visibility and collegiality within the scientific community. The Institute was able to reinvigorate its cytogenetics program by providing adjunct appointments to Lydia McMorrow, associate professor at Thomas Jefferson University; Barry Barnoski, director of cytogenetics at Cooper Hospital/University Medical Center; and Philip McCoy, a cytometrist at the Robert Wood Johnson Medical School.

Beck's approach to recruitment and retention of research talent revealed much about his conception of the scientific enterprise as a human system. He understood that the Institute's size and resources minimized its chances of securing scientific stars that were not in the twilight of their luminous careers.

His recruitment style was not unlike collegiate football coaches who built successful dynasties in the 1990s by forsaking old practices. Instead of picking players solely by proven ability to fill fixed positions, winning coaches simply began picking the best all-round athletes. Similarly, all other things being equal, when faced with a choice between a researcher who precisely represented a sought-out specialty and a young researcher who was just outside targeted parameters but blessed with extraordinary intellectual promise, David Beck would try to pick the smartest person every time.

Once recruited, investigators were expected to perform and to support their endeavors with grants. But they could expect something in return. It quickly became apparent that the new administration was organized for one purpose only: to serve the Coriell scientists and maximize their productivity. One way of accomplishing that formidable objective was to acquire the most up-to-date technology. Proper equipment made all the difference in a scientist's ability to complete an experiment quickly and accurately, to analyze data, query external databases, and communicate with the external scientific community. When Beck arrived, the Institute lacked a viable computer network. By 1995 a new Novell computer network was in place and plans were underway to create an Internet-accessible database for the cell repositories. Soon sophisticated new computer imaging systems were enhancing researchers' scrutiny of chromosomes and genetic markers. Computerized DNA sequencing equipment was extending the capabilities of investigators. Establishing an automated nerve center for research went a long way toward improving productivity, morale, recruitment, and grantsmanship.

Administrative support of science involved not only adding powerful tools but also eliminating peripheral duties, allowing investigators to spend their time investigating. For decades Bob Wilson effectively assumed that latter role as his special province. His announcement at the end of 1992 of his intention of retiring in January 1994 after forty years of service portended an awesome gap to fill.[5] Before he stepped down, the Institute appointed Joseph Mintzer as chief operating officer and vice president for administration. Mintzer had served as vice president for outpatient services at the Delaware County Memorial Hospital and of clinical services at Hahnemann University Hospital. He knew how to shape organizations to allow physicians to concentrate on the practice of medicine. At Coriell, he would apply those insights to facilitating exquisite science. He moved quickly to rationalize and simplify administrative procedures and to implement economical, efficient financial and operational management systems. His personable demeanor and intellectual curiosity won favor with the scientific staff, and his ability to communicate internally and externally helped forge a productive partnership with the president. Another emerging partnership eased Mintzer's transition. Wilson's administrative assistant, Carole Smith, provided the new vice president not

[5] When Wilson stepped down, the Institute appropriately dedicated in his name the Coriell "Kitchen," the sterilization laboratory he personally designed to process glassware to assure successful cell culturing.

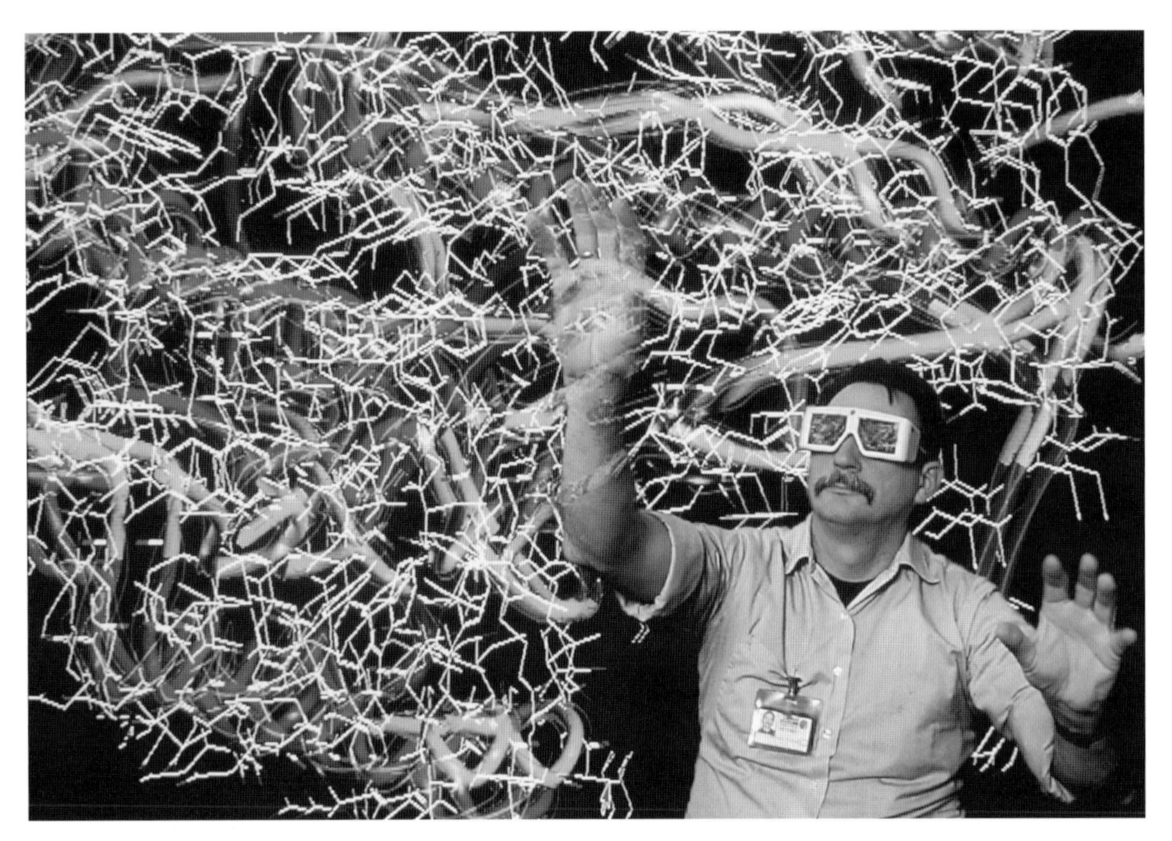

Dr. Gary Butler views a protein in "3-D." Other scientists in the growing programs use state-of-the-art systems including DNA sequencers, real-time PCR machines, automatic computerized karyotyping systems, and fluorescence-activated cell sorters.

only exceptional organizational talent but also three decades of corporate memory and instinct.

Premium support could not alter the peripatetic complexion of scientific careers. By the end of the century, the Institute had recruited ten new faculty members and yet the scientific staff was not significantly larger than it was at the decade's start. Ironically, in the late 1990s, a buoyant economy and improved prospects of federal support for scientific research tended to encourage institutional mobility among investigators. What counted was making Coriell scientists as productive as possible during their tenures and insuring that the programs to which they contributed were strengthened by their research.

It seems that every benefit has an adverse consequence. Trustees became accustomed to their new president delivering reports in "good news-bad news" format. Fortunately for the Institute, administrative, technical, and scientific support personnel supplied a backbone of institutional memory and fidelity. Inspired by loyalty to Dr. Coriell, an unusually long-tenured staff became David Beck's precious inheritance. In 1992, the ten most senior staff members collectively provided the Institute with almost three centuries of experience. A third of the Institute's family had served for at least a decade. Un-

In 1997, NIGMS Genetics Program Director Judith Greenberg, David Beck, chairman of the NIGMS Cell Repository Working Group Richard Spritz, and Jeanne Beck celebrate the collection's twenty-fifth anniversary. At the same time, the Institute initiates a vigorous program of marketing its technology to the pharmaceutical and biotechnology communities.

fortunately, many employees were fast approaching retirement. For example, Dorothy Gruber, who started the Coriell library from scratch a quarter of a century earlier, stepped down in 1992.[6] Supervisor of the cell culturing laboratories since their founding, Selena Dwight, whom Warren Nichols celebrated as "cell culturist supreme," announced that she would leave the Institute in January 1993.[7] Her critically important post was smoothly assumed by heir apparent Gloria J. (Jeanne) West, whom Dwight had capably mentored.

In 1992, Art Greene retired with over 170 co-authored publications to his credit. He humbly accepted the naming of a cell culture laboratory in his honor and introduced geneticist Sharon Suchy to her new role as assistant director of the John T. Dorrance, Jr. International Cell Science Center. When Suchy resigned in 1995, Jeanne Beck, who had been working as research director for the National Disease Research Interchange in Philadelphia, replaced

[6] Dorothy Gruber established the Institute's library in 1967. A decade later, following her training as a MEDLINE search analyst, the library became the first and for some time only MEDLINE Center in Southern New Jersey. By that time, Institute investigators were provided ample access to remote journals through consortial and cooperative relationships Gruber established with other health science libraries. The library merged with the UMDNJ's Education and Research Library in 1989.

[7] The loyalty of volunteers should not be overlooked in this "cohort analysis" of staff. Also in 1993, the Auxiliary to the Coriell Institute for Medical Research commemorated thirty years of service.

Dr. Lorraine Toji analyzes DNA samples with assistant Ron Soltesz.

her. Greene surrendered his part-time position at the repositories when Judith Greenberg, Ph.D., David Beck's successor as NIGMS project officer, suggested it was time for Richard Mulivor to mentor an apprentice who could take charge in the event of an emergency. The need for that precaution was sadly realized on October 27, 1996, when the 51-year-old Mulivor died unexpectedly following a brief illness. Jeanne Beck capably served as acting director until Dr. Robert Johnson's recruitment.

Activity in the Dorrance Center illustrated David Beck's ability to translate strategy into organizational behavior. It was easy to pronounce that the cell banks should relate to cutting-edge research. It was more difficult to provide financial support, time, and encouragement to cell repository scientists to engage in the part-time research that would provide intellectual stimulation and increased awareness of advanced trends. Dr. Suchy's principal responsibility as assistant director was to keep abreast of the rapid changes in human genetics and to insure that the Center's collections reflected those advances. She was, however, encouraged to continue her own research into genetic abnormalities present in Down syndrome. When Jeanne Beck became deputy director of the cell banks in 1998, she continued her efforts—critical to the evolving utility of the repositories themselves—to develop a technique for expanding DNA in the absence of cell culture. Dr. Jay Leonard, who joined the Institute in 1992 to direct the cytogenetics laboratory for the NIGMS collection, was likewise urged to renew the research interests he had pursued as a postdoctoral student at Johns Hopkins. In 1993 Dr. Lorraine Toji, who had worked closely with Warren Nichols from the early 1970s until his departure, was promoted to associate professor in recognition of her efforts to establish and maintain a molecular genetics program in the repositories. Since 1984, her work has been a key element in the success of the NIGMS repository.

By the end of the decade, investment in the strategy for the cell repositories was paying unparalleled dividends. A major portion of the stabilizing growth of the Institute's revenue stream stemmed from application of new technologies, matching of collections with greatest scientific need, funding from the breast cancer projects, renewed contracts from the NIGMS and NIA, diversification, penetration into the for-profit client and biotechnology markets, aggressive competition for collections held elsewhere, and sophisticated pricing and marketing tactics. Training programs in cell culturing connected the Coriell Institute to Thomas Jefferson University and Rowan University, and created a pool of talent that could eventually replenish human resources in the expanding repositories. The cell bank operation had been set on this positive trajectory in 1992 and by April of the following year David Beck could report that "good news" to the board, which promptly braced itself for the "bad news." The liquid nitrogen freezer room, the president announced, was filled to capacity. It was time to plan for the ninth building expansion in the Institute's history.

By July 30, 1998, when the Institute broke ground for its planned $5.6 million addition, overcrowding of cell storage facilities and research space had become a serious problem. Construction began on the 24,092 square foot addition in October and was completed ahead of schedule the following year. The project more than doubled cryogenic storage space, brought the administrative offices into an intimate connection with the laboratories, and created a sorely needed, recognizable corporate façade and "front door" presence on Haddon Avenue. The fundraising effort that enabled the expansion was a model capital campaign that reflected the continuing largess of the Coriell community and the consummate skills of the development and public affairs teams.

In addition to the capital campaign for expansion, the Institute made significant progress throughout the decade, improving community outreach, enhancing public recognition, expanding its donor base, diversifying funding sources, controlling its investment policy, and nurturing the state's funding stream. By the end of the decade, the endowment had tripled to about $11 million. Market-driven increases in the value of the Coriell portfolio accounted for approximately three-quarters of that enhancement. The Institute today is a strong, viable organization that understands that its financial stability and independence remain subject to vicissitudes beyond its control.

Control of commercial applications of scientific research and expertise was very much within the Institute's grasp. Again, backing strategy with ac-

Joe Mintzer, Tom Ganor, Lewis Coriell and David Beck in the footprint of the planned 24,000-square-foot laboratory addition.

tion, James Palmer established a Commercial Development Committee in 1995. Championed by board chairman John A. Philbrick III, the committee became a seedbed of ideas and an effective channel for diversifying the Institute's income stream. One concept that emerged from the committee appeared so promising that trustee Frank Giordano, then serving as chair of the executive committee, incorporated a company, CorCell, to engage in the business of collecting blood from newborn umbilical cords and preserving stem cells contained in the cord blood for potential future use by the donors. Transplantation of cord blood stem cells is useable as treatment against a variety of cancers and genetic diseases. Unlike invasive, painful, and costly bone marrow collection, cord blood acquisition was a simple procedure and a foolproof form of biological insurance. Vice president Joe Mintzer thought it was such a good idea that he and his expectant wife Beth became the Institute's first donors.

After meticulous review, the state's department of health issued Coriell a license to collect and store umbilical core blood in December 1996. By the middle of 1998 the company had attracted nearly a thousand clients. The board's backing of the enterprise followed sometimes strenuous but always insightful discussions about the relationship of not-for-profit institutions to for-profit venture. And the president's recruitment of a medical director to

Joseph and Beth Mintzer's son Joe is the Institute's first umbilical cord blood donor.
Courtesy of The Courier-Post

run Coriell's umbilical cord blood stem cell laboratory illustrates the Institute's characteristic commitment not only to capitalize on science as good business but also to use business to further scientific investigation.

As the business evolved, the relationship between the Institute and CorCell ended in 2000. It was replaced at the end of that year by the establishment of the New Jersey Cord Blood Bank (NJCBB), funded by a $5 million no-interest loan from the state of New Jersey. Assemblyman Paul DiGaetano sponsored the bill securing the loan for the state's first publicly accessible cord blood bank.[8]

The Institute's president had been pursuing the notion of a stem cell biology program at least since the inception of Palmer's committee. Board members as well as Coriell faculty were able to learn more about umbilical cord blood stem cell studies from seminars conducted by invited visiting scientists. Since the field was new to the Institute, its researchers steadily increased their expertise in stem cell biology in order to build a knowledge base to support the recruitment of specialists beginning in July 1998. The Institute developed five stem cell projects from the original venture: pancreatic, neuronal, hematopoietic (blood forming), adipose (fat), and muscle/cartilage. Today the stem cell program is a vital component of the Institute's scientific agenda.

[8] On March 22, 2002, the NJCBB was certified by the National Marrow Donor Program and its cord blood holding listed with this national database.

Drs. David Moscatello, Rick Cohen and Richard Huhn lead the Institute's stem cell biology program.

The Definition of Science

David Beck championed a holistic approach to scientific activities at the Institute, one that demanded the convergence of as many components as possible to add synergistic value to each initiative. That characteristic gestalt was manifest in the creation of a Cooperative Family Registry for Breast Cancer Studies in November 1994. As well as any recent initiative, that project exemplifies and even defines science as practiced at the Coriell Institute.

The eager inclination to collaborate became a hallmark of the Institute in the 1990s, and nothing better illustrates the power of joint endeavor than the Institute's effort to accelerate research on breast cancer. The project was a collaboration within a collaboration, in that Cooper Hospital/University Medical Center's Generosa Grana had helped to develop a clinical network of breast cancer patients throughout New Jersey, a state especially hard hit by the costly disease. Cooper and Coriell teamed up to create a breast cancer repository to serve as a research base for the entire scientific community. Thanks to Grana's previous relationship with Fox Chase, the collaboration was extended to include the Fox Chase Cancer Center, which not only provided a large, diverse population base for the registry but also lent its information management capacity to the endeavor. The National Cancer Institute soon funded the project with a $1.7 million, five-year grant as a part of an international consortium. Jeanne Beck coordinated the project and was responsible for the breast cancer cell collection itself. The larger repository was not limited to biological materials; it included clinical histories and epidemiological data as well.

The project exhibited the interlocked relationship of the repositories and the research programs and catalyzed the campaign to develop new ways to make the cell banks useful. Breast cancer cells are difficult to grow in culture. Traditional cell culturing techniques pioneered at the Institute could not supply sufficient genetic material to speed up worldwide scientific progress against the disease. Accordingly, Jeanne Beck, Chung Kim, and Honghua Li joined forces to perfect a method called "whole genome amplification" to increase the amounts of DNA that could be extracted from tumor specimens. The basic technique, utilizing polymerase chain reaction (PCR), was developed by Norman Arnheim, Li's mentor at the USC.

Internal collaboration benefited from the specialized knowledge of Drs. Toji, Leonard, and Hoover and exhibited the rewards of the Institute's deliberate trek toward focused, critical mass. The combined expertise of scientists,

As part of a collaborative experiment conducted on John Glenn's space shuttle Discovery *flight in the fall of 1998, Drs. Jeanne Beck and Robert Johnson retrieve endothelial cells from liquid nitrogen with participating Wistar Institute scientist Dr. Elliot Levine for breast cancer studies on MIR.* Courtesy of The Courier-Post technicians, and supervisors in the Coriell Cell Repositories made the project possible. For science, the perfected technology would be transferable to many other types of cells, such as nerve cells. For medicine, the repository itself would potentially benefit families at risk for other sorts of cancers, since susceptibility to breast cancer was correlated with risk of colon, prostate, and ovarian cancers as well.

The project exhibited the seriousness with which the Institute embraced its educational mission. Breast cancer captured the public's imagination, and that interest created a "bully pulpit" from which to educate the public about the power of genetic science. Jeanne Beck regularly traveled around the state to women's organizations and other groups to discuss genetic screening, family risk, and basic research's role in the fight against breast cancer. The very idea of a registry for breast cancer posed new ethical and legal dilemmas that required public dialogue. As a member of the Commission on Cancer Research's breast cancer advisory group, Beck enjoined the debate over the need for genetic privacy of its citizens. She testified before committees of both houses of the state legislature. At the time of its enactment, the resultant legislation was the most comprehensive law of its kind in the nation.

By the end of the century, the Cooperative Family Registry for Breast Cancer Studies had grown into a huge international initiative, involving six medical research institutions in three countries and providing a family registry for both breast and ovarian cancer. Based on the success of the project, Coriell and Cooper finalized an agreement in February 1998 to initiate a similar study to identify genetically diverse patients with a family history of prostate cancer. The Institute's unparalleled technological mastery is making possible new collections for stroke, obesity, and macular degeneration. Above all, it is important to appreciate, this initiative was just one of many dynamic undertakings during the prolific decade.

The project embodied practically every feature of the Institute's strategic plan. It began with an affiliation Lewis Coriell championed for decades, escalated into a broad external collaboration, intertwined basic research with clinical medicine, infused the repositories with research-based technologies, increased basic knowledge applicable to other endeavors and transferable to other diseases, created opportunities for cooperation and cross-fertilization within Coriell laboratories, augmented the cell bank collections and enlarged their constituencies. It expanded the Institute's educational mission, gave it a public forum for airing its views on health policy issues, increased its visibility and influence, secured federal underwriting, attracted new sources of funding, and brought the Institute into closer working relationship with the state legislature and the Cancer Commission. It cooperated with otherwise competing research institutes, expanded a rich institutional legacy by bringing biological sciences into contact with the social sciences, engaged administrators and scientists in a common endeavor, spawned similar undertakings, and personally touched the families of employees. Here was synthesis.

Historians and sociologists have long recognized that science is more than bench research. Viewed as a complex social system, science is acquiring

Cytogeneticist Dr. Jay Leonard performs chromosomal analysis.

technology, recruiting talent, providing supporting personnel, building infrastructure, creating departments, establishing optimum working environments, raising funds, designing and marketing products and services, projecting public images, lobbying legislatures, cultivating shareholders, maintaining morale, and performing countless related activities that contribute to successful, useful abstract thinking about complex natural phenomena. By this functional definition of science, David Beck—the incisive administrator—has remained the consummate scientist.

CODA

No dirge was played when Lewis L. Coriell died. Succumbing to cancer, which he had labored to eradicate from the earth, he willed himself to stay alive until his ninetieth birthday on June 19, 2001. A few days earlier, his doctors at Cooper Hospital allowed him to cross the street one last time to celebrate his birthday with the entire Coriell Institute staff, members of his family, and many former colleagues at a gala surprise party at the Institute. Throughout his final months of life, he stayed close to his Institute and his Institute stayed close to him.

Living memory is fleeting. There will come a time in the history of the Coriell Institute for Medical Research when its champions will no longer recollect its founder. Posterity should therefore know that this gentle, larger-than-life man traversed the twentieth century as a giant.

AFTERWORD

BY DAVID P. BECK

PREDICTING THE FUTURE may be only slightly more difficult than deriving an objective account of the past. It would certainly be difficult to chart a path for the Coriell Institute in the twenty-first century without understanding the Institute's fundamental contributions and their place in the course of biomedical research in the twentieth century.

The lessons of history, however, can disconcert as well as reassure. Predictability may be a criterion for scientific experiment, but science itself is an opportunistic and therefore unpredictable process. In large measure, the Coriell Institute's success has resulted from its ability to build solidly upon its historical foundations. Since 1953, when the Institute was founded and James Watson and Francis Crick discovered the structure of DNA, it has been clear that cell biology and molecular genetics were the waves of the future. Now, as the human genome is sequenced and genetic diseases are yielding the cellular and molecular secrets of their underlying causes, the cell culturing technology that Dr. Coriell developed a half century ago remains a fundamental tool for providing the raw materials for gene research. Progress in medicine will depend on the new fields of genomics (learning how to use this genetic sequence information) and proteomics (learning how to use the proteins in our cells which are derived from that genetic information). These terms will suffuse our daily language and likely our future medical care.

The Institute is confident that it is positioned to continue and even accelerate its contributions to understanding human disease and human genomics in an increasingly competitive international scientific community precisely because it has remained true to its heritage. It has, in other words, succeeded in creating a dynamic, symbiotic interactivity between its fundamental mission of conducting basic biomedical research and its core technology: the culture, cyrostorage, characterization, and distribution of cells. It will continue to develop new ways to characterize and curate cells and the critical raw materials extracted from them, apply these developments to the study of genetic diseases, especially complex diseases such as behavioral illnesses, and keep these strategies germane to molecular genetic and cellular research at the Institute and worldwide.

Since the establishment of the first cell repository at the Institute in 1964, Coriell's sixty plus cyrostorage tanks have housed millions of vials of cell, representing thousands of genetic diseases. It has distributed more than 125,000 cell cultures and more than 150,000 DNA samples in fifty-five countries to researchers who recognize the Institute's preeminence in developing cell lines, maintaining quality control, and managing databases associated with the collections. Experiments using materials from Coriell collections have resulted in over 12,000 scientific citations. This panoply of numbers reveals the Institute's continuing commitment to Dr. Coriell's legacy of service to the international scientific community and establishes a clear foundation for the continued diversification and growth of the Coriell Cell Repositories.

The richness of the Coriell Institute's collections complements and facilitates the cutting-edge research programs conducted by Institute faculty. Understanding the range of genetic variation and diversity in humans and non-human primates and the biology of the stem cells that renew our tissues are areas of outstanding scientific promise and long-term growth, and they are the principal areas of focus for the Institute's research programs. One of the most powerful areas of study made possible by the Human Genome Project is genetic variation, more broadly known as comparative genomics. Learning more about the genetic composition of an individual, an ethnic group, or indeed other species will help us understand, for example, longevity or susceptibility to hypertension or cancer. We also need better ways to identify genes involved in multifactorial genetic diseases such as cancer and diabetes. Likewise, the use of stem cells for future therapeutic strategies requires understanding their biology and the molecular controls on their development programs. Coriell laboratories will focus more and more on stem cells and the factors that control their function.

The Institute has been involved in stem cell research and banking umbilical cord blood, from which blood-forming stem cells are derived, since the mid-1990s. We are especially proud to serve as New Jersey's first *public* cord blood bank, and we expect this role to grow and continue for many years. As with the creation of the Environmental Research Laboratory a quarter-century ago, the New Jersey Cord Blood Bank represents the Institute's traditional commitment to serve state and region. The exciting possibilities of stem cells and cord blood banking are key parts of the long-term scientific agenda of the Institute.

That agenda is not influenced by scientists alone. When, for example, trustee Edward M. Satell recently donated $1 million to endow the Richard D. Satell Laboratory for Cancer Research, he encouraged that stem cell research be applied to the Institute's historical interest in cancer research. Such discerning investment accelerates the pace of progress, makes the Coriell Institute increasingly competitive in its quest for research grants and scientific discoveries, and recalls the critical importance and sustaining role of private philanthropy in the Coriell Institute's history.

Science, as the preceding narrative has suggested, is the product of many intellectual, cultural, social, and economic forces. In the final analysis, the characteristic of the Coriell Institute that is most deeply rooted in its past and most essential to its future is a shared vision that draws upon the collective wisdom of the entire Coriell Institute family. During my tenure as president, the Institute has been guided by an exceptional cadre of trustees under the capable leaderships of James Palmer, John A. Philbrick III, Alan Wechsler, and, most recently, William T. Carson, Jr., who is currently heading an ambitious campaign to enhance the Institute's endowment fund. Every individual who has ever served as board member, scientist, administrator, technical and support staff, member of our scientific advisory committee, auxiliary, contributor, and interlocutor is a part of this organization's brave history and should be gratified and enthusiastic, as am I, by the Institute's progress and promise.

The scientific staff has always constituted the source of the Institute's success and its future. Photograph taken April 2002.

Bibliography

PRIMARY SOURCE MATERIAL for this work consisted principally of interviews with individuals cited in the Acknowledgment section of the *Preface*; minutes of the meetings of the Institute's board of trustees; germane documents appended to those minutes; annual and biannual reports of the Institute; its *Biennial Scientific Reports*; its especially useful newsletter *Discover*; and miscellaneous organizational files, correspondence, media releases, and reports. Secondary source material included newspaper articles and editorials chiefly appearing in the *Camden Courier-Post*, the *Philadelphia Inquirer*, the *Philadelphia Bulletin*, and the *New York Times*. Quotations drawn from *Courier-Post* accounts cited and dated in the narrative will not be referenced in the notes. The state legislature records its actions and roll call votes in its *Journal of the Senate* and *Minutes of the General Assembly*. Enacted bills can be found in the appropriate volumes of *New Jersey Statutes Annotated*, published by West Publishing Company. Where the author needs to acknowledge an intellectual debt or to show the source of quotation or contextual perspective, references are supplied below by chapter. These notes, however, will not reference hundreds of secondary bibliographic, journalistic, and Web-based sources of information consulted or the scores of interviews and conversations conducted in order to produce the preceding narrative. The single most useful tool used in research for this book was the Internet search engine *Google*.

Chapter One

Quotations of Robert E. Kohler are from the preface to his monograph, *Partners in Science: Foundations and Natural Scientists, 1900–1945* (Chicago: University of Chicago Press, 1991), pp. xiii and xiv.

Chapter Two

Genealogical information about the Coriell family in America was gathered from a number of sources including Nelson W. Evans, *A History of Scioto*

County Together with a Pioneer Record of Southern Ohio, 1796–1903, published in Portsmouth, Ohio, 1903 by its author; and a recent but undated typescript by Dallas Lee Coryell entitled *The Coryells: An American Family and 300 Years of Its History*.

Valuable insights about Lewis Coriell's early years are contained in a series of five "Dad Vignettes" that he wrote for his grandchildren with his son Jim's encouragement between September 1998 and February 1999. Among the many journalistic sketches of the young Lewis Coriell's life, Kathleen A. Rowley's *Courier-Post* article (October 14, 1969) is richly detailed and highly accurate. The brilliantly conceived, historically based novels of A.B. Guthrie, Jr., and of Ivan Doig convey the texture of life in early twentieth-century Montana far better than dusty county histories. Doig's biographical account of his Montana upbringing, *This House of Sky: Landscapes of the Western Mind* (New York: Harcourt Brace & Company, 1978), provides a wonderful window onto the era. For insights into the meaning of Sinclair Lewis's *Arrowsmith* for aspiring researchers, see Charles E. Rosenberg, "Martin Arrowsmith: The Scientist as Hero" in Rosenberg, *No Other Gods: On Science and American Social Thought* (Baltimore: Johns Hopkins University Press, 1976), pp. 123–31.

Ed Regis, *The Biology of Doom: The History of America's Secret Germ Warfare Project* (New York: Henry Holt, 1999) provides a backdrop to Dr. Coriell's experiences at Fort Detrick. That year also, Alastair Hay published two important articles in Vol. 15 of *Medicine, Conflict and Survival* (London: Frank Cass, 1999): "Simulants, Stimulants and Diseases: The Evolution of the United States Biological Warfare Programme, 1946–60" (pp. 198–214) and "A Magic Sword or a Big Itch: An Historical Look at the United States Biological Weapons Programme" (pp. 215–34). Dr. Coriell described his work at Children's Hospital of Philadelphia in a transcribed interview conducted by Shirley Bonnem on April 3, 1992, in preparation for her history of CHOP entitled *Two Decades: An Informal Report (1974–1994)*, published by CHOP in 1995. The volume's epilogue, "In Perspective: 1855–1974," written by Mary Crane Hope, provided essential context for Dr. Coriell's career in Philadelphia. The author's understanding of the history of virology and tissue culture was aided by Greer Williams, *Virus Hunters* (New York: Alfred A. Knopf, 1959).

The status of post-war biomedical research in the United States and the role of the National Institutes of Health are discussed in Daniel M. Fox, "The Politics of the NIH Extramural Program, 1937–1950," *Journal of the History of Medicine and Allied Sciences* 42 (1987): 447–66; Victoria A. Harden, *Inventing the NIH: Federal Biomedical Research Policy, 1887–1937* (Baltimore: Johns Hopkins University Press, 1986); Stephen P. Strickland, *Politics, Science, and Dread Disease: A Short History of United States Medical Research Policy* (Cambridge: Harvard University Press, 1972); Donald C. Swain, "The Rise of a Research Empire: NIH, 1930–1950," *Science* 138 (1962): 1233–37; and, Daniel S. Greenberg, *The Politics of Pure Science: An Inquiry into the Relationship between Science and Government in the United States* (New York: New American Library, 1967). These references also inform subsequent chapters.

George Aaron was quoted in a *Philadelphia Inquirer* article, "Two Phila. Groups Take Camden Hospital Control" (February 15, 1949).

CHAPTER THREE

Jeffrey M. Dorwart and Philip English Mackey, *Camden County, New Jersey, 1616–1976: A Narrative History* (Camden: Camden County Cultural & Heritage Commission, 1976) is a standard account of the municipality and county. See also Thomas Fleming, *New Jersey: A History* (New York: Norton, 1984). Newspaper accounts and reminiscences supply the details about Camden Municipal Hospital, but two magistral accounts of the American hospital provide essential context: Charles E. Rosenberg, *The Care of Strangers: The Rise of America's Hospital System* (New York: Basic Books, 1987) and Rosemary Stevens, *In Sickness and In Wealth: American Hospitals in the Twentieth Century* (New York: Basic Books, 1989). The single best source of the modern history of the political state of New Jersey is Barbara G. Salmore and Stephen A Salmore, *New Jersey Politics and Government: Suburban Politics Comes of Age*, 2nd ed. (Lincoln: University of Nebraska Press, 1998). Also useful is Gerald M. Pomper, ed., *The Political State of New Jersey* (New Jersey: Rutgers University Press, 1986). The remarks of Leslie Ewing and George Aaron on county control of the Municipal Hospital were quoted by reporter William Gaffney in *Courier-Post* articles appearing December 20 and December 22, 1949, respectively.

The best of many fine accounts of the conquest of polio, in my opinion, is Jane S. Smith, *Patenting the Sun: Polio and the Salk Vaccine* (New York: W. Morrow, 1990). I am deeply indebted to it for fact and interpretation. The *Saturday Evening Post* feature on the gamma globulin polio protection study, written by Steven M. Spencer, appeared November 1, 1952. My account of the Enders group discovery is richly informed by Williams, *Virus Hunters*, pp. 251–69.

CHAPTER FOUR

Contextual perspective for this chapter relied upon Smith, *Patenting the Sun*; Richard Carter, *Breakthrough: The Saga of Jonas Salk* (New York: Trident Press, 1966); and Tony Gould, *A Summer Plague: Polio and Its Survivors* (New Haven: Yale University Press, 1995).

CHAPTER FIVE

Interpretive context and much useful information for this chapter is found in Paul Starr, *The Social Transformation of American Medicine: The Rise of a Sovereign Profession and the Making of a Vast Industry* (New York: Basic Books, 1982); Greer Williams, *Virus Hunters*; and Victoria A. Harden, *Inventing the NIH*. My historical understanding of changing conceptions of cancer was deepened by David Cantor, "Cancer" in the *Companion Encyclopedia of the History of Medicine*, vol. 2, ed. W. F. Bynum and Roy Porter (London: Routledge, 1993), pp. 537–61.

Chapter Six

Derek de Solla Price, *Big Science, Little Science* (New York: Columbia University Press, 1963) provides keen insights about the sociology of scientific research. Mahlon Hoagland authored two helpful guides to genetic science: *The Roots of Life: A Layman's Guide to Genes, Evolution and the Ways of Cells* (Boston: Houghton Mifflin Company, 1978) and *Discovery: The Search for DNA's Secrets* (Boston: Houghton Mifflin Company, 1981).

Materials relating to the Biochemical Research Foundation are reposited (Reference # 734) at the Orphans Court of Philadelphia, Room 415, City Hall, Philadelphia, PA.

Chapter Seven

With respect to national health policy and its relationship to biomedical research, I have relied for general historical and interpretive context on Starr, *Social Transformation*, pp. 290–411 and Stevens, *Sickness and Wealth*, pp. 284–320. Stevens's quotes are found on her pages 284 and 294, respectively. Dr. Coriell's remarks about the NCI's budget reduction for cancer research were quoted by Kathleen A. Rowley in her *Courier-Post* article, "Dr. Coriell Seeking Hike in Cancer Research Aid" (November 20, 1969). See also John T. Kalberer, Jr., "Impact of the National Cancer Act on Grant Support," *Cancer Research* 35 (March 1975): 473–81, and Robert Q. Marston, "Dilemmas of Decision-Making; NIH: A Century of Science for Health," *Nature* 326 (October 22, 1987): 683–85. On the Lasker lobby and the "War on Cancer," see Harden, *Inventing the NIH*, pp. 182–87. The quote of "the NIH's astute chronicler" is Harden's (page 186).

The quoted views of Drs. Coriell and Nichols on the independent viability of the Institute have been taken from the minutes of the meeting of the executive committee on June 3, 1968. The report entitled "A Medical-Dental School in South Jersey" was published in September 1968 by the Camden Board of Freeholders. Much of the historical background of the initiative is contained in that report. Also useful is Stanley S. Bergen, Jr., "Medical Education in New Jersey: The Development of UMDNJ," *Journal of the Medical Society of New Jersey* 81 (No. 9, September 1984): 791–97. For the story of the Institute's healthcare neighbor, see Margaret O. Kirk, *Cooper: The Story of Cooper Hospital* (Camden: Cooper Hospital/University Medical Center, 1987). Dr. Coriell's comments on Governor Cahill's ideas for medical education were quoted by Robert M. Herron in his *Courier-Post* article, "'No Walls' Med School 'No Good' " (November 17, 1971).

New Jersey's battles over broad-based taxation and "thorough and efficient" public education significantly shaped institutional strategy in the 1970s. For this essential political context, see Salmore and Salmore, *New Jersey Politics and Government*, pp. 244–52, 260–67, and Albert Burstein, "Education Policy" in Pomper (ed.), *Political State of New Jersey*, pp. 199–213.

Dr. Moore's group's study "Search for a Human Breast Cancer Virus" appeared in *Nature* 229 (No. 5287; February 26, 1971): 611–14. See also

Moore et al., "Some Aspects of the Search for a Human Mammary Tumor Virus," *Cancer* 28 (No. 6; December 1971): 1415–24. The *Newsweek* article appeared on page 129 of the magazine's April 19, 1971 number.

CHAPTER EIGHT

The interrelated saga of Cooper Hospital during this period—including the osteopathic-allopathic controversy—is summarized in Kirk, *Cooper*, pp. 167–88. The quotation about David Kaloupek is on page 185. Kaloupek's January 4, 1982, report is entitled "Options for Research and Support Facilities."

Governor Kean recounted his Superfund strategy and environmental policies in his political autobiography, *The Politics of Inclusion* (New York: The Free Press, 1988), pp. 103–07. The national cancer statistics cited in the narrative come from the 1975 *Atlas of Cancer Mortality for U. S. Counties, 1950–1969* (DHEW Publication [NIH] 75-780). The state statistical study cited is *Cancer Mortality in New Jersey, 1975–1979* (NJ DEP, Office of Cancer Research, Trenton, 1983.) The CINJ/CMDNJ article is Louria et. al., "Cancer in New Jersey: An Overview," *Journal of the Medical Society of New Jersey* 73 (No. 9; September 1976): 749–52. The quotation therefrom appears on page 752. See also Gerard J. McGarrity, *Cancer in Southern New Jersey: A Report to the Camden County Board of Chosen Freeholders* (Camden: CIMR, 1987). A reliable interpretive account of the development and passage of the Cancer Research Act is contained in T. Patrick Hill, "The Politics of Cancer," *New Jersey Reporter* (June 1987), pp. 14–19, 33. John Fay's quote appears on page 16.

CHAPTER NINE

The quotations of Senator Rand, Chairman Kallelis, and President McGarrity are taken from the Institute's media releases, newsletter, and annual report. The legislative actions and status of various bills concerning the passage of laws that affected events described in this chapter can be found in the germane issues of the *New Jersey Legislative Index*, published by the Legislative Index Company.

CHAPTER TEN

David Beck is quoted from an interview with the author on October 27, 1999; much of the material used in preparing this chapter is contained in that interview and those of November 8 and November 29, 1999. For the effect of *Sputnik* on science education in the public school curriculum, I have relied on Peter B. Dow, *Schoolhouse Politics: Lessons from the Sputnik Era* (Cambridge: Harvard University Press, 1991). Two helpful articles summarizing the Institute's programs in the 1990s and beyond are Jennifer Fisher Wilson, "Coriell Extends its Scope," *The Scientist* 15 (Number 11; May 28, 2001); Nicole Gray, "Will Wonders Never Cease?," *New Jersey TechNews* 5 (Issue 7; September 2001).

~

APPENDICES

BOARD MEMBERS

CORIELL BOARD CHAIRMEN

EXECUTIVE COMMITTEE CHAIRMEN

FRIENDS OF CORIELL

CORIELL AUXILIARY

THE MISSION OF THE CORIELL INSTITUTE is discovering the causes of cancer and other genetic diseases in order to improve the health of humankind . . . through scientific research, banking of cells and tissues, and education. At the Coriell Institute for Medical Research, our mission is to support the gift of good health.

BOARD OF TRUSTEES

The Board of Trustees of Coriell Institute for Medical Research provides essential governance and fiduciary oversight for the operations of the scientific research programs, all banking activities, and educational endeavors.

BOARD MEMBER	ELECTED/RETIRED
A. Marshall Acuff, Jr.	2002–
John A. Affleck	2000–
John Aglialoro	1982–1987
Dr. Forrest H. Anthony	1992–1996
Samuel H. Ballam, Jr.	1982–1988
Lewis Barton	1965–1967
Dr. David P. Beck	1992–

Board Member	Elected/Retired
Dr. Jeanne C. Beck ***	2000–
Leo C. Beebe *	1991–2001
William H. Bell, Jr.**	1970–2001
Dr. Patrick K. Bender ***	1998–2000
Ian J. Berg	1994–1999
Dr. Stanley Bergen	1972–1998
Dr. Karl H. Beyer, Jr.	1976– 1980
William W. Bodine, Jr.	1982–1983
Dr. Alfred M. Bongiovanni	1963–1977
E. Gerald Bowman	1958–1966
Gerald A. Brawner, Esq.	1985–1986
Dr. Gary H. Butler ***	1996–1998
Joseph H. Cappalonga	1989–1993
Joseph Carley	1982–1983
Charles H. Carpenter	1954–1976
William T. Carson, Jr. *	1991–
John S. Carter	1953–1970
Buntzie Ellis Churchill	1986–1991
Marvin Cohen	1974–1979
Harvey J. Comita	1992–2001
Dr. Stuart D. Cook	1999–2000
Dr. Earl D. Coriell	2002–
Dr. Lewis L. Coriell **	1953–2001
Dr. Jean Cortner	1976–1982
Charles Cox	1979–1982
Mrs. Charles Cox	1982–1982
Jay G. Cranmer	1989–1990
Rae Crowther	1970–1980
John F. D'Aprix	1992–1996
Gabe E. Danch	1980–1985
W. Robert Davis *	1966–1999
Dr. Arnold E. Denton	1990–1993
Melville P. Dickenson, Jr.*	1998–

* denotes Life Trustee

** denotes Life Trustee Emeritus

*** denotes Coriell faculty representative

BOARD MEMBER	ELECTED/RETIRED
Edward C. Dolbey	1979–1982
Brian H. Dovey	1994–1999
William J. Doyle	1994–
John T. Dorrance, Jr.	1953–1989
Peter E. Driscoll, Esq.*	1992–
Leila G. Dyer	2002–
Dr. Norman H. Edelman	1992–1995
Dr. John E. Errickson, Jr.	1963–1966
Dr. Angela S. Fanelli	1990–1998
Louis C.R. Farrelly	1996–2000
Alexander Feinberg, Esq.	1967–1980
Mrs. W.H.K. Fleck	1954–1984
Edwin J. Foltz, Esq. **	1982–
James R. Foran	1988–
Brian R. Ford	1989–2000
JoAnne T. Fredericks	2001–
Vincent E. Furey, Jr.	1985–1988
Frank Giordano **	1989–
Donald M. Gleklen, Esq.	1994–1996
Virginia Graham	1974–1983
Frederick P. Greiner, Esq.*	1953–1994
Holly H. Griffin	1991–1998
Dr. Samuel P. Gurin	1966–1969
Peter Hamilton	1998–1998
Mrs. Brooks J. Harral *	1984–
Michael J. Hayes	1954–1979
Joseph S. Holman **	1982–
Walter S. Holmes, Jr.	1984–1987
Dr. Marie L. Hoover ***	1994–1996
Samuel T. Hudson **	1986–
Angela M. Huggins	1995–
David Huggins	1992– 1995
Raymond R. Hull	1953–1954
Joseph H. Jacovini	1990–1999
Ron Jaworski	1991–1997
John K. Kaiser	1990–1992
William Kalellis *	1954–

BOARD MEMBER	ELECTED/RETIRED
Dr. Roscoe P. Kandle	1966–1971
Lewis L. Katz	1992–1995
Thomas J. Keane	1993–1998
Eleanor Kelemen **	1988–
Frank K. Kelemen	1963–1986
W.J.L. Kennedy	1982– 1985
Irving Kessler	1982– 1982
Josephine S. Klein	2000–
Richard P. Klopp	1985–1986
Bernard J. Korman, Esq.	1986–1988
George F. Kugler, Jr., Esq.**	1979–
Bryant W. Langston	1953–1969
David C. Langworthy *	1953–1978
Anthony LaRosa	1992–1993
Charles N. Lord	1997–
Kenneth MacDonald	1953–1980
Dr. Perry MacNeal	1953–1966
Constance M. Madara	1993–
Samuel W. Madara	2002–
Claudine B. Malone	1986–1989
Mary Alice D. Malone	1992–
Gay Mayer	1974–1992
Dr. G. J. McGarrity	1990–1991
John Meade, Jr.	1976–1986
Donald E. Meads	1983–1987
Mrs. Albert B. Melnik	1954–1980
Louis H. Meyer	1966–1974
Eugene Mori	1953–1975
Takashi Moriuchi	1989–1999
William R. Morris	1965–1980
Dr. Richard A. Mulivor ***	1992–1994
Paul L. Mulvee	1966–1972
Rabbi Fred J. Neulander	1989–1991
Jack C. Newell	1990–1995
Dr. Warren W. Nichols	1972–1991
Wilbur H. Norton	1953–1966
William O'Brien	1971–1984

Board Member	Elected/Retired
John B. O'Hara	1983–1989
Dr. Edward Osborn	1971–1977
Gerald R. Pacella	1992–1998
James Palmer **	1982–2000
Robert A. Paul	2001–
Dr. Harold Louis Paz	1996–1999
Albert V. Pescatore	1980– 1980
John V. Petrycki	1984– 1991
John A. Philbrick III**	1989–
Philip A. Piro *	1991–
Dolores S. Plasket	1981– 1991
Judith P. Poole	1993–
Dr. Joel Porter	1994–1999
Charles J. Prizer	2001–
Eleanor Read	1998–
Dr. William T. Read*	1966–1998
Henry Reichner **	1982–
Dr. Jonathan E. Rhoads **	1957–2002
Robert A. Richards, Jr.	1986–1992
Janice L. Richter, Esq.	1995–
W. Leslie Rogers	1971–1973
William J. Ryan, Esq.	1982– 1984
Michael L. Sanyour *	1992–
Dr. Robert A. Saporito	2000–
Edward M. Satell	1999–
Robert J. Schmertz	1974–1975
Samuel A. Schreiber	1996–1999
Philip E. Scott	1953–1965
Dr. Reuben Sharp	1956–1966
Harold A. Shaub *	1981–1998
Stephen R. Shilling	2002–
Steven D. Siegfried	2000–
A. Weir Stedman	1973–1985
Dr. Joseph Stokes, Jr.	1953–1964
Dr. S. Emlen Stokes	1953–1972
F. William Storck **	1977–2000
Wayne A. Stork	2002–

Board Member	Elected/Retired
William A. Stretch	1953–1970
Newbold Strong	1998–
Custis B. Swope	2002–
Mrs. S. Herbert Taylor	1966–1974
S. Robert Teitelman, Esq.*	1982–
Dr. Luther L. Terry	1966–1972
Dr. Lorraine H. Toji	1990–1992
Peter D. Utsinger	1997–1997
Neil VanderDussen	1974– 1980
Thomas L.Vanderslice	1953–1954
Dr. Edward D. Viner	1993–
Dr. Arnold Webster	1985–1988
Alan Wechsler *	1982–
Thomas R. Whitesell	1986–1994
Richard Wickes	1954–1968
Kyle Will	1974–1976
Robert G. Williams **	1986–
Clarence Z. Wurts	1994–1998
Charles Yates	1979–1980
Karen B. Yoh	1998–

(as of June 2002)

Coriell Board Presidents/Chairmen

Dr. Lewis L. Coriell	1953
Philip E. Scott	1953–1958
Mrs. W.H.K. Fleck	1959–1963
Bryant W. Langston	1964–1965
John S. Carter	1965–1967
Frederick P. Greiner, Esq.	1968–1971
David C. Langworthy	1972–1973
W. Robert Davis	1974–1976
William H. Bell, Jr.	1977–1984
William Kalellis	1984–1989
Samuel T. Hudson	1989–1991
James Palmer	1991–1994
John A. Philbrick III	1994–1998
Alan Wechsler	1998–2001
William T. Carson, Jr.	2001–

Executive Committee Chairmen

Harold A. Shaub	1985–1992
Frank Giordano	1992–1998
Leo C. Beebe	1998–February, 2001
Peter E. Driscoll, Esq.	February, 2001–

Friends of Coriell

Since 1990, the Friends of Coriell have worked to increase the visibility of the Coriell Institute and to raise funds for its research programs.

Geri Caparrelli
Joyce Connell
Marcia W. Coward
Kathy Gilbert
Dottie Giordano
Sally Harral
Janel Johnson
Jo Ann Kay
Peg Knight
Rosemary Leach
Connie Madara
Pat McGlynn
Pat Miller
Beverly Mitchell
Rosemary Nichols
Patricia O'Rourke
Betty Oliker
Sandy Parker
Ann Parker
Judith Poole
Marianne Raphaely
Maureen Santoro
Samantha Schiff, MA, MS
Joyce Stein
(as of April 2002)

Coriell Auxiliary

Since 1963, the Coriell Auxiliary has worked to inform South Jersey residents of the Institute's contributions to scientific discoveries and has raised funds for various research projects.

Gladys Allison
Gerda Ballinger
Doris Barlow
Frances Brenner
Denise Buscher
Janet Coccia
Elizabeth D'Allesandro
Marguerite Daubert
Carolyn Deakins
Catherine Finnegan
Susanna Ford
Ruth Goldman
Doris Greene
Riet Heinink
Jane Holben
Mary Holben
Marie Hoover, Ph.D.
Vicki Kwiatkowski
Abigail Lake
Mildred Lenker
Joan McFadden
Kitty Middleton

Eunice Miller
Mary Murakami
Linda Murakami
Laura Panzera
Harriet Patterson
Connie Pezzuro
Veronica Pompei
Grace Reichwein
Judith Sarama
Pearl Stein
Helen Stupp
Lorraine Toji, Ph.D.
Catherine Wert
Gloria Jeanne West
(as of April 2002)

INDEX

ROWAN UNIVERSITY CAMPBELL LIBRARY
3 3001 00913 748 9